13. JAN. 1992

B I

10. DEC

X

AUTHOR	CLASS
LAYCOCK. S,	T51

TITLE	No.
Warblin's fro' an owd songster.	490953042

This boo[...] [...]est date
shown a[...] [...]rrowed

LIBRARY HEADQU[...] [...]STON, PR1 8RH

D1436342

a30118 030561496b

57

Yours truly,
Samuel Laycock.

WARBLIN'S FRO' AN

OWD SONGSTER.

By SAMUEL LAYCOCK.

WITH AN INTRODUCTORY SKETCH BY W. TREVOR

𝔖𝔲𝔟𝔰𝔠𝔯𝔦𝔟𝔢𝔯𝔰' 𝔈𝔡𝔦𝔱𝔦𝔬𝔫.

OLDHAM: W. E. CLEGG, 30, MARKET PLACE.

LONDON: SIMPKIN, MARSHALL, HAMILTON, KENT & CO. LIMITED.

MANCHESTER: JOHN HEYWOOD.

MANCHESTER: ABEL HEYWOOD & SON.

[DEDICATION]

TO THE

SHARERS OF MY JOYS AND SORROWS—

MY DEAR WIFE AND CHILDREN—

THESE "WARBLIN'S"

ARE AFFECTIONATELY DEDICATED

BY THE "OWD SONGSTER."

PREFACE.

———

Twenty-nine years ago, at the time when the great struggle between the Northern and Southern States of America was taking place, which gave rise to what is still known in Lancashire as the "Cotton Panic," I published my first small volume of Poems and Songs.

That little bantling was very cordially received by the press, and it met with a most liberal patronage at the hands of an appreciative public. Eleven years later, a somewhat larger edition of my writings was published; and this second child of my fancy met with the same kindly welcome and generous treatment.

I would here record my heart-felt thanks to the Reviewers who gave my first volumes such an encouraging and flattering reception; and to the friends who then aided me with their sympathy and practical support. For several years these two volumes have been out of print; and I have been repeatedly urged by my many friends to bring out, in one book, a complete collection of the best of my life's work; with which request I now comply.

In this volume many new poems will be found which have not previously been printed; and others which have from time to time appeared only in sheet form, or in the magazines and newspapers of the day, In bringing out this more presentable, and pretentious volume, I feel that I should be ungrateful if I did not express my indebtedness to the Artists, and other friends, who have so willingly and generously assisted me in my efforts to make my latest work successful. Although compelled to exclude from this collection a large number of poems and songs of a private nature, and others relating to subjects of passing interest, I venture to think that in what I now submit to the public, it will be seen that I have always had before me some well-defined and useful object; and I trust I have not wholly failed to pourtray the worthy sentiments of lowly Lancashire folk in their own familiar dialect. If I have succeeded in doing this, in ever so small a degree, the "Owd Songster" will feel that his "Warblin's" have not been in vain.

SAMUEL LAYCOCK.

Foxhall Road,
Blackpool,
September, 1893.

Prefatory Sketch of the Author.

—◆◆—

SAMUEL LAYCOCK was born at Marsden, near Huddersfield, on the 17th January, 1826, a year of great drought and scarceness. His father, John Laycock, was a handloom weaver. Trade was extremely bad, provisions were dear, breadflour cost six shillings a dozen, and among the poor there was great privation, so that he might well say :—

> " Aw've often yerd mi feyther tell
> 'At when aw coom i' th' world misel
> Trade wur slack."

When six years old he attended, for a short time, a day school taught by a Congregational minister ; he also went to the Sunday school, where, as was not uncommon in those days, writing was taught, and it was here he acquired the free flowing hand which conduces so greatly even yet to the pleasure of reading his communications. " So far as I can recollect," he says, " we seldom, if ever, missed going to school and chapel on Sundays. My father used to carry on his back those of us who were too young to walk."

When nine years old he commenced work in a woollen mill for two shillings a week, and, though his hours of labour were from six in the morning till eight at night, he managed to do something in the way of self-improvement.

In 1837, when eleven years old, the family removed to Stalybridge. He now entered the cotton mill, and for seventeen years followed the occupation of a weaver, and his first effort at rhyming, written on a copticket, was addressed to a fellow-operative.

Speaking of his parents, he remarks, " They were very strict with us, and made us keep good hours, and always attend school and chapel on Sundays. I can easily see now, at my advanced age, what a blessing this must have been, especially to a man of my sensitive temperament, to be surrounded by so many good influences, and kept from so many temptations."

For the next eight years he was clothlooker at mills in Stalybridge and Dukinfield, when, in 1862, the great Civil War in America caused what is known as the "Cotton Panic," and Laycock, amongst others, found himself without occupation.

As a record of patient endurance and unquenchable hopefulness the history of that portion of our Lancashire life has never been surpassed ; and it is noteworthy that the ingenuity and public spirit of the time were wisely directed to finding something useful for "idle hands to do ;" and so elementary schools for men, and sewing classes for women, were established on every hand.   In his "Sewin' Class Song" Laycock has most accurately portrayed the determined cheerfulness which marked the conduct of the suffering workpeople throughout those dark days :—

   ' Come, lasses, let's cheer up an' sing, it's no use lookin' sad,
   " We'll mak eawr sewin' skoo to ring, an' stitch away like mad."

Indeed, his writings during that period, inspired as they were by constant exhibitions of patient privation, are a very fair indication of the intelligent sympathetic attitude of Lancashire folk toward the great American struggle.

In 1868 continued ill-health induced him to settle at Blackpool, and it is from that popular seaside resort that many of his sermons in verse have been sent forth.

Laycock, as an interpreter of thought and feeling, is full of that energetic buoyancy and relish for fun so peculiar to Lancashire working folk ; and though essentially the poor man's poet, having sounded the depths of poverty and felt the pinch of want, there is in him nothing of disappointed meanness, and nothing morbid.   Indeed, he impresses one as being mostly on the verge of playing some practical joke.   Even in his " Ode to th' Sun," so impressive from one point of view, there is an original confidential familiarity with the great orb of day, almost comical in its surprising ease and conversational fluency.   So with " Rowl away, theaw grand owd ocean."   We are pleasantly carried along with this same easy fluency, whilst still conscious that the Lancashire dialect does not readily lend itself to the description of grand scenes.

" Welcome, Bonny Brid," must tell its own tale.   In this short poem there is an interchanging tenderness and delicate humour, which, for felicity of expression, is unrivalled in any poem of its kind.

There is in him, too, a strain of deep reverence, without which humour is liable to descend to mere cynicism.   In " An Evening Prayer " occur these impressive lines :—

> " The moon shed forth her silvery light
> " O'er mountain, dale, and ocean ;
> " And all I saw and heard that night
> " Inspired me with devotion."

It is, however, as a teacher of sound morals, and delineator of homely Lancashire folks and ways, that Laycock will be remembered.   He appeals to us in "our own tongue," and he reaches the heart.

He has done his own work, and in his own way has taught us the value of hnman sympathy and the power of humble goodness, and through him many a quiet blessing has fallen upon Lancashire hearthstones, and wholesome laughter has brightened many a fireside.

The painter who transfers to canvas the forms of beauty in a passing cloud, the mellow light of an autumn evening, or the dimpling laugh on a child's sweet face, inspires feelings not only of admiration but of gratitude, for we feel that but for the exercise of his genius, these transient visions would have been but as forgotten dreams.

It is so with our best thoughts and feelings.   We have our brief seasons of elevated thought, in which the mind refreshes itself amid scenes of its own creation, and sensibly grows in strength by its own purifying efforts.

This is our life at its best, and it is at times such as these that we long for adequate powers of expression.

The subjects which prompt our meditation and move our sympathies may from our very surroundings be homely and even commonplace, but the man who can give them expression and permanent record is to us a benefactor, and we keep him in grateful memory as one who arrested some of our fleeting joys, and who peopled our little world with forms and faces familiar, but always welcome.

W.   TREVOR.

CONTENTS.

———✳———

LIST OF ILLUSTRATIONS.

Warblin's fro' an Owd Songster.

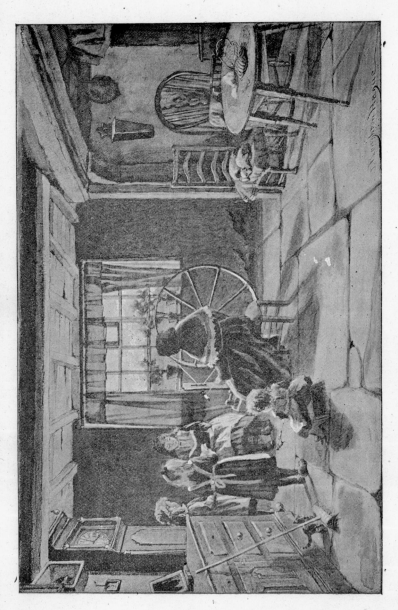

At Number One i' Bowton's Yard, mi gronny keeps a skoo';
But hasn't mony scholars yet; hoo's only one or two;
They say th' owd woman's rayther cross;—well, well, it may be so;—
Aw know hoo'd trod us weels once, an aw'd mi ears an'

BOWTON'S YARD.

AT number one, i' Bowton's yard, mi gronny keeps a skoo,
    But hasn't mony scholars yet, hoo's only one or two;
      They sen th' owd woman's rather cross,—well, well, it may be so;
Aw know hoo box'd me rarely once, an' pood mi ears an' o.

At number two lives widow Burns—hoo weshes clooas for folk
Their Billy, that's her son, gets jobs at wheelin' coke;
They sen hoo coarts wi' Sam-o'-Neds, at lives at number three;
It may be so, aw conno tell, it matters nowt to me.

At number three, reet facin' th' pump, Ned Grimshaw keeps a shop;
He's Eccles-cakes, an' gingerbread, an' treacle beer, an' pop;
He sells oat-cakes an' o, does Ned, he has boath soft an' hard,
An' everybody buys off him 'at lives i' Bowton's yard.

At number four Jack Blunderick lives; he goes to th' mill an' wayves;
An' then, at th' week-end, when he's time, he pows a bit an' shaves;
He's badly off, is Jack, poor lad; he's rayther lawm, they sen,
An' his childer keep him deawn a bit—aw think they'n nine or ten.

At number five aw live mysel', wi' owd Susannah Grimes,
But dunno loike so very weel—hoo turns me eawt sometimes;
An' when awm in there's ne'er no leet, aw have to ceawer i' th' dark;
Aw conno pay mi lodgin' brass, becose awm eawt o' wark.

At number six, next dur to us, an' close o' th' side o' th' speawt,
Owd Susie Collins sells smo' drink, but hoo's welly allis beawt;
But heaw it is that is the case awm sure aw conno tell,
Hoo happen maks it very sweet, an' sups it o hersel!

At number seven there's nob'dy lives, they left it yesterday,
Th' bum-baylis coom an' mark'd their things, and took 'em o
    away ;
They took 'em in a donkey-cart—aw know nowt wheer they
    went—
Aw recon they'n bin ta'en and sowd becose they owed some
    rent.

At number eight—they're Yawshur folk—there's only th' mon
    an' woife,
Aw think aw ne'er seed nicer folk nor these i' o mi loife ;
Yo'll never yer 'em foin' eawt, loike lots o' married folk,
They allis seem good-tempered like, an' ready wi' a joke.

At number nine th' owd cobbler lives—th' owd chap 'at mends
    my shoon,
He's getting very weak an' done, he'll ha' to leov us soon ;
He reads his Bible every day, an sings just loike a lark,
He says he's practisin' for heaven—he's welly done his wark.

At number ten James Bowton lives—he's th' noicest heawse
    i' th' row ;
He's allis plenty o' sum'at t' eat, an lots o' brass an' o ;
An' when he rides an' walks abeawt he's dress'd up very fine,
But he isn't hawve as near to heaven as him at number nine.

At number 'leven mi uncle lives—aw co him uncle Tum,
He goes to concerts, up an' deawn, an' plays a kettle-drum ;
I' bands o' music, an' sich things, he seems to tak' a pride,
An' allis maks as big a noise as o i' th' place beside.

At number twelve, an' th' eend o' th' row, Joe Stiggins deals i'
    ale ;
He's sixpenny, an' fourpenny, dark-coloured, an' he's pale ;
But aw ne'er touch it, for aw know it's ruined mony a bard—
Awm th' only chap as doesn't drink 'at lives i' Bowton's yard.

An' neaw awve done aw'll say good-bye, an' leave yo' for awhile;
Aw know aw have n't towd mi tale i' sich a first-rate style ;
But iv yo're pleased awm satisfied, an' ax for no reward
For tellin' who mi nayburs are at live i' Bowton's yard.

At number nine th' owd cobbler lives—th' owd chap 'at mends mi shoon ;
He's gettin' very weak an' done, he'll ha' to leov us soon ;
He reads his Bible every day, an' sings just loike a lark,
He says he's practisin' for heaven—he's welly done his wark.

CLEAWDS AN' SUNSHOINE.

WELL, readers, awm glad 'at we're met once ogen ;
    An' tho' we're a year or two owder,
    Let's hope 'at eawr love for each other an' God
    Hasn't grown ony feebler or cowder.
Aw think aw may venture to flatter mysel'
  'At awve met wi' some on yo befoor ;
So iv yo'll alleaw me that pleasure ogen,
  Aw'll try to amuse yo once moor.

It's pleasant to meet an' shake honds wi' owd friends,
  Tho' it very oft pains us to foind
'At th' sun o' prosperity's withered some hearts
  'At once wur booath lovin' an' kind.
An' some 'at we knew when they'rn lasses an' lads
  Are neaw, loike one's self, gettin' hoary ;
Whoile others have finished loife's battle deawn here,
  And neaw they're gone forrud to glory.

Th' owd Reaper keeps slashing away wi' his scythe,
  First o' one hand, an' then on the other ;
Neaw some darlin' pet lamb's rudely hurried away,
  Then some silver-haired sister or brother.
There's mony a dear loved one pack'd up an' gone whoam
  Sin' last yo an' me met together ;
They've thrown eawt their anchors, their barques are neaw
    moored—
  Let's hope they're enjoyin' good weather.

We shall ole have to go—young an' owd, rich an' poor,
  Whatever eawr kindred or nation ;
Death sweeps all before him, an' cares nowt at o
  For noather rank, title, or station.
Well, wheer are we for—thoose of us 'at's left ?
  Have we settled what haven we'll book to ?
Is th' craft at we sail in seaworthy an' seawnd ?
  Is th' pilot a safe un to look to ?

Eawr souls are loike musical instruments.   Ah!
    An' they're here to be put into tune.
This earth's nobbut th' schoolheawse or practisin' greaund—
    Th' grand concert tak's place up aboon.
Let's everyone see 'at eawr lamps are well trimm'd,
    An' th' lights burnin' clearly an' steady;
An' when th' Bridegroom comes knockin' at th' dur, may He
        foind
    'At we're ole on us waitin' an' ready.

Dear readers, for once you'll excuse me, aw'm sure,
    For pennin' so serious a strain;
For yo know very weel 'at it's moor i' my loine
    To write in a humorous vein;
But a feelin' o' this mak' comes o'er one at times,
    'At we connot shake off if we would;
Awd sooner bi' th' hauve tak' mi pen i' mi hand
    To pleos yo a bit iv aw could.

So come neaw, just straighten yore faces a bit,
    An' try to look cheerful an' jolly.
Yo fling ole yore cares o' one side a bit, John—
    An' yo mop up thoose tears o' yores, Polly;
An' tho' gloomy cleawds may be hoverin' o'er,
    Flingin' shadows o'er th' loife ov a mon,
Let's spread eawrsel's eawt for th' good things 'at God sends,
    And drink in ole th' sunshoine we con.

"COARTIN' DAYS."

REET days ! Heaw soon they pass away !
    Th' best days Heaven sends to men !
    Aw wish aw wurn't so owd an' gray
    Aw'd cooart a bit ogen ;
An' every spot wheer Kate an' me
    Have often met befoor,
To sit an' tell eawr tales o' love,
    Aw'd try to see once moor.

There's th' tree aw used to clamber up ;
    An' yonder's th' garden wo ;
An' th' owd church clock on th' village green—
    Aw think aw see 'em o.
Awve noan forgetten th' chimney-nook,
    That owd familiar place
Wheer Kate would often sit an' look
    So fondly i' mi' face !

Tho' years have passed sin' thoose breet heawers,
    Aw'm noan ashamed to tell—
Aw used to go an' gather th' fleawers
    'At grew i' th' primrose dell ;
An' these awd twoine i' th' nut-breawn hair
    O' Kate, mi darlin' pet ;
An' then th' dear lass would look so fair—
    Aw think aw see her yet.

A kind an' thoughtful girl wur Kate,
  An' gentle as a dove;
Hoo never learned to scorn or hate,
  Her heart wur full o' love;
Her features allis wore a smoile,
  An' these o' moine wur th' same.
Aw used to ceawer me deawn at th' stoile,
  An' whistle till hoo came.

Oft aw recall thoose happy heawers,
  When 'neath the moonlit sky
Two lovers paced yon silent beawers—
  Mi' bonny Kate an' I.
One lovely neet, i' th' month o' June,
  Whoile under th' hawthorne tree,
Aw axed her if hoo'd wed me soon.
  Hoo smiled, an' said—"Aw'll see."

Just then Giles Bloomfield drove his flock
  Close by that owd church teawer;
We lingered chattin' theer till th' clock
  Proclaimed the midnight heawer.
That neet we named the happy day;
  An' aw remember still,
Heaw in the church aw heard her say—
  "Have Robin? Yes, I will!"

THEE AN' ME.

HA'RT livin' at thi country seat,
    Among o th' gents an' nobs ;
   Tha's sarvant girls to cook thi meat,
    An' do thi bits o' jobs.
Aw'm lodgin' here wi' Bridget Yates,
   At th' cot near th' Ceaw Lone Well ;
Aw mend mi stockin's, peel th' potates,
   An' wesh mi shurts misel' !

Tha wears a finer cooat nor me ;
   Thi purse is better lined,
An' fortin's lavished moor o' thee,
   Than th' rest o' human kind.
Life's storms 'at rage abeawt this yead,
   An' pelt so hard at me—
That mony a time aw've wished aw're dead,—
   But seldom trouble thee.

Tha'rt rich i' ole this world can give ;
   Tha's silver, an' tha's gowd ;
But me—aw find it hard to live,
   Aw'm poor, an' gettin' owd.
These fields an' lones aw'm ramblin' throo—
   They o belong to thee ;
Aw've only just a yard or two
   To ceawer in when aw dee.

When tha rides eawt th' folks o areawnd
   Stond gapin' up at thee,
Becose tha'rt worth ten theawsand peawnd',
   But scarcely notice me.
Aw trudge abeawt fro' spot to spot,
   An' nob'dy seems to care :
They never seek my humble cot,
   To ax me heaw aw fare.

If tha should dee, there's lots o' folk
 Would fret an' cry, noa deawt ;
When aw shut up, they'll only joke,
 An' say, " He's just gone eawt !
Well, never heed him, let him goo,
 An' find another port ;
We're never to a chap or two,
 We've plenty moor o' th' sort."

Tha'll have a stone placed o'er thi grave
 To show thi name an' age ;
An o tha's done 'at's good an' brave,
 Be seen o' history's page.
When aw get tumbled into th' greawnd,
 There'll ne'er be nowt to show
Whose restin' 'neath that grassy meawnd,
 An' nob'dy'll want to know.

But deawn i' th' grave, what spoils o th' sport,
 No ray o' leet can shine ;
An' th' worms 'll have hard wark to sort
 Thy pampered clay fro' mine.
So, when this world for th' next tha swaps,
 Tak' wi' thee under th' stone
Thi cooat ov arms, an' bits o' traps,
 Or else tha'll ne'er be known.

Pack up thi albert, hoop, an' pin,
 An' opera-glass an' o ;
Be sure tha sees 'em o put in,
 Before tha gangs below.
Then iv some hungry worm should come,
 To root abeawt thi bones,—
Tha may stond a better chance nor some
 If it's known tha'rt Mister Jones.

But up above, there's One at sees
 Thro' th' heart o' every mon ;
An' He'll just find thee as tha dees,
 So dee as weel as t' con.
An' when deawn here this campin' ends,
 An' o eawr fau'ts forgiven,—
Let thee an' me still shew we're friends,
 Bi shakin' honds i' heaven !

TEETOTAL? OF COURSE AWM TEETOTAL!

TEETOTAL? Of course awm teetotal!
    Is there owt wrong i' that, do yo think?
    Con yo foind me a mon under heaven
      Made grander or nowbler wi' drink?
Neaw we need noather lawyers nor doctors
    To help us to sattle disputes;
For it dosen't need very much larnin'
    To judge of a tree by its fruits.

Th' other day, as aw're goin' thro' Owdham,
    Aw met wi' a chap 'ut aw knew—
He appeared to be eawt seekin' orders,
    So aw axed what he'd getten to do.
" Well," he said, " Awm a dealer i' sperrits."
    But didn't aw look at th' owd lad,
As good as to say—" Arto jokin',
    Or arto gone stark starin' mad?"

So theaw's gone into th' sperrit loine, hasto?
    Well, theaw's getten a very queer trade!
Are they sperrits they get at these drink shops,
    Or do they attend Doctor Slade?
What's to do 'at theaw carries no samples?
    Mon, theaw'd foind it to act like a charm
Iv theaw'd one or two well-seasoned topers
    Along wi' thee under thi arm.

Well, we arn't ole blest wi' one fancy,
    Nor do ole look at things i' one leet.
Some are fond o' owd stuff 'ats gone putrid,
    An othersome loike their meat sweet;
But there's nowt to admire in a drunkard—
    He isnt' loike th' work o' God's hand;
For there s nowt i' thoose drink-bloated features
    'As stroikes one as nowble or grand.

God's image is theer after all's done.
    But heaw is it marred do yo think ?
Not wi' feedin' off beefsteaks an' onions,
    Nowt o'th' sooart; it's wi' drinkin' strong drink.
But yore some on yo moderate, are yo ?
    Yo never do drink to excess ?
Well, yore tackin' th' same liquor as drunkards,
    Wi' this difference—yo use rayther less.

Beware !   That degraded owd toper
    Wur once as pure-moinded as yo ;
A kind-hearted Sunday-schoo' teacher—
    It's th' drink 'at's made th' difference—that's o.
Aw believe i' God's grace—it'll help yo,
    So long as yore doin' what's reet ;
But it never makes alcohol harmless,
    Nor rotten potatoes turn sweet.

Iv yo'n faith i' yore prayers, yo can try 'em.
    Go an' tak' a run jump into th' say ;
An' except yore good practical swimmers
    Yo'll dreawn, as heaw hard yo may pray.
Neaw will yo alleaw me to show yo,
    I' th' form ov a bit ov a song,
'At God's laws are ne'er altered or brocken
    To help us to mend up a wrong ?

What we reap must depend upo' th' sowin' ;
    We shall ole of us get what we've earned ;
Iv we play wi' a wasp it'll sting us ;
    Thoose 'at play wi' a foire get burned.
An' tho' blessed loike Shakespere or Milton
    Wi' great moinds to reason or think,
We'se get daubed iv we creep up a chimney,
    An' drunk iv we tak' to mich drink.

A RESPECTABLE MON.

ETWEEN these shoe soles an' this hat,
    Stonds a very respectable mon ;
An' nob'dy 'll contradict that,
    An' why ?   Becose nobody con.

There's none o' yo're hypocrites here,
    Deceivin' o th' folk 'at they see ;
Aw'm nowt nobbut what I appear,
    There's none o' yo're durt abeawt me.

Respectable ! well, an' what's that ?
    Does it meon to be polished a bit—
Sport a silver-knobbed cane, an' silk hat,
    Un' be coe'd Mister Muggins ?   Not it.

Yo' see this owd jacket, aw guess ;
    Well, it covers as decent a brick
As ever wur moulded !—oh, yes,
    I' every way quite " up to Dick."

There's Joe Dandy, Tom Vain, an' Bob Breet ;
    These think weel o' theirsels, one may see ;
But they winno stond bringin' to th' leet,
    And comparin' wi' someb'dy loike me.

They may curl up their noses an' laff,
    When they happen to meet me on th' way ;
They may turn eawt their slang an' their chaff,
    But aw'm th' yead above them ony day.

Aw know aw'm noan donn'd up so smart,
    An' yo' wouldn't give much for this hat ;
But aw hope aw've a good honest heart,
    An' it's summat t' be preaud on, is that.

Aw con boast noather heawses nor londs,
   An' wealthy relations aw've noan ;
But aw've getten mi brains, an' mi honds,
   An', thank God ! aw con co' these mi own.

Ah, mi own, an' they're shackled bi none ;
   Fro mi toes to mi toppin' aw'm free ;
An' let tyrants do o' 'at they con,
   Aw meon to be so till aw dee.

Aw've getten th' good sense to behave,
   An' respect thoose at's put in to rule ;
But aw'll never be reckoned a slave—
   Aw'll never be used as a tool.

Aw've no patience wi' dandified gents !
   One's sick o' so mitch o' this pride ;
They're soakin' wi hair oils an' scents,
   But there isn't mitch else beside !

Neaw aw towd yo' when furst aw begun,
   Aw're a very respectable mon ;
Bless yo're life, aw wur noan i' mi fun—
   Find a daycenter chap iv yo' con.

Heaw yo're grinnin' at what aw've just said !
   Aw dar' say yo' think aw'm noan reet ;
But aw'll stick mi owd hat o' mi yead,
   An' be trudgin' ; good neet, folk ; good neet.

FOOT PASSENGERS, KEEP TO THE RIGHT.

IT'S been said 'at there's sarmons i' stones;
    Well, judgin' bi thoose i' eawr fowd,—
      Awm a bit i' th' same mind as Tom Jones,—
    'At sich sarmons must feel rayther cowd.
This o' mine, tho' it's noan o' th' furst stamp,
    It's as good as this heart con indite;
Mi text, ta'en fro' th' post ov a lamp,
    Is " Foot-passengers, keep to the right."

An' furstly, aw'd ha' yo' beware
    O'th' dandy 'at tak's greater pains
To convince us he's nice curly hair,
    Than he does to convince us he's brains.
There's words o' deceit on his tongue,
    Calculated fair prospects to blight:
If yo' tread i' his steps yo'll be wrong;
    Young fellows! keep on to the right.

Let th' standard yo' go by be true;
    Measure man by his mind, not his purse;
There's mony a great squire 'at's a foo',
    An' a drunken foo' to', an' that's worse.
We've lots o' rich men one could name,
    'At are hurried whoam drunk every night;
Well, this a scandalous shame,
    So, " Foot-passengers, keep to the right."

Let th' motives 'at guide yo' be pure,
    Proceedin' fro' hearts full o' love;
Deal gently wi' th' errin' an' th' poor,
    For kind acts are recorded above.
To lead folk to virtue an' God,
    Exert o yo'r influence an' might;
Bid 'em guard against fashion's smooth road,
    Ask 'em kindly to keep to the right.

Keep eawt o' thoose traps 'at are laid,
    Th' Breawn Ceaw, th' Black Horse, an' th' Blue Bell,
There's a curse on their damnable trade,
    An' on th' death-dealin' drink 'at they sell!
While yo, tramp throo this wearisome world,
    Keep th' goal 'at yo' aim at i' sight;
Let th' banner o' truth be unfurled,
    Wi' this motto on—" Keep to the right."

Some tempter may come wi' his wiles;
    Try to get yo' to tread i' th' wrong track;
Tack no heed to his words an' sweet smiles,
    But, like Jesus did, say " Stand back!"
Tack no notice o' praises or freawns;
    Dunno fret o'er yo'r locks growin' white;
Hoary heads 'll be glorified creawns,
    To thoose 'at keep on to th' right.

If dark gloomy cleawds should appear,
    To o'ershadow yo'r hearths an' yo'r homes;
Light yo'r lamps, an' tak care they burn clear,
    An' be ready when th' bridegroom comes.
Should th' sky appear cleawdless aboon,
    An' yo'r prospects be hopeful an' bright,
Beware! for a storm may come soon:
    Be cautious, an' keep to the right.

When Death yo'r last summons shall bring,
    To be sharp an' pack up an' be gone,
Yo' con calmly, triumphantly sing—
    " Aw'll be wi' thee as soon as aw con "
An' heaw th' angels i' heaven will rejoice,
    When yo bid us yo'r last "good night!"
An' yo'll hear Christ's own welcomin' voice,—
    " Come up hither, my friend, to the right!"

TH' QUACK DOCTOR.

HERE you are! I'm the great and renowned Doctor
Bell!
    Oh yes, I'm the man who can soon make you well;
    You see this small box that I hold in my hand,
Well, it holds the best salve ever made in the land
For all kinds of ulcers and sores you can name,
The salve now before you has got a great fame.

A lady who lives near the " Shamrock and Rose,"
Had a carbuncle right at the tip of her nose;
Well, she came to my stall here one Saturday night
And purchased one box, now she's perfectly right;
I have cured an old man of a very sore lip,
And a poor little boy of a boil on his hip;
I engage to remove all the ailments of man
As soon and as cheaply as anyone can.

Now, to give some idea of my knowledge and skill
I will bring to your notice my world-renowned pill;
There's a pill now before you unequalled on earth,
The man is not born who can tell you its worth;
For removing obstructions no better is made,
" Old Parr " and all others are thrown in the shade,
As a plain illustration of what I now say
I will mention a fact which I heard yesterday.

A gentleman living not far from this town,
And I may as well give you his name—Mr. Brown;
This gentleman had a large safe in his shop,
The key of which he'd the misfortune to drop;
Now, this safe contained most of his cash and his bills,
Well, having oft heard of my excellent pills,
He sent for a box and straightway applied
One or two of the pills to the keyhole outside,
When, strange to relate, they burst open the door,
And bills, notes, and cashbox lay spread on the floor!

B

Now, I think you'll admit friends, from what you've just heard,
That the pills need no praises from me, not a word ;
If they'll open a safe, their laurels are won,
And they'll ne'er shy at anything under the sun.

Here you are, once again, in my fingers I hold
A most certain cure for a cough or a cold,
Any lady or gentleman now standing by
Who is troubled with hoarseness, I ask them to try
My unrivalled wafer, the " Princess of Wales,"
And I'll venture to forfeit five pounds if it fails.
An acquaintance of mine and a learned M.P.,
With talking so much he was hoarse do you see ;
Well, he ate one or two of my wafers one night,
Next morning his throat had got perfectly right :
He sent me a letter, and in it he said—
Were it not for my wafers he might have been dead.

Well, ladies and gents, there's one article more
That I wish to produce from my wonderful store,
And that is my world-renowned Syrup of Plums,
For earache, for toothache, and pains in the gums,
Any party now standing before me to-night,
May be cured on the spot, and made perfectly right.

Now, ladies and gentlemen, do not delay ;
You can't purchase medicine like this every day,
Only twopence per box for the pills, that is all,
And one penny the salve, the charge is but small.
The wafers, in packets, are one penny each,
A price that must come within everyone's reach.
To those persons afflicted with pains in the gums,
Twopence-halfpenny per ounce for my Syrup of Plums ;
Now, you know who I am, friends, the great Doctor Bell,
If you swallow my stuff you are sure to do well !

MALLY AN' JONAS.

COME, Mally, owd woman, it's near forty year,
　　Sin' thee an' me furst coom together;
　We've had mony a breet smile, ah, an' mony a sad tear,
　　An' experienced booath good an' bad weather.
As eawr 'Lizabeth's gone to look after thi geawn,
　An' eawr Tum's rubbin' th' mare deawn i' th' stable,
What thinks ta, owd lass, iv we sitten us deawn,
　An' have a nice chat while we're able?

Owd age is fast whitenin' eawr yeads one con see;
　An' these shanks o' eawrs are no' so nimble
As they wur when aw held thee th' furst time on mi knee,
　An' tha rapp'd me o'er th' yead wi' thi thimble.
I' fancy aw often look back to thoose days,
　When tha lived wi' thi aunt i' th' Flag Alley;
There wur nob'dy awm sure had a prattier face,
　An' aw did think some weel on thee, Mally!

Aw bowt thee some ear-rings o' reet solid gowd,
　An' some side-combs to stick i' thi hair;
An' when we walked eawt, aw wur lots o' times towd,
　Tha wur th' han'somest lass i' o th' fair.
True, sin then a great deol o' thi charms have gone dead,
　An' tha'rt nowt near as lusty an' clever;
But, spite o' thi wrinkles an' silvery yead,
　Aw love thee as dearly as ever.

There's one thing aw've noticed owd lass, an' it's this,—
　That whenever tha's had ony trouble,
An' tha's come an' pretended to borrow a kiss,
　Tha allis would pay me back double.
Neaw, when ta'en an' compared wi' a woman like thee,
　What's beauty, position, or riches!
But tha seems to be shapin' for cryin' aw see,
　So get on wi' mendin' mi britches.

" Neaw, drop it, do, Jonas, tha's said quite enuff ;
   Mon, tha'rt worse than tha wur when we're courtin' ;
An' at that time tha turned eawt a lot o' queer stuff,
   'At needed some weedin' an' sortin'.
Awm surprised at a grey-yeaded fellow like thee ;
   Still, it's nobbut thi fun 'at tha'rt pokin ;
An', someheaw, tha never con let me a-be
   When tha'rt ceawrin' i' th' corner an' smokin'.

Aw see 'at there's one o' thi waist-buttons gone,
   An' one o' thi gallowses brocken ;
Tha needn't ha' gone abeawt this way mon,
   If tha'd oppen'd thi meawth an' just spocken.
Awm expectin' eawr 'Lizabeth here very soon ;
   An' eawr Will's abeawt leavin' Jane Tupper ;
If tha'll push a few lumps o' dry wood under th' oon,
   Aw'll see abeawt mackin' some supper.

As it's Setterday neet, we shall want summat nice ;
   Heaw would t' relish some tripe or some trotters ?
As tha knows, lad, we've had some good stuff once or twice
   At that shop th' next but one to owd Potters.
If tripe doesn't suit thee when goin' to bed
   Aw con mak thee a mess o' good porritch ;
We've some capital meal 'at owd Carrier Ned
   Browt wi' him fro' Gregson's at Nor'itch.

But tha musn't forget tha's to wesh thee a bit,
   An' go deawn to th' shop for some stuff ;
We want a few beons, an' some corn for th' owd tit,
   An' tha wants some 'bacco an' snuff.
It's Sunday to-morn ! Oh aw like it to come,
   For it's th' best day we have i' ole th' seven,—
A day when one's soul con look on tow'rds whoam,
   An', on earth, get a foretaste o' heaven ! "

OH! THIS BOIL!

OH dear! oh dear! aw do feel queer,
Pooin' mi face an' ceawerin' here
   O this while.
  Reach me that stoo' here, will ta, Kit?
An' let me rest mi leg a bit:
   Oh! this boil!

Iv these are boils aw want no moor,
Aw'd rayther have a *roast*, aw'm sure;—
   Pig or goose.
Robin, thee mind that cheer o' thine;
Tha mun keep off this leg o' mine,
   It's no use.

Confeawnd this stinkin' drawin' sauve,
It mak's me bawl eawt like a cawve;
   What a bore!
Aw dar'no stur misel' a peg,
For fear lest aw should hurt mi leg,
   It's so sore.

Aw've sweat wi' toothwarch mony a time;
Aw've had mi fingers brunt wi' lime;—
   Aw have so!
Aw've walked wi' blistered feet for miles,
But aw'm prepared to swear this boil's
   Wor' nor o!

Aw think th' owd plague's abeawt at th' worst;
Kit, when does think it's beawn to burst?
   Tell me that;
For oh! aw do feel dreadful bad;
Iv it dosen't get weel soon, aw'll go mad,
   An' punse th' cat.

Aw dar'no laff, aw dar'no cry,
Aw'm freet'ned aw should hurt mi thigh,
   Th' skin's so tight.
Aw've shewed mi boil to Limpin' Ned;
He says aw shouldn't ha' getten wed;—
   Sarves me right!

Hard-hearted wretch! inhuman cleawn!
To kick a fellow when he's deawn
   Isn't reet.
He met ha' kept that to hissen,
At leost while aw'd got up ogen
   On mi feet.

Oh dear! whenever mun aw stur?
Aw've never been eawtside o'th' dur
   For a week.
Aw've ceawered so long inside this room,
'At aw haven't getten a bit o' bloom
   On mi cheek.

Aw'm gradely done,—aw'm reet fagg'd eawt
Aw shall ha' to vomit soon aw deawt;—
   Come here, Ted!
An' stur, theaw good for nothin', theaw!
Ho-up! ho-up! it's comin' neaw,
   Howd mi yead.

O dear! aw am gone sick an' queer;
Tak' me an' lay me on th' couch cheer
   For awhile.
Oh! what a torment, to be sure!
What? healthy things! aw want no moor,
   Oh! this boil!

HELP YO'RSEL'S, LADS.

DUNNO steal, nor nowt, mi brothers;
 That's noan what aw meon—not it.
 Now, it's this—look less to others—
  Try to help yor'sels a bit.
Neaw, aw'm noa great politician,
 Up to th' een in't, same as some;
Aw believe a mon's position
 May be mended mooast awhom.

Thurty year aw've been a toiler,
 Th' mooast o'th' toime i'th' cotton mill;
Sweat as hard as th' best among yo'—
 Ah, an' lads, aw'm workin' still!
Workin' when yo're noicely dozin'—
 Workin' wi' a weakly frame—
Thinkin', feelin', an' composin',
 Not to get mysel a name,

But to try an' raise mi brothers—
 Thoose 'at labour by mi soide—
Sons o'th' same dear English mothers—
 Britain's glory, strength, an' proide.
Oh, may God, i' heaven aboon us,
 Help me i' mi humble task!
Gi'e me th' will an' strength to do it!
 Brothers, this is o aw ask.

Let's be thowtful, let's be sober,
 Get eawr drinks fro' nature's wells:
Put less confidence i' others,
 An' a bit moor i' eawrsels.
Some consider th' Tories reet uns—
 Friends o'th' workin' men an' sich;
Other some co th' Liberals breet uns—
 Noan o' these can help us mich.

At th' elections here aw've yeard yo'
   Set up mony a rare good sheawt ;
Well, an' what will this wark bring us ?
   No' mich cheese an' bread, aw deawt.
Bless yo, lads, it is but little
   Onyone deawn here con do:
Th' best o' men are nobbut mortal,
   Often selfish—seldom true.

Brother toilers, let's no longer
   Trust to this or that big mon ;
Th' chaps at Lunnun con do nowt mich—
   Help yo'rsels, lads, o yo' con.
Let me ax yo' t' give o'er drinkin' ;
   Nob'dy's peawer to raise yo' up ;
Nob'dy can prevent yo' sinkin',
   While yo'r slaves to summat t' sup.

Th' world's a ring—we're wrostlers in it ;
   Life's a conflict, let's " wire in,"
Struggle monfully an' bravely,
   Same as thoose 'at meon to win.
Iv successful, let's keep humble ;
   Iv we are no', never heed ;
Th' best o' men mun sometimes tumble,
   Th' bravest warriors sometimes bleed.

Toime's to precious to be wasted ;
   Loife's to' short to fling away ;
Let's o set to work i' earnest,
   Hopin' t' see a breeter day.
Dunno look to mich to others ;
   Drink deep draughts fro' wisdom's wells ;
Carve yo'r own way eawt, mi brothers ;
   Help yo'rsels, lads ! help yo'rsels !

TO POVERTY.

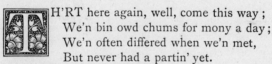H'RT here again, well, come this way;
    We'n bin owd chums for mony a day;
    We'n often differed when we'n met,
    But never had a partin' yet.
Aw conno say awm fond o' thee,
Then why does t' stick so fast to me?
Aw know aw used t' be some an' mad,
Theau plagued me so when aw're a lad.

Tha knows that time when Robin Clegg
Fell off th' barn dur an' broke his leg?
Poor lad! aw took him on mi knee,
An' should ha' helped him but for thee.
What con a body do 'at's poor?
Aw cried a bit, but nowt no moor.
Well, never moind, he geet it set,
An' thee an' me are owd chums yet.

Aw've tried for years to shake thee off—
An' when th' last winter theaw'd a cough,
Aw hoped to see thee laid i' th' greawnd,
But th' summer weather's browt thee reawnd.
Well, poo thi cheer up—warm thi shanks,
Aw'll sit an' watch thee play thi pranks;
Aw meon to shunt thee when aw con,
Till then aw'll face thee like a mon.

Thae'll ha' fair play, tha needn't fear—
Now, now, thae'll see no shufflin' here!
Aw'll tell thee plainly theaw'rt a pest,
An's spoilt me mony a good neet's rest;
Theaw stole mi supper t'other neet,
An' sent me t' bed wi' cowd wet feet.
Aw didn't relish this—Would theaw?
Well, come, we'll let it pass o'er neaw.

Heaw is it theaw ne'er goes to see
Big folks 'at's better off nor me?
There's plenty up an' deawn i'th' lond,
'At theaw'd do weel to tak' bi' th' hond,
An' leod 'em every day to schoo'.
There's young Nat Wild—poor silly foo'—
He's lots o' brass, but noan mich wit,
Go play thi pranks wi' him a bit.

Aw've had mi friends—fond, firm, an' true,
An' dear relations not a few;
But noan o' these han stuck to me
As firmly an' as long as thee.
An' after o it's hardly reet
To goa an' turn thee eawt i' th' street,
And one not knowin' wheer thae'rt beawn
Aw conno do it—sit thee deawn.

FEIGHT FAIR.

H dear ! what foin' eawt there is ;
    It does look bad, for sure :
    We'n th' young at loggeryeads wi' th' owd,
      An' th' rich at war wi' th' poor.
Professin' Christians quarrel too ;
  M.P.'s get eawt o' square ;
A pity this : but come, mi lads,
  Let's everyone feight fair.

While toddlin' thro' this world o' eawrs
  Th' best on us getten hit ;
An', tho' we'd rayther live at peace,
  We han to feight a bit.
There's wrongs one dosen't like to see ;
  We'n rights we conno spare ;
There allis sum'at t' feight abeawt ;
  But come, mi lads, feight fair.

We'n Superstition t' battle wi',
  Owd Prejudice an' o ;
An' we shall foind it hardish wark
  Opposin' these, aw know.
Ne'er mind, let's buckle to ogen,
  An' meet us, if they dare ;
They'll ha' to shift afore so long ;
  Feight fair, mi lads, feight fair.

There's foak to feight 'at never larned
  To aim a gradely blow ;
They'n noather science, skill, nor sense ;
  Neaw these are th' worst of o ;
They'll fire their shots, an' wheer they leet
  They noather know nor care ;
Th' owd-fashund way o' arguin' this ;
  But, never mind, feight fair.

Well, then, there's hollow-yeaded folk
   (Of course they'n lots o' tongue),
'At fancy their ideas are reet,
   An' other folks's wrong.
Let's treat these kindly, pity 'em,
   An' lay their follies bare ;
A dose like this may do 'em good ;
   Let's try it, lads ; feight fair.

Yo'll ha' some ruffish feightin' t' do,
   An' rare hard tugs wi' some,
Altho' they know nowt, good or bad,
   Bo what they'n larned awhoam.
Wi' th' weapons these ull bring i'th' field
   No deawt they'll mak' yo' stare ;
But, then, they're o they han to use,
   They are, indeed ; feight fair.

When Error stonds i'th' way o' truth,
   An' Wrong i'th' way o' Right ;
To clear the way, an' see fair play,
   Set to wi' o yo'r might.
But act wi' reason, tak' yo'r time,
   An' have a bit o' care ;
Be firm, an' yet be gentle, too ;
   Feight fair, mi lads, feight fair.

Feight fair wi' everyone yo' meet,
   Wi' rich, poor, young, an' owd ;
An' value noble actions moor
   Nor oather fame or gowd.
An' lads, as far as in us lies,
   Let's do what's reet an' square ;
An' when there's feightin' to be done,
   Let's aim at feightin' fair.

OWD PLAYMATES.

WHEER are my dear owd playmates neaw—
  Thoose lads aw loved so weel?
 Wheer's Allen Ridgway, Jemmy Breawn,
  An' little Bobby Steel?
An' that dear lad 'at used to come
  An' play wi' me i'th' fowd,
Wi' th' dimpled chin, an' rosy cheeks,
  An' curly locks o' gowd?

It's getten thirty year, an' moor,
  Sin' we we'rn lads at th' schoo';
Heaw toime goes trudgin' on, for sure!
  An' foalk go with it too.
But, oh! aw've noan forgetten yet
  Thoose childish sports o' eawrs—
Rompin' abeawt o'er hill an' dale,
  'Mong moss, an' ferns, an' fleawers.

Wheer are they neaw—those playful lads?
  Wheer's honest-hearted Will,
'At used to come fro' Whiteley Ho'
  An' lodge wi' Missis Gill?
He's long bin restin' in his grave;
  Poor lad! he geet a cowd,
An' th' scarlet fever took him off,
  When short o' nine year owd.

Dick Lunn's alive an' hearty yet,
  But isn't hawve as gay:
No foot-bo punsin' neaw for him,
  Nor rowlin' o'er i'th' hay;
He's toathry wrinkles on his broo,
  An' care-worn, too, aw see;
No deawt he's had some hardish rubs,
  An' worse for wear, like me.

An' then there's Widow Simpson's lad—
    Poor thing ! he deed when young.
Aw fancy aw can see him yet,
    An' yer his prattlin' tongue.
It broke his poor owd mother's heart,
    To lose her hope an' pride ;
An' neaw i'th' country churchyard, yon,
    They're lyin' side bi side.

Aw loved to linger near that grave ;
    Aw've sat theer scores o' heawrs ;
An' th' silent tears aw've letten fo,
    Han moisten'd th' fair wild fleawers ;
An' tho' there's some may reckon this
    Unworthy brain or pen,
Aw'm glad to think, an' preawd to own,
    We'd childer's feelin's then.

Heaw are we neaw—thoose on us left ?
    Is sympathy asleep ?
Or do we laugh wi' thoose 'at laugh,
    An' weep wi' thoose 'at weep ?
Has age improved us ?   Are these hearts
    More manly, kind, an' true ?
Or han we less good feelin' neaw
    Nor when we'rn lads at th' schoo ?

Let's hope we're better, an' as age
    Creeps o'er us, may we feel
At th' bit o' toime we'n bin i'th' world
    We'n fowt loife's battle weel.
An' may thoose lads 'at deed when young,
    An' thoose 'at live t' be owd,
All meet ogen wheer every yead
    Shall wear a creawn o' gowd !

(FROM THE ORIGINAL PICTURE BY CUTHBERT GRUNDY, R.C.A.)

Come an' see us every mornin';
  Come, these droopin' spirits cheer;
Peep thro' every cottage window,
  Tha'll be welcome everywheer.
Show thisel' i' o thi splendour;
  Throw that gloomy veil aside;
What does t' creep to th' back o' th' cleawds for,
  Tha's no fau'ts nor nowt to hide.

ODE TO TH' SUN.

HAIL, owd friend! aw'm fain to see thee:
 Wheer has t' been so mony days?
Lots o' times aw've looked up for thee,
 Wishin' aw could see thi face.
Th' little childer reawnd abeawt here,
 Say they wonder wheer tha'rt gone;
An' they wanten me to ax thee
 T' show thisel' as oft as t' con.

Come an' see us every mornin';
 Come, these droopin' spirits cheer:
Peep thro' every cottage window;
 Tha'll be welcome everywheer.
Show thisel i' o thi splendour;
 Throw that gloomy veil aside;
What dost t' creep to th' back o'th' cleawds for?
 Tha's no fau'ts nor nowt to hide.

Flashy clooas an' bits o foinery
 Help to mend sich loike as me:
Veils improve some women's faces,
 But, owd friend, they'll noan mend thee.
Things deawn here 'at we co'n pretty
 Soon begin to spoil an' fade;
But tha still keeps up thi polish,
 Tha'rt as breet as when new made.

Tha wur theer when th' hosts o' heaven
 Sweetly sang their mornin' song;
But tha looks as young as ever,
 Tho' tha's bin up theer so long.
An' for ages tha's bin shinin'—
 Smilin' o' this world o' eawrs;
Blessin' everythin' tha looks on,
 Makin' th' fruit grow—oppenin' fleawers.

It wur thee 'at Adam looked on,
    When i'th' garden bi hisel';
An' tha smoiled upon his labour—
    Happen helped him—who can tell?
It wur thee 'at Joshua spoke to
    On his way to th' promised land;
When, as th' good owd Bible tells us,
    Theaw obeyed his strange command.

Tha'll ha' seen some curious antics
    Played deawn here bi th' human race;
Some tha couldn't bear to look on,
    For tha shawmed an' hid thi face.
Mony a toime aw see thee blushin',
    When tha'rt leavin' us at neet:
An' no wonder, for tha's noticed
    Things we'n done 'at's noan been reet.

After o tha comes to own us,
    Tho' we do so mich 'at's wrong;
Even neaw tha'rt shinin' breetly,
    Helpin' me to write this song.
Heaw refreshin'! heaw revivin'!
    Stay as long as ever t' con;
We shall noan feel hawve as happy,
    Hawve as leetsome, when tha'rt gone.

Oh! for th' sake o' foalk 'at's poorly,
    Come an' cheer us wi thi rays;
We forgetten 'at we ail owt
    When we see thy dear owd face.
Every mornin' when it's gloomy,
    Lots o' foalk are seen abeawt;
Some at th' door-steps, some at th' windows,
    Watchin' for thee peepin' eawt.

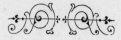

UNCLE DICK'S ADVOICE TO WED WOMEN.

NEAW, women, God bless yo! yo know aw'm yo'r friend,
An' as long as aw'm able to stur, aw intend
To do what aw con, booath wi' tongue an' wi' pen,
To praise yo, an' get yo weel thowt on bi' th' men.
At th' same toime aw shall noan be for howdin' mi tongue,
Iv aw foind 'at yo'r guilty o' doin' what's wrong.
Aw dar' say yo know very weel what aw meon ;
Aw want yo t' keep th' heawses o tidy an' cleon ;

An' be sure —when yo'r husbands come in ov a neet—
To ha' th' har'stone new mopp'd an' th' fender rubb'd breet ;
See 'at everything's noicely put by in its place,
An' welcome 'em whoam wi a smile on yo'r face.
When it's weshin' day, get done as soon as yo con ;
Aw'll assure yo it's very unpleasant for John
To come into th' heawse ov a noonin or neet,
An' foind th' durty clooas spread abeawt at his feet.

Aw'll be hang'd iv aw've patience wi' th' slatternly hags,
Sich as som'toimes aw see when aw'm goin' deawn th' flags ;
It's no wonder their husbands should set off an' drink ;
Will they stop wi' sich slovens as thoose, do yo think ?
Now, aw'll warrant they winnot, for *aw* never should ;
Aw'd " hook it " as sharply as ever aw could.
Whoa could ever expect one to ceawer in a hole,
Wheer a woman sits smookin', as black as a coal ?

Iv a fellow gets wed to a cratur' like this—
Unless he's some very queer notions o' bliss—
Aw think he'll prefer bein' off eawt o' th' dur
To ceawrin' o' th' har'stone wi' someb'dy loike her.
But oh ! a chap's blest when he gets a *good* woife,
To help him thro' th' world, and to sweeten his loife ;
An' one or two youngsters to romp on his knee ;
Neaw, aw've tried it, an' know what it is, do yo see.

It's noice when a little thing meets one on th' way,
An' sheawts, " Come on, daddy, come on to yo'r tay."
Eh, women, aw'll venture to gie my owd hat
Iv yo'll foind ony music 'ats sweeter nor that.
Oh ! it's grand when one enters th' inside o' their cot,
An' foinds 'at th' woife's made it a *heaven* ov a spot ;
An' her stondin' theer, bless her, to welcome yo in,
Wi' o 'at's abeawt her as clean as a pin !

An' it does seawnd some sweet, when hoo tells yo hoo's fain
To see yo come whoam weel an' hearty again.
Iv one's wantin' a bit o' *real pleasure*, it's here—
Bein' welcomed an' cared for bi' thoose yo' love dear.
There's nowt 'at's moor dear to a chap i' this loife,
Nor th' breet smilin' face ov a fond lovin' woife.
Well, women, what are yo for doin', neaw, come ?
Will yo promise an' try to keep th' husbands awhoam ?

Let 'em feel—when their wark's done—'at th' loveliest spot
'At there is under heaven, is *their own humble cot.*
Ah ! there's lots o' poor fellows aw've known i' mi loife,
'At's bin driven fro' whoam bi' a slovenly woife :
When they'n come in at neet, wearied eawt wi' their toil,
I' th' stead o' bein' met wi' a sweet lovin' smoile,
There's nothin' but black-lookin' holes met their een,
An' a woife an' some childer, a shawm to be seen.

Neaw, women, aw beg on yo, do what yo con
To mak things look summat loike reet for a mon ;
There'll be less drunken husbands, awm sure, if yo will ;
An' less money spent across th' road, at th' " Quiet Gill.'
Yo'll be paid for yo'r trouble wi' th' comfort it brings,
An' havin' moor brass for foine bonnets an' things.
Iv yo want to be happy, aw'd ha' yo be quick,
An' practice th' advoice o' yo'r friend, Uncle Dick.

UNCLE DICK'S ADVOICE TO SENGLE WOMEN.

NO deawt it ud look a deol better o' me
    To moind mi own wark, an' let th' women a-be ;
    But awm anxious to gie yo a bit ov advoice,
    For awm fond on yo, bless yo, yo looken so noice,
Wi yo're bonny blue een, set loike gems i' yo'r yead ;
Aw very nee wish 'at aw'd never bin wed ;
But there'd noan be mich chance iv aw' wurno, perhaps,
For aw reckon yo'r th' mooast on yo fitted wi chaps.

God bless yo, yo'r loike tender plants 'at's i' th' bud ;
Iv aw'd peawr to protect yo fro' danger, aw would ;
When th' cowd winds are blowin', to keep yo fro' harm,
Aw'd cover yo up weel, an' keep yo reet warm;
An' aw'd tak' care 'at th' sun didn't spoil yo an' o,
For aw'd nurse yo loike folk nurses plants for a show.
Neaw aw want a young woman—afore hoo gets wed
To Willie, or Albert, or Jammie, or Ned—

To try an' foind eawt if he's fond ov his books—
Never mind what he wears, nor heaw pratty he looks ;
Never heed heaw he brushes an' fettles his yure :
These things are attractive to one to be sure ;
But let her forget his fine clooas, if hoo con,
An' mak' sure o' one thing—an' that is—'at John's
Getten summat coed brains i' th' inside ov his nob.
Dunno ax iv he's getten a watch in his fob ;

Dunno mak' so mich bother respectin' his age,
Nor what he can get in a week as a wage ;
For there's mony a young fellow get's plenty o' brass
'At's never no business to cooart a young lass ;
For it's very well known 'at he's only a foo'—
Th' street-corner's his chapel, an' th' ale-heawse his schoo'.
Neaw, a young woman acts very foolish, aw think,
'At gets wed to a fellow 'ats fond ov his drink ;

For hoo connot expect to be happy, awm sure—
Ho'll be likelier far to be wretched an' poor.
So, lasses, yo bargain weel, whoile yo'r agate,
An' not ha' to after-think, when it's to' late ;
For there's lots o' poor deawn-trodden women aw know
'At once wur as happy as ony o' yo ;
When they started a-cooartin' their prospects wur breet—
Walkin' eawt arm-i'-arm wi' their lovers at neet :

Their minds free fro' trouble an' cankering care,
An' as women are neaw, buildin' "castles i' th' air,"
Never dreomin' but what sich accomplished young men
Would be allus as lovin' as what they wur then.
But men are loike women—they sometimes do wrong—
An' loike them, too, they mak' too mich use o' their tongue ;
Its surproisin' what noice-seawndin' tales they can tell—
Aw darsay aw've towd mony a hundert misel.

Well, lasses, iv ever yo meon to get wed,
Prepare yo'rsels for it.   Aw once yeard it said,
'At a chap deawn i' Slawwit—a village close by—
Ax'd his newly-made woife t' mak' a potato pie.
Neaw, hoo never had made nowt o' th' sooart in her loife,
But hoo towd him hoo'd try, like a dutiful woife ;
So hoo geet some potatoes, some mutton an' stuff,
An' at first hoo appeared to get on weel enuff ;

But, as th' tale gooas, it seems hoo went wur tor't th' last—
When hoo coom to put th' crust on, hoo geet gradely fast ;
Hoo couldn't for th' loife on her ger it th' reet size,
An' wondered why th' husband should want sich loike pies ;
Hoo rowled it, an' pood it, an' frabb'd a good bit,
But whatever hoo did, couldn't ger it to fit.
At last, when hoo'd done till hoo'rn getten reet stowd,
Hoo went to her mother's—a piece fur up th' road,

An' towd her what bother hoo'd had wi' this pie ;
" Well, come," said th' owd woman, " tha's no need to cry ;
Soa tha'rt fast, an' tha's come to thi mother to th' schoo';
Get a knife, an' then cut reawnd th' edges, tha foo' !"

UNCLE DICK'S ADVOICE TO SENGLE MEN.

A S sengle young women have had some advoice,
    Aw think it ud hardly be fair or look noice
    If friend Uncle Dick didn't set to ogen,
    And try to say summat to sengle young men.
Well, as yo'r weel aware, lads, aw've bin young misel',
So a hint or two met be o' use—who can tell ?
Aw'm noan yet a very owd fellow, it's true,
Still aw've gone through a deol 'at yo'll have to go through.

Neaw th' bit ov advoice 'at aw have to impart,
Let me tell yo's weel meant, an comes warm fro' mi heart ;
For aw know very weel what it is to be young ;
Aw remember the toime when aw whistled an' sung
As aw used to be trudgin' along to mi wark,
As cheerful, as merry, as blithe as a lark ;
Little thinkin' 'at care 'ud o'ertak' me so soon,
To mar an put everythin' reet eawt o' tune.

But we foind, while trampin' this rough world o' eawrs,
A great deol o' thorns, but a very few fleawers.
It's weel 'at it is so ; wur this a good shop,
We should aim at no better, but want to stop.
Well, neaw, will yo kindly excuse an owd mon,
While he's tryin' to gie th' best advoice 'at he con.
Beware o' bad habits : cigars an' strong drink
Are doin' moor harm to young folk nor they think.

Aw mony a toime wish eawr big men ud mak laws
To punish young lads seen wi' pipes i' their jaws.
Neaw isn't it a painful, a humblin' seet,
To witness mere childer go smookin' through th' street ?
Young lads ! iv yo ever intend to be men,
Shun poipes an' cigars ; never touch 'em ogen.
Aw'm sorry to gie yo'r pet habits such raps,
But smookin' an drinkin' oft ruin young chaps.

Well, aw reckon there's some little coartin' t' be done—
Some woman's affections 'at han to be won.
An here let me warn yo t' beware what yo do—
If yo' mak a bad match yo'll be certin to rue.
If tha meons to get wed, John, look eawt for a lass
Wi' some brains an' good fingers—care nowt abeawt brass,
For iv that's o tha get's tha'll repent o thi life
At that did'nt get howd ov a sensible woife.

Neaw, chaps, dunno yo be loike some 'at aw've seen—
Led away wi' red cheeks, rosy lips, an blue een.
Pratty women are very attractive, aw know ;
They'll do for us t' look at a bit—but that's o.
Neaw, dunno go tellin' it up an deawn th' teawn
'At beauty's a thing 'at aw want to run deawn ;
For a honsome young woman tak's th' lead, ther's no deawt,
I' o th' bonny things at eawr Maker's turned eawt.

What aw want yo to do, chaps, is this—get some woives
'At are loikely to wear weel, an' sweeten yo'r loives ;
'At'll love yo an' comfort yo' mony a long day,
When age comes, an' beauty's o faded away.
Get some woives 'at'll ha some affection to show,
An' cling to yo firmly i' weal an i' woe.
That's th' best sort o' beauty 'at winno go cowd,
But sticks to a mon when he's helpless an owd.

Well, aw'll drop it neaw lads ; aw'm at the' eend o' mi bant,
An aw dar' say aw've said quite as mich as yo want.
Aw've tried to appeal booath to th' heart an to th' yead,
An' hope yo'll be better for th' little aw've said :
Just tak these few hints as they come fro' mi pen,
And put 'em i' practice, young fellows, an' then—
Some day, when yo foind things are workin' so noice,
Yo'll thank Uncle Dick for his bit ov advoice.

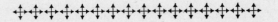

UNCLE DICK'S ADVOICE TO WED MEN.

WHAT to say to wed fellows aw conno weel tell ;
Altho aw've been wed two or three times mysel'.
It's a awkwardish job, an it's noan very noice
To be actin' th' owd uncle, an givin' advoice.
But th' wed women keep botherin' an wantin' me t' write
Iv aw dunno, aw know they'll do nowt nobbut flite.
My woife's among th' rest, hoo kicks up a rare fuss,
An says at there's reawm for improvement i' us.

Well aw dar' say there is, were noan angels, aw know ;
Now, now, chaps, there's nowt o' that stamp here below ;
Even women, as fair as they happen to be,—
They're sent into world witheawt wings, one can see ;
An' it's weel as it is so, for if they could fly,
That woife o' Tom Breawn's ud be off up i' th' sky ;
And there's moor beside her 'at ud soon disappear,
For they're tired o' bein' hampert an' kicked abeawt here.

Neaw why should it be so ? come, chaps, is this reet ?
Awm for bein' reet plain an straight forrud to-neet.
Does tha yer, Tom ? heaw is it theaw treats wi' neglect
That woman tha promised to love an protect ?
Heaw is it th'art gradely wi' folk eawt o' th' dur,
But when tha gets whoam th'art so peevish wi' hur ?
Eh, Tom, iv there's owt tha should love i' this loife,
Awm sure it's yore Poll, for hoo mak's a good woife.

Why, mon, tha's forgetten that mornin' awm sure,
When tha took her to th' altar, so fair an so pure ;
An' talk abeawt angels, an bonny blue een,
To mi thinkin' a prattier lass never wur seen.
When yo seet off to th' church, bells wor ringin' so sweet,
And th' nayburs God blessed her when passin' deawn th'
          street,
An her feythur an' mother—they mingled their prayers,
'At tha'd mack a good whoam for that dear lamb o' theirs.

Has ta done so, owd brid ? nowt o'th' sooart mon, tha knows
'At hoo's sufferin' just neaw fro' thi kicks an thi blows ;
It wur nobbut last neet, tha wur on at th' " King Ned,"
An' becose hoo went for thi, an ax'd thee t' go t' bed—
Tha up wi' thi fist, an' witheawt e'en a word,
Tha knocked her on th' paivins ;—it's true mon, aw've yeard.
Eh, Tom, lad, aw'd oather be better nor thee—
An' keep off that mischievous drink—or aw'd see.

A chap when he's wed should feel sattled i' loife—
Stay at whoam of a neet wi' his books an' his woife ;
An' if it so leets 'at there's youngsters to nurse,
It's his duty to help, for there's nothin' looks worse
Nor a chap to be gaddin' abeawt eawt o'th' dur,
An his woife wi' th nursin' an th' wark left to her.
Neaw awm sure it ud look far moor monly an' fair
If we stay'd in to help 'em, an did th' biggest share.

Aw con fancy aw yer somb'dy say, " Uncle Dick !
Aw wish yo'd stop gabblin' an talkin' so quick.
Let's have a word wi' yo,—it's o very noice
For a chap to be writin' an givin' advoice ;
But we wanten yo'r wife here, no deawt hoo could tell
Heaw toime after toime yo'n bin guilty yo'rsel ;
When ogen yo'r inclined to give others a rap,
Think on an' begin' at Jerusalem, owd chap."

Well, well, lads, aw will, for awm guilty, no deawt ;
We'n o bits o' failin's—we're noan on us beawt.
Even th' best on us, when we're weel polished an' breet
Winno bear a good siftin' nor bringin' to th' leet.
So let's start an' mend, let's begin an be good,
For eawr woives ud be rarely set up if we would.
Let's prove eawrsel's honest an monly an' true,
An then th' women ull try, an' they'll mend a bit too.

GEORGE PERKINS. 1893.

Tha'rt welcome, little bonny brid:
But shouldn't ha' come just when tha did:
    Times are bad.
We're short o' pobbies for eawr Joe,
But that, of course, tha didn't know,
    Did ta, lad?

Lancashire Lyrics!

(TWELVE IN NUMBER).

WRITTEN DURING THE "COTTON PANIC."

WELCOME, BONNY BRID!

TH'ART welcome, little bonny brid,
But shouldn't ha' come just when tha did ;
    Toimes are bad.
We're short o' pobbies for eawr Joe,
But that, of course, tha didn't know,
    Did ta, lad ?

Aw've often yeard mi feyther tell,
At when aw coom i' th' world misel'
    Trade wur slack ;
An' neaw it's hard wark pooin' throo—
But aw munno fear thee, iv aw do
    Tha'll go back.

Cheer up ! these toimes 'll awter soon ;
Aw'm beawn to beigh another spoon—
    One for thee ;
An', as tha's sich a pratty face
Aw'll let thee have eawr Charley's place
    On mi knee.

God bless thee, love, aw'm fain tha'rt come,
Just try an mak' thisel awhoam :
    Here's thi nest ;
Tha'rt loike thi mother to a tee,
But tha's thi feyther's nose, aw see,
    Well, aw'm blest !

Come, come, tha needn't look so shy,
Aw am no' blamin' thee, not I ;
    Settle deawn,
An' tak' this haupney for thisel,
There's lots o' sugar-sticks to sell
    Deawn i' th' teawn.

Aw know when furst aw coom to th' leet,
Aw're fond o' owt 'at tasted sweet ;
     Tha'll be th' same.
But come, tha's never towd thi dad
What he's to co thee yet, mi lad—
     What's thi name ?

Hush ! hush ! tha mustn't cry this way,
But get this sope o' cinder tay
     While it's warm ;
Mi mother used to give it me,
When aw wur sich a lad as thee,
     In her arm.

Hush-a-babby, hush-a-bee,—
Oh, what a temper ! dear-a-me
     Heaw tha skrikes !
Here's a bit o' sugar, sithee ;
Howd thi noise, an then aw'll gie thee
     Owt tha likes.

We've nobbut getten coarsish fare,
But, eawt o' this tha'll get thi share,
     Never fear.
Aw hope tha'll never want a meal,
But allis fill thi bally weel
     While tha'rt here.

Thi feyther's noan been wed so long,
An' yet tha sees he's middlin' throng
     Wi' yo' o.
Besides thi little brother Ted,
We've one upsteers, asleep i' bed,
     Wi' eawr Joe.

But tho' we've childer two or three,
We'll mak' a bit o' reawm for thee,
     Bless thee, lad !
Tha'rt th' prattiest brid we have i' th' nest,
So hutch up closer to mi breast ;
     Awm thi dad.

THERE'S NO GOOD I' CEAW'RIN' I' TH' DUST.

COME, Dick, let's have howd o' thi hond,
    Whot a dreadful long face tha keeps pooin,
    These bad times tha'll ne'er manage to stond,
        Except tha minds weel whot tha'rt doin'.
Iv aw've owt i' mi heawse or mi purse,
    'At tha'rt really i' th' need on, aw'll lend it,
Aw see thi owd cooat's gettin' worse,
    But aw'll look thi a patch up to mend it.

Aw wish aw'd mi hat full o' gowd,
    Aw'd mak' someb'dy glad wi' mi givin';
Aw'd miss noather young folk nor owd,
    'At wanted a lift wi' their livin'.
There's theawsands o' poor folk, aw know,
    O'er hard times an' poverty grievin';
There's one or two lives i' th' next row
    Aw should feel rare an' preawd o' relievin'.

But it happens aw'm poor, like theirsel',
    An' aw know very weel they're noan shammin';
Bless thi, Dick, lad, there's nob'dy can tell
    Heaw long we're to keep on a clammin'.
They should help us a bit, them as con,
    Or some'll ne'er live to see th' end on't;
There's mony a poor woe-stricken mon,
    Would be glad ov assistance, depend on't!

We'n lots o' brave fellows i' th' street,
    Low-spirited, deawncast, an' needy,
Wi' hardly a shoe to their feet,
    An' cooats o' their backs gettin' seedy.
It's hard when a chap's done his best,
    Boath i' plannin', an' savin', an' strivin',
To keep th' little brids i' their nest,
    An' yet connot get 'em a livin'.

But it's no use o' whinin' loike this,
   Th' dark cleawd 'll gi way for a breeter ;
Aw'll gi' mi owd woman a kiss,
   An' then tune up mi poipe, an' sing sweeter.
Let's noan look so deawncast an' sad,
   There's things i' th' world yet 'at's worth seein',
As long as there's life to be had,
   It's no use o' talkin' o' deein.

There's no good i' ceawrin' i' th' dust,
   Iv aw wur to have mi own choosin',
Afore aw'd be covered wi' rust,
   Aw'd wear eawt wi' rubbin' an' usin'.
Aw'll try an' aw'll keep up mi yed,
   Tho' aw live a few months upo' shoddy,
Aw'm determined aw'll never go dead,
   As long as aw've soul i' mi body.

Go whoam, Dick, an' streighten thi face,
   An' keep it as streight as tha'rt able,
An' aw'll warrant tha'll see better days,
   An' plenty o' meat o' thy table.
Dunno skulk i' this world loike a meawse,
   Howd thi yed up, an' keep up thi courage ;
Iv tha'rt clammin', just co' at eawr heawse,
   An' aw'll gi' thi a spoonful o' porridge.

Ne'er fret abeaut th' times bein' bad,
   For they'll mend again sometime, depend on't ;
There'll be plenty o' wark to be had,
   An' plenty o' wage, too, at th' end on't.
Let us bid care an' trouble good-neet,
   For there's ne'er no good i' repinin' ;
Look up ! iv it's noan i' one's seet,
   Yon sun up above's allis shinin'.

AW'VE HARD WARK TO HOWD UP MI YED.

WHEEREVER aw trudge neaw-a-days,
    Aw'm certain to see some owd friend
Lookin' anxiously up i' my face,
    An' axin' when times are beawn t' mend.
Aw'm surprised heaw folk live, aw declare,
    Wi' th' clammin' an' starvin' they'n stood ;
God bless 'em, heaw patient they are !
    Aw wish aw could help 'em, aw would.

But really aw've nowt aw con give,
    Except it's a bit ov a song,
An' th' Muses han hard wark to live,
    One's bin hamper'd an' powfagg'd so long ;
Aw've tried to look cheerful an' bowd,
    An' yo know what aw've written an' said,
But iv truth mun be honestly towd,
    Aw've hard wark to howd up mi yed !

There'll be some on us missin' aw deawt
    Iv there isn't some help for us soon ;
We'n bin jostled an' tumbled abeawt,
    Till we're welly o knocked eawt o' tune ;
Eawr Margit, hoo frets an' hoo cries,
    As hoo sits theer, wi' th' choilt on her knee
An' aw connot blame th' lass, for hoo tries
    To be cheerful an' gradely wi' me.

Yon Yankees may think it's rare fun,
  Kickin' up sich a shindy o'th' globe ;
Confound 'em, aw wish they'd get done,
  For they'd weary eawt th' patience o' Job !
We shall have to go help 'em, that's clear,
  Iv they dunno get done very soon ;
Iv eawr Volunteers wur o'er theer,
  They'd sharpen 'em up to some tune.

Neaw it's hard for a mortal to tell
  Heaw long they may plague us this road ;
Iv they'd hurt nob'dy else but thersel,
  They met fo eawt and feight till they'rn stow'd.
Aw think it's high time someb'dy spoke,
  When so many are cryin' for bread ;
For there's hundreds an' theawsands o' folk,
  Deawn i' Lancashire hardly hawve fed.

Th' big men, when they yer eawr complaint,
  May treat it as " gammon " an' " stuff,"
An' tell us we use to' much paint,
  But we dunnot daub paint on enuff,
If they think it's noan true what we sen,
  Ere they charge us wi' tellin' a lie,
Let 'em look into th' question loike men,
  An' come deawn here a fortnit an' try.

SEWIN' CLASS SONG.

COME, lasses, let's cheer up, an' sing, it's no use
    lookin' sad,
    We'll mak' eawr sewin' schoo' to ring, an' stitch
    away loike mad ;
We'll try an' mak' th' best job we con o' owt we han to do,
We read an' write, an' spell an' kest, while here at th' sewin'
    schoo'.
   Chorus—Then, lasses, let's cheer up an' sing,
        It's no use lookin' sad.

Eawr Queen, th' Lord Mayor o' London, too, they send us lots
    o' brass,
An' neaw, at welly every schoo', we'n got a sewin' class ;
We'n superintendents, cutters eawt, an' visitors an' o ;
We'n parsons, cotton mesturs, too, come in to watch us sew.
   Chorus—Then, lasses, let's cheer up an' sing, &c.

Sin th' war begun, an' th' factories stopped, we're badly off, it's
    true,
But still we needn't grumble, for we'n noan so mich to do ;
We're only here fro' nine to four, an' han an heawer for noon,
We noather stop so very late nor start so very soon.
   Chorus—Then, lasses, let's cheer up an' sing, &c.

It's noice an' easy sittin' here, there's no mistake i' that,
We'd sooner do it, a foine seet, nor root among th' Shurat ;
We'n ne'er no floats to unweave neaw, we're reet enough,
    bi th' mass,
For we couldn't have an easier job nor goin' to th' sewin' class.
   Chorus—Then, lasses, let's cheer up an' sing, &c.

We're welly killed wi' kindness neaw, we really are, indeed,
For everybody's tryin' hard to get us o we need ;
They'n sent us puddin's, bacon, too, an' lots o' decent clo'es,
An' what they'll send afore they'n done there's nob'dy here 'at
    knows.

Chorus—Then, lasses, let's cheer up an' sing, &c.

God bless these kind, good-natured folk, 'at sends us o' this
    stuff,
We conno tell 'em o we feel, nor thank 'em hawve enuff ;
They help to find us meat an' clooas, an' eddicashun, too,
An' what creawns o', they give us wage for goin' to th' sewin'
    schoo'.

  Chorus—Then, lasses, let's cheer up an' sing, &c.

We'n sich a chance o' larnin' neaw we'n never had afore :
An' oh, we shall be rare an' wise when th' Yankee wars are o'er;
There's nob'dy then can puzzle us wi' owt we'n larned to do,
We'n getten polished up so weel wi' goin' to th' sewin' schoo'.

  Chorus—Then, lasses, let's cheer up an' sing, &c.

Young fellows lookin' partners eawt had better come this way,
For, neaw we'n larned to mak' a shirt, we're ready ony day ;
But mind, they'll ha' to ax us twice, an' mak' a deol ado,
We're gettin' rayther saucy neaw, wi' goin' to th' sewin' schoo'.

  Chorus—Then, lasses, let's cheer up an' sing, &c.

There'll be some lookin' eawt for wives when th' factories start
    ogen,
But we shall never court wi' noan but decent, sober men ;
Soa vulgar chaps, beawt common sense, will ha' no need to
    come,
For sooner than wed sich as these, we'd better stop a whoam.

  Chorus—Then, lasses, let's cheer up and sing, &c.

Come, lasses, then, cheer up an' sing, it's no use lookin' sad,
We'll mak' eawr sewin' schoo' to ring, an' stitch away loike mad;
We live i' hopes afore so long, to see a breeter day,
For th' cleawd at's hangin' o'er us neaw is sure to blow away.

  Chorus—Then, lasses, let's cheer up an' sing, &c.

IT'S HARD TO CEAWER I' TH' CHIMNEY NOOK.

IT'S hard to ceawer i' th' chimney nook,
　　Fro' weary day to day;
　An' no kind word, nor lovin' look
　　To drive one's care away!
Mi clooas are welly o worn eawt,
　An' neaw aw'm sich a seet,
Aw dunno loike to walk abeawt,
　Unless it's dark at neet.

To get us bread, mi mother sowd
　Eawr mattrasses an' sheets;
An' oh, it is so bitter cowd,
　These frosty, winter neets!
Two ladies kindly co'd one day,
　An' put us deawn some shoon;
They said they'd sheets to give away,
　An' we must ha' some soon.

Eawr Mary Jane's a bonny lass,
　Wi' two such rosy cheeks;
Hoo goes to th' Refuge Sewin' Class,
　An' has done neaw for weeks.
Poor thing! hoo's badly starved, aw know,
　Hoo's scarcely owt to wear;
Aw do so wish 'at somed'y'd co,
　'At's getten owt to spare.

Her petticoats are o worn eawt;
　Her Sunday frock's i' holes;
An' then her boots—hoo's welly beawt—
　They want booath heels an' soles.
Aw wish mi feyther had a job,
　He looks so strange an' wild;
He'll sit for heawers at th' side o'th' hob,
　An' cry just like a child.

D

No wonder he should pine an' fret,
    An' look soa discontent;
For th' gas bill isn't settled yet,
    An' th' lon'lord wants his rent.
Mi mother's bin to th' shop to-neet,
    To fetch a bit o' tay;
Hoo says they hardly looken reet,
    Becose hoo conno pay.

An' who can blame 'em?   Nob'dy can;
    They're wur nor us, bi th' mass!
Iv they're to pay for what they han,
    They're loike to ha' some brass;
We'n lived as careful as we con
    Aw'm sure, but after o
A great big shop score's runnin' on,
    For tothry peawnd or so.

Aw've etten bacon till aw'm sick;
    Eawr Jimmy has an' o;
An' iv yo'll ax mi uncle Dick,
    He'll tell yo th' same, aw know.
An' porritch aw've had quite anoo,
    For they dunno suit, aw find;
Aw conno do wi' soup an' stew,
    They fill one full o' wind.

Aw'm glad o' every bit aw get,
    An' rare an' thankful feel;
Aw've allis getten summat yet,
    To mak' misel' a meal.
Thank God, we'n never ax'd i' vain,
    For folk are kind, aw'm sure;
God bless 'em o for what they've gan;
    One conno say no moor.

TH' SHURAT WEAVER'S SONG.

ONFOUND it ! aw ne'er wur so woven afore,
    Mi back's welly brocken, mi fingers are sore ;
    Aw've bin starin' an' rootin' among this Shurat,
    Till aw'm very near getten as bloint as a bat.

Every toime aw go in wi' mi cuts to owd Joe,
He gies mi a cursin', an' bates mi an' o ;
Aw've a warp i' one loom wi' booath selvedges marr'd,
An' th' other's as bad for he's dress'd it to hard.

Aw wish aw wur fur enuff off, eawt o' th' road,
For o' weavin' this rubbitch aw'm gettin' reet stow'd ;
Aw've nowt i' this world to lie deawn on but straw,
For aw've only eight shillin' this fortni't to draw.

Neaw aw haven't mi family under mi hat,
Aw've a woife an' six childer to keep eawt o' that ;
So aw'm rayther among it at present yo see,
Iv ever a fellow wur puzzled, it's me !

Iv one turns eawt to steal, folk 'll co me a thief,
An' aw conno' put th' cheek on to ax for relief ;
As aw said i' eawr heawse t' other neet to mi woife,
Aw never did nowt o' this sort i' mi loife.

One doesn't like everyone t' know heaw they are,
But we'n suffered so long thro' this 'Merica war,
'At there's lot's o' poor factory folk getten t' fur end,
An' they'll soon be knock'd o'er iv th' toimes don't mend.

Oh, dear! iv yon Yankees could only just see
Heaw they're clemmin' an' starvin' poor weavers loike me,
Aw think they'd soon settle their bother, an' strive
To send us some cotton to keep us alive.

There's theawsands o' folk just i' th' best o' their days,
Wi' traces o' want plainly seen i' their face;
An' a future afore 'em as dreary an' dark,
For when th' cotton gets done we shall o be beawt wark.

We'n bin patient an' quiet as long as we con;
Th' bits o' things we had by us are welly o gone;
Aw've bin trampin' so long, mi owd shoon are worn eawt,
An' mi halliday clooas are o on 'em "up th' speawt."

It wur nobbut last Monday aw sowd a good bed—
Nay, very near gan it—to get us some bread;
Afore these bad times cum aw used to be fat,
But neaw, bless yo'r loife, aw'm as thin as a lat!

Mony a toime i' mi loife aw've seen things lookin' feaw,
But never as awk'ard as what they are neaw;
Iv there isn't some help for us factory folk soon,
Aw'm sure we shall o be knocked reet eawt o' tune.

Come give us a lift, yo' 'at han owt to give,
An' help yo're poor brothers an' sisters to live;
Be kind, an' be tender to th' needy an' poor,
An' we'll promise when th' times mend we'll ax yo no moor.

TH' OWD BARBER EAWT O' WARK.

HERE aw'm ceawerin' beawt custom fro' mornin' to
    neet,
        Aw wonder what's th' matter, there's summat noan
            reet;
Heaw it is aw've nowt t' do aw conno weel tell,
Unless folk's beginnin' o' shavin' theirsel.
Aw should loike to do moor nor aw have done to-day,
For aw've one or two bills 'at aw'm wantin' to pay;
An' aw'm certain o' one thing, there'll be a foine row,
Iv aw dunno pay Turner for gildin' mi pow.
An' then there's th' cigar chap—he's comin' this week;
An' aw owe four-an'-sixpence to Clay for some breek.
Iv someb'dy doesn't come in, an' bring me some brass,
Aw shall very soon be in a pickle, bi th' mass!
There's th' doctor reawnd th' corner, he used to come here,
Never missed twice a week bein' perch'd i' this cheer;
But neaw he walks past, an' ne'er gies me a co'—
Aw wonder iv *he's* stopped for cotton an' o'!
As aw're comin' past Morton's front window at noon,
When aw'd bin on to Johnny M'Kay's wi' mi shoon,
Aw'll be blest if th' owd chap wur no' cuttin' his hair
Wi' a pair o' big shears—it's true, aw declare!
Ah! tha'll look a foine seet when tha's finished, aw thowt:
Iv he'd come an' ax'd me aw'd ha cut it for nowt.
It's toime aw'd a job, for mi lather an' brush—
Hello! there's a customer comin' neaw, hush!
Oh, it's only eawr Timothy bringin' mi tay—
Aw shall ate a deal moor nor aw've getten to-day.
What's th' reason owd Jammy o' Neds doesn't come?
Aw wonder iv th' woife pows an' shaves him awhoam.

Aw know why Bob Travis ne'er gi'es me a co',
He's letten his beard an' his mustash grow;
He's towd me this week 'at he doesn't intend
To be shaved ony moor till trade begins t' mend.
We shall ha' to shut up, shall us barbers, that's ole;
For we connot pretend to find gas an' coal,
Nor we conno' pay taxes an' rates eawt o' nowt;
An' then there's these razors, they han to be bowt,
Beside other matters one has abeawt th' place,
Sich as hair oil, an' teawels for wipin' their face;
There's mi lather brush, hair brush, there's soap an' th' glass,
An' that great big wesh-bowl—they o tacken brass.
When one's nowt comin' in mich it acts very bad,
It's enuff to mak' people i' business go mad.
Neaw things wur no' soa when aw oppen'd this room,
For aw couldn't attend folk as fast as they coom.
Jem Thompson, poor chap, he's no better nor me,
He says he can hardly mak' ends meet an' tee;
An' he used to do rarely, did Jem, he did so,
For he mends umbrellas, grinds razors an' o.
Aw wish aw wur single, aw'd hook it fro' here,
Aw'd sell o' mi razors, mi strop, an' this cheer;
Aw'd soon steer mi bark on the ocean wave,
For aw'd go see iv th' Yankees wur wantin' a shave.
Iv aw didn't succeed, an' could get nowt to eight,
Aw could list for a sodier, an' help 'em to feight.
But aw'll go an' shut up, while there's middlin' o' leet,
For there's nob'dy wants powin' an' shavin' to-neet.
Aw've waited, an' waited for folk till aw'm stow'd,
But aw'll noan stond it long, if aw do aw'll be blow'd.
Th' idea ov a chap ceawrin' here bi hissel,
Singin' " Lather 'em, shave 'em, shave 'em well."
Iv aw'd somb'dy in here just to stick to mi coat,
Aw'd get ow'd of a razor an' cut mi throat,
An' try t' other world, for there's nowt to do here—
Aw'd go see iv they're wantin' a barber deawn theer.

GOD BLESS 'EM, IT SHOWS THEY'N SOME THOWT.

IS there nob'dy to thank these good folk?
    No poet to scribble a line?
  Aw wish aw could write yo' a song,
    Aw'd mak' yo' reet welcome to mine.
There's Waugh, he's bin writin' for years,
  An' mony a good tale, too, he's towd;
But he says nowt abeawt these bad times,
  Aw wonder, neaw, heaw he con howd.

Iv aw could draw pictures loike him,
  An' ceawr deawn an' write hawve as weel,
Aw'd tell folk heaw thankful aw am,
  But aw couldn't tell th' hawve 'at aw feel.
When aw tak' up a papper to read,
  Aw con see there heaw ready folk are
At helpin' poor creatures i' need,
  An' givin' us o they con spare.

We'n gentlemen, ladies an' o',
  As busy i' th' country as owt,
Providin' for th' Lancashire poor;
  God bless 'em, it show's they'n some thowt!
Iv they'll only keep on as they do,
  We shall o be rigg'd eawt very soon;
There's one party givin' us frocks,
  An' another lot sendin' us shoon.

Th' Australians han sent us some gowd,
   For feedin' an' clothin' o' th' poor ;
An' they say it's noan o we mun have,
   For they're busy collectin' us moor.
An' th' Indians are helpin' an' o ;
   Aw reckon they're grateful for th' past,
So they'll give us a bit of a lift,
   For helpin' them eawt when they'rn fast.

We'n clogs an' we'n clooas gan us neaw,
   There's both second-honded an' new ;
Some are givin' us soup twice a week,
   An' others are givin' us stew.
We're rare an' weel done to aw'm sure,
   For we're fed, an' we're clothed, an' we're towt ;
They pay'n us for goin' to th' schoo',
   An gi'en' us good larnin' for nowt.

God bless 'em for o 'at they've done,
   An' aw hope they'll keep doin' as well,
Till th' dark cleawd 'at hangs o'er's blown away,
   An' we're able to do for eawrsel'.
Excuse me for writin' these loines,
   For it's no use, aw conno' be still,
As long as they help us to live,
   Aw'll thank 'em, if nob'dy else will.

AW'VE TURNED MI BIT O' GARDEN O'ER.

A W'VE turned mi bit o' garden o'er,
    An' set mi seed an' o ;
    Soa neaw aw've done aw'll rest a bit,
    An' sit an' watch it grow.
It's noice to have a little spot,
    Where one can ceawer 'em deawn,
A quiet, comfortable place,
    Eawtside o' th' busy teawn,
Where one can sit an' smoke their poipe,
    An' have a friendly chat,
Or read th' newspapper o'er a bit,
    Or talk abeawt Shurat ;
Or listen to some owd man's tale,
    Some vet'ran come fro' th' wars ;
Aw loike to yer 'em spin their yarn,
    An' show their wounds an' scars.

One neet aw thowt aw'd tak' a walk
    As far as th' Hunter's Teawer,
To beg a daisy root or two :
    Tom's gan me mony a fleawer.
They're bloomin' i' mi garden neaw,
    Aw've sich a bonny show ;
Aw've daisies, pinks, carnations, too,
    An' pollyants an' o.
Yo couldn't think heaw preawd aw feel,
    O' every plant an' fleawer ;
Aw couldn't ha' cared for childer moor—
    Aw've nursed 'em mony a heawer.
But tho' they neaw look fresh an' fair,
    They'll droop their yeds an' dee ;
They hanno long to tarry here—
    They're just loike yo an' me.

Dark-lookin' cleawds are gatherin' reawnd,
  Aw think it's beawn to rain ;
There's nowt could pleos me better neaw,
  Aw should be rare an' fain !
Mi bit o' seed wants deggin' o'er,
  To help to mak' it spreawt ;
It's summat loike a choild's first teeth,
  'At wanten helpin' eawt.
But aw'll be off, afore aw'm wet,
  It's getten reet agate ;
An' while it comes aw think aw'll get
  A bit o' summat t' eat ;
For oh ! it is a hungry job,
  This workin' eawt o' th' door ;
Th' committee should alleaw for this,
  An' give one rayther moor.

Aw should so loike a good blow eawt,
  A feed off beefsteak pie ;
But aw can ne'er get nowt loike that
  Wi' th' bit aw draw, not I !
Aw'm glad enough o' porritch neaw,
  Or tothrey cowd potates ;
If aw can get enoo o' these,
  Aw'st do till th' factory gates.
It's welly gan o'er rainin', so
  Aw'll have another look,
An' see heaw th' garden's gettin' on ;
  An' then aw'll get a book,
An read an heawer or two for th' woife,
  An' sing a bit for Ted ;
Then poo mi clogs off, fasten th' doors,
  An' walk up steers to bed.

WHAT'S UP WI' THEE, TUM?

"MON, tha howds deawn thi yead loike a thief,
    An tha's noan getten th' pluck ov a leawse;
    Neaw, what's th' use on thee nursin' thi grief?
    Ger up, or aw'll give thee a seawse:
Mon, tha'rt welly a shawm to be seen,
    Are ta meawtin', or what does ta ail?
Come, mop up that weet fro' thi een,
    For aw've browt thee some bacon and male.

"Aw dar say tha'rt hungry, owd lad,
    An thi woife, theer, hoo looks like a ghost;
Yo'r Jonathan's welly as bad,
    An yo're Nelly, poor thing, hoo looks lost.
Hast a bit ov a pon ony wheer,
    'At 'll fry yo a collop or two?
An aw'll run for a pint o' smo' beer,
    Fro' owd Mally Dawson's i' th' broo."

"Ne'er mind, Jim, we need no smo' drink;
    We can manage beawt swillin' it deawn;
An, thank thee, aw mony a toime think
    Tha'rt th' best-natured chap i' this teawn.
God bless thee, an thank thee ogen;
    Iv it wur not for thee an' yo're Sam
Bringin' summat to eat, neaw an then,
    Aw believe we should o have to clam.

"This mornin' owd Alice, th' next dur,
    Coom in wi' a potfull o' tay;
An oh, some an thankful we wur,
    For it's o we'n had t' live on to-day.
Aw've bin eawt a beggin' sin noon,
    Just look heaw mi stockins are wet;
It's wi' havin' big holes i' mi shoon,
    But tha knows, Jim, they're th' best one can get."

" Well, well, lad, aw know heaw yo are,
   An aw'm noan so mich better mysel';
Heaw long aw may have eawt to spare
   It's hard for a body to tell ;
But as long as aw've getten owt t' give
   Tha'rt sure to be one aw shall sarve ;
Aw shall help an owd shopmate to live,
   An see 'at tha'rt noan left to starve.

" Send yo're Nelly to th' cobblers to neet—
   Aw meon cobbler Jack's deawn i'th' fowd—
An aw'll beigh thi some shoon to thi feet,
   For tha'rt gettin' thi deoth wi cowd ;
An aw'll speak to owd Mistress Scholes,
   To look th' woife up a bit ov a dress ;
For that hoo has on's full o' holes—
   But hoo's getten nowt better, aw guess.

" Neaw, Tum, lad, tha'rt cryin' aw see,
   Come, cheer up as weel as tha con ;
Tha's noan bin forgotten, tha'll see ;
   There's foalk as con feel for thee, mon.
Tha's noan bin beawt trouble, aw know ;
   It's no wonder to me tha should fret ;
But there's room i'th' world yet for us o
   Mon ; tha's no need to hang thisel yet.

" Tum ! aw knew thee when tha wur a lad,
   Livin' th' next dur but one to th' Breawn Ceaw ;
Thi heart then wur leetsome an' glad ;
   What aw want is—to see it so neaw.
Tha'rt welcome to my little mite,
   For aw connot afford a big sum ;
But as long as aw've getten a bite,
   Tha shall ha' th' hawve on't—that tha shall, Tum."

AW'VE JUST BEEN A-LOOKIN' AT TH' SCHOLARS.

AW'VE just been a-lookin' at th' scholars;
 God bless 'em! heaw happy aw feel
To find 'at they'n been so weel done to,
 An' see 'em ole lookin soa weel.
There's Charley—he's getten new breeches;
 An' Hannah Maria's new shoon;
While owd Billy Wade's youngest dowter,
 Hoo does cut a dash to some tune!

There has been some plannin' an' skeomin',
 There has been some sugarless tay—
An' buttercakes etten beawt butter,
 To get these foine things for to-day!
Neaw, isn't it really surprisin',
 Heaw well th' little childer appear,
When brass is soa hard to get howd of,
 An' wearin' things gettin' soa dear.

If it wurno' for th' kind-hearted women
 (God bless 'em o) helpin' us throo—
While things are soa dreadfully awkard—
 Aw dunna know what we must do.
Iv Mary Ann wants a new bonnet,
 Or Frederick James a new cap,
They'll manage to get 'em a-someheaw,
 They'll oather beg, borrow, or swap.

There's lots o' owd faded silk dresses
 Been used to mack little frocks on;
We've cut an owd cooat o' mi' fayther's
 To make up a suit for eawr John.
Aw've seen little Emily Thompson—
 Hoo wur some an' pratty for sure!
There's nob'dy would ever imagine
 Her fayther an' mother are poor.

But foalks have to skeom an' do ole roads,
　　An' th' rich abeawt here never dreom,
Heaw one hawve o' th' nayburs abeawt 'em,
　　For a bare toarin' on have to skeom.
For, while they've getten so mitch to stur on,
　　'At they hardly know what to do wi' 't,
There's mony a poor chilt reawnd abeawt 'em
　　Wi' hardly a shoe to its feet.

Eh, aw wish aw wur wealthy, like some foalk,
　　An' had summat to spare aw could give,
Aw'd do what this heart o' moine prompts me,
　　Aw'd help thoose abeawt me to live !
Aw'd leeten poor folk o' their burdens,
　　Aw'd cheer mony a heart 'at wur sad ;
While thoose 'at wur troubled an' deawncast,
　　Aw'd try to mak' cheerful an' glad.

Heaw is it 'at foalks are so hampert
　　Wi' sich an abundance i' th' lond ?
Heaw is it 'at some are i' tatters
　　While others are gaudily donn'd ?
Heaw is it 'at some can be livin'
　　I' splendour, at foine marble halls,
While others are clemmin' an' starvin',
　　Wi' nowt i' their seet but bare walls ?

God's good, an' provides us wi' plenty ;
　　There's mate an' there's clooas for us o,
But these good things—they're hard to get howd on—
　　These blessin's 'at ceasin'ly flow—
They seem to be stopp'd on their journey,
　　An' laid deawn at th' rich foalks door ;
Well, its happen tor th' best 'at it is so ;
　　God help those 'at's needy an' poor !

CHEER UP A BIT LONGER.

HEER up a bit longer, mi brothers i' want,
    There's breeter days for us i' store ;
    There'll be plenty o' "tommy" an' wark for us o,
      When this dark-lookin' cleawd's blown o'er.
Yo'n struggled reet nobly an' battled reet hard,
    While things han been lookin' so feaw ;
Yo'n borne wi' yo're troubles an' trials so long,
    'At it's no use o' givin' up neaw.

Feight on, as yo han done, an' victory's sure,
    For th' battle seems very near won ;
Be firm i' yore sufferin' an' dunno give way,
    For they're nowt nobbut ceawards 'at run.
Yo' know heaw they'n praised us for stondin' so firm,
    An' shall we neaw stagger an' fo ?
Not we ! if we nobbut brace up an' be hard,
    We con stond a bit longer aw know.

It's hard to keep clemmin' an' starvin', it's true ;
    An' it's hard to see th' little things fret,
Becose there's no buttercakes for 'em to eat,
    But we'n allis kept pooin' throo yet.
As bad as times are, an' as feaw as things look,
    One's certain they met ha' bin worse ;
For we'n getten a trifle o' summat so fur,
    Tho' it's been poorish poikin,' of course.

Aw've begged on yo' t' keep up yore courage before,
    An' neaw let me ax yo' once moor;
Let's noan get disheartened, there's hope for us yet,
    We needn't despair tho' we're poor.
We connot expect it'll allis be foine;
    It's dark for awhile, an' then clear;
We'n mirth mixed wi' sadness, an' pleasure wi' pain,
    An' shall have so long as we're here.

This world's full o' changes for better or worse,
    An' this is one change among th' ruck;
We'n a time o' prosperity, time o' success,
    An' then we'n a reawnd o' bad luck.
We're baskin' i' sunshine at one time o' th' day,
    At other times ceawrin' i' th' dark;
To-day finds us hearty, an' busy as owt,
    To-morn, may be, ill an' beawt wark.

God bless yo', mi brothers, we're nobbut on th' tramp,
    We never stay long at one spot;
An' while we keep knockin' abeawt i' this world,
    Disappointments will fall to eawer lot;
So th' best thing we con do, if we mean to get through,
    Is to wrastle wi' cares as they come;
If we're tired an' weary,—well, let's never heed,
    We con rest us weel when we get whoam.

Cheer up, then, aw say, an' keep hopin' for th' best,
    For things are goin' t' alter, an' soon:
Ole these wailin's an' discords are beawnd to dee eawt,
    An' gie way for a merrier tune.
'Bide on a bit longer, tak' heart once ogen,
    An' do give o'er lookin' so feaw;
As we'n battled, an' struggled, an' suffered so long,
    It's no use o' givin' up neaw.

HOMELY ADVICE TO TH' UNEMPLOYED.

THO' unfit to tak' part i' loife's battles
 Or feight wi th' same pluck as befoor;
As a comrade, an' late brother-toiler,
 Aw feel anxious to help yo' once moor.
Aw've fowt long an' hard as yo' know, lads;
 But aw'm gettin' near th' end o' mi days;
Aw shall soon have to strip off this armour,
 An' let somb'dy else tak' mi place.

Tak' advice fro' a grey-yeaded comrade,
 Let justice be blended wi' blows:
An' be sure 'at yo' dunnot mak' th' blunder
 O' mistackin yore friends for yore foes.
Some o' th' wealthy deserve ole they'n getten;
 They'n been workin', an' savin' their gowd,
While yo'n had yore honds i' yore pockets,
 Or, perhaps, played at marbles i' th' fowd.

Tak' an owd friend's advice, an' feight fair, lads;
 Be aware o' what's known as "bad blood;"
An', whatever yo' do, keep fro' mischief;
 Breakin' windows will do yo' no good.
Yo' do reet to speak eawt when yo're clemmin',
 An' let ole yore troubles be known;
But this can be done witheawt threat'nin',
 Or endangerin' th' nation or th' Throne.

Lads, aw know what it meons to be pinchin',
 For aw've had a front seot i' that schoo';
Oatcake an' churn milk for a "baggin'"
 An' a penny red herrin' for two!
It tries a poor starvin' mon's patience,
 An' his feelin's are hardish to quell,
When he sees his rich naybours are feastin'
 An' he can get nowt nobbut th' smell.

E

This is one o' those wrongs 'at want reightin';
　　There's a screw loose i'th' job there's no deawt;
There's a foe hangin' reawnd 'at needs feightin';
　　Set to work, lads, an' ferret it eawt.
An' while battlin' for th' right, let's be "jannock;
　　Thoose 'at's reet have no need be afraid.
Are these wrongs browt abeawt bi eawr nayburs?
　　Or are they—what's likelier—whoam-made?

While th' wealthy are feastin' we're starvin,
　　An' for this, lads, there must be a cause;
Aw know pratin' Tom will put this deawn
　　To injustice an' th' badness o' th' laws.
Well, there may be some truth i' what Tom says,
　　But aw know what th' real cause is aw think:
For while Tom's wife an' childer are starvin',
　　He's spendin' his earnin's o' drink.

Yo' may prate o'er yore wrongs until doomsday,
　　An' blame what are called th' upper class;
But ole yore complaints will be useless,
　　Till yo'n th' sense to tak' care o' yore brass.
Turn o'er a new leaf, fellow-toilers,
　　An' let common sense be yore guide;
If there's one happy spot under heaven,
　　Let that spot be yore own fireside.

Get a ceaw, if yo' con, an three acres,
　　An' i' future, employ yore spare heawers
I' readin' good books; an' yore windows,
　　Fill these up wi' plants an wi' fleawers.
Get yore wives an' yore childer' areawnd yo',
　　Sing an' whistle among 'em loike mad;
An' if this doesn't mak' yo' feel happier,
　　Throw th' blame on "A LANCASHIRE LAD."

(FROM THE ORIGINAL PICTURE BY J. R. G. GRUNDY, R.C.A.)

Rowl away, theaw grand owd ocean,
Dash thi spray on th' pebbly shore ;
Like some giant i' devotion,
Singin' praises evermore.

ROWL AWAY, THEAW GRAND OWD OCEAN.

ROWL away, theaw grand owd ocean,
    Dash thi spray on th' pebbly shore ;
  Like some giant i' devotion,
    Singin' praises evermore.
Talk o' true an' earnest worship !
  Great revivals ! dear-a-me !
Why, there isn't a sect i' th' nation
  'At con hawve come up to thee.

Baptists, Independents, Quakers,
  Followers o' Young an' Joe ;
Ranters, Unitarians, Shakers ;
  These are nowt—tha dreawns 'em o.
Organ, singers, parson, people,
  Let these mak' what noise they will ;
Ring o' th' bells they han i' th' steeple,
  Tha poipes eawt aboon 'em still.

Oh, aw loike to yer thee roarin ;
  Loike thee when i' gradely trim ;
When wi' mighty voice tha'rt pourin'
  Eawt some grand thanksgivin' hymn !
Priests han mumbled, people muttered,
  What's bin looked upon as foine ;
Still their praises are no uttered
  Hawve so heartily as thoine.

O, heaw charmin' 'tis at midneet !
  Heaven's breet lamps lit up aboon ;
Thee deawn here, like some vast mirror,
  Silvered o'er wi' th' leet o' th' moon !
What are these 'at look like childer,
  Bi their mother gently led ?
Th' moon's browt th' stars to have a bathe here,
  Just before they're put to bed !

Th' sun may shed his brilliant lustre;
  Th' moon display her queenly peawer;
Th' bonny twinklin' stars may muster
  All their force at th' midneet heawer.
Th' woind may roar i' wild commotion,
  Or may blow a gentle breeze:
Still, ah, still owd briny ocean,
  Theaw can charm me moor nor these.

Oh, aw loike to yer thy music,
  Moor nor th' bells 'at sweetly chime;
For thy voice is ever seawndin'
  Grandly solemn an' sublime!
Eawr poor efforts, tho' inferior,
  Very often have t' be bowt;
But, tho' thine's so mich superior,
  Tha ne'er thinks o' chargin' owt.

When God's people fled fro' bondage,
  Tramp'd thro' th' wilderness so long;
An' fair Miriam played on th' timbrel,
  Did ta help 'em i' their song?
When preawd Pharaoh's host o'ertook 'em,
  An' th' poor things i' terror stood;
Do we read 'at theaw forsook 'em?
  Nay, but helped 'em o' tha could.

Londin' here fro' th' great Atlantic,
  Sometoimes tha does use us bad;
Foamin', ravin', fairly frantic;
  Tossin' ships abeawt loike mad!
Other toimes tha's bin quite different,
  Noather awkward, cross, nor nowt;
Same as if tha'd bin asleep theer,
  Just as calm an' still as owt.

Oh, we connot blame thee, ocean;
　Oftentoimes we've yerd it said,
'At tha uses th' gentlest motion,
　When tha'rt movin' nearest th' dead.
Whoile a mon's o' reet an' hearty,
　He may foind thee rayther ruff;
Iv he lies theer deod an' helpless
　Then, owd friend, tha'rt kind enuff.

Foalk 'at feel there's summat wantin';
　Drinkers deep o' sorrow's cup;
These should yer thi merry chantin',
　Bless us tha'd soon cheer 'em up!
Oh, an' tha'rt a kind physician;
　Well it is tha wants no fee;
Weakly folk i' my condition
　Couldn't pay, they'd ha' to dee.

Mony a toime aw've sit deawn, sadly
　Broodin' o'er mi load o' woe,
Feelin' gradely sick an' badly,
　Crush'd wi' cares 'at few can know.
O at once these cares han vanished;
　Not a fear left, not a deawt;
Every gloomy thowt's bin banished,
　When aw've yeard thee poipin' eawt.

Foalk 'at live i' teawns an' cities,
　Conno yer thee same as me;
Oh! but it's a theawsand pities!
　Everyone should hearken thee.
Rowl away, then, grand owd ocean;
　Dash thi spray on th' pebbly shore;
Tha ne'er flags i' thy devotion—
　Allis singin'—evermore.

QUALITY ROW.

EIN' a poor workin' mon, it's but little aw know
Abeawt th' people livin' i' Quality Row;
An' to tell yo' th' plain truth, it's but seldom one
    gooas,
Unless it's to hawk, or to beg some owd clooas.
Heawever, aw went th' other day wi' a friend,
An' a few bits o' trifles picked up theer aw've penn'd
In a plain, whomly style, for there's nowt very fine
Abeawt these ruff, ramblin' sketches o' mine.

Mister Bolus, M.D., lives at th' furst heawse i' th' row,
An' thoose at are ailin' will do weel to co.
Neaw, he's allis awhom, except when he's eawt,
An' he's allis his specks on, except when he's beawt.
It's noan o' mitch consequence what a chap ails,
For he's very successful, except when he fails.
'At his charges are moderate there's none can deny,
Except neaw an' then, when they get rayther high.

Th' next dur lives a parson, a kind-hearted mon,
'At glories i' doin' ole th' good 'at he con:
If anyone's poorly, an wants him to pray,
He's willin' to gooa oather neet-time or day.
When he meets a poor chap he'll get howd ov his hond,
An' shake it as iv he're th' richest i' th' lond;
Whenever aw meet him, he touches his hat,
An there's noan mony parsons i' th' teawn will do that.

Th' next dur to this parson, at heawse number three,
There's a young ladies' schoo' kept bi Miss Nancy Lee;
Aw've a cousin 'at gooas, an' aw met her one neet,
An' hoo is rarely polished! hoo is some an' breet!
An' hoo does spread her fithers abeawt when hoo walks,
An' screws up her meawth when hoo simpers an' talks!
Hoo's goin' up to Lunnon hoo tells me next week,
To translate the word "turnip" to Latin an' Greek.

Well, th' next aw shall notice is heawse number six,
There's a fellow lives theer 'at makes clay into bricks ;
He's moderate steady, teetotal, aw think,
Except at odd times when he's gettin' his drink.
Aw neaw an' then leet on him comin' my way,
When he's been on at th' " Punch Bowl " soakin' his clay ;
But as clay isn't easy to mould when it's dry,
Aw say nowt, but let him go quietly by.

At heawse number seven (dear-a-me, what a life ?)
An owd bachelor lives—a poor fellow beawt wife ;
If yo'll peep under th' curtain some neet when yo' pass,
Yo'll see him ceawerd mopin' an' ceawntin' his brass.
He should have a big heawseful o' childer to keep,
Then he wouldn't be seen potterin' abeawt, haw've asleep ;
For they'd loosen his joints for him weel, never fear,
An' keep him fro' gettin so reawsty an' queer.

Aw've another to mention,—it's heawse number nine ;
A relation lives theer,—a rich uncle o' mine ;
He owns some good shops between Owdham an' Lees,
'At aw venture to think will be mine when he dees.
Aw'm aware 'at eawr Charley does o' 'at he con,
To poke his nose in, an' get thick wi' th' owd mon ;
But it's ole to no use, he'll be chetted, he'll see,
For mi Uncle John promised he'd leov 'em to me.

Well, aw think aw'll give o'er, yo'll be weary aw deawt,
An' aw've mentioned o th' folk 'at aw know mitch abeawt.
Aw've missed two or three 'at are livin' i' th' row,
But iv they feel slighted aw'll give 'em a co ;
An' tho' aw've noan getten much talent or time
For drawin' eawt sketches i' Lancashire rhyme,
Aw may try to please yo' a bit wi' mi' pen,
Someday, when aw've been reawnd that quarter ogen.

STARVED TO DEATH.

TARVED to death, did you say? dear-a-me!
    Why, bless us, wheerever i'th' world could it be?
    Wur he somewheer i' Greenland, wheer th' north
        winds blow?
Or ramblin' o'er th' moors, an' lost i'th' snow?
Or wur he away i' some lonely place,
Wheer th' sun seldom shoines on a human face;
I' some far-away desert 'at's seldom trod—
Wheer th' soil appears fresh fro' th' hands o' God?

Nay, nay, he're noan starved on a foreign strand,
But here, awhom, i' this Christian land,
Wheer th' seawnd o'th' church-goin' bell is heard,
An' charity's preached in the name of eawr Lord.
Wheer the priest an' the Levite on luxuries dine,
An' nowbles an' statesmen get fuddled wi wine;
It wur here, i' owd England, this "Queen of the Isles"—
This garden o' eawrs, on which Providence smiles.

It wur here 'at he deed,—i'th' lond ov his birth;—
I'th' wealthiest city on God's fair earth.
Starved to death within seet an' seawnd
O'th' merchant princes 'at prosper areawnd!
Ah, starved to death in a Christian land.
Eh dear! this is hard to understand—
Yore brother an mine lyin' stiff an' cowd,
In a city o' splendour, a mart o' gowd.

Starved to death! a loife flung away!
God's image starved eawt o'th' poor vessel o' clay:
A dear choilt o' somb'dy's, a brother o' eawers,
Wi' similar feelin's an' mental peawers,
Thrown away as iv nothin' worth;
Not one friend to assist him on ole God's earth.
O, brothers an' sisters, pray what can we do?
O, thinkers an' writers—here's sum'at for you.

Come, thunner it eawt i' clarion tones,
'At we're starvin' th' bees while we pamper th' drones.
Thunner it eawt, an' let it be known,
Fro' th' pauper i' th' warkheawse to th' queen on th' throne.
We can boast o' eawr greatness an' prowess i' war,
An' eawr fame as a nation's oft' talked of afar ;
An' shall it, wi' truth, o' owd England be said,
That her sons an' her dowters are starvin' for bread ?

Is this what we co feedin' th' hungry an' th' dry,
Or doin' to others as we'd be done by ?
Nay, we rayther think not ; we should think it wur queer
If we'rn deein' o' hunger, an' nob'dy came near.
While one's livin' i' " clover," he's friends ole reawned ;
Iv he's crush'd wi' misfortune, they're hard to be feawnd.
Let us rectify ole these sad blunders, an' try
To be brothers i' sorrow as weel as i' joy.

Yo' 'at preitch Christ's religion, come, practise it too ;
Here's a field for yore labour,—here's sum'at to do :
Look abeawt on th' wayside for some witherin' fleawer,
An' give it o' th' help 'at may lie i' yore peawer.
Dunno fall into th' error o' wastin' yore breath,
I' talkin' to th' hungry o' judgment an' death ;
If yore fishin' for souls, yo'n a very poor bait ;
Yo'll be loiklier to catch 'em wi' sum'at to ate.

We met as weel talk to a chap 'at's noan reet,
An' tell folk to walk 'at's lost th' use o' their feet,
As attempt to feed th' hungry wi' orthodox creeds,
Or quieten a stomach wi' crosses an' beads.
Let's scorn to insult wi' sich simperin' cant,
As to talk abeawt deein' to folk 'at's i' want ;
Let us act moor loike Christians, an' every one strive
To let 'em have sum'at to keep 'em alive.

WRITTEN FOR A MEETING HELD AT GREAT ECCLESTON.

SO this is Great Eccleston, is it ? Well, well—
Aw thowt aw should loike to see th' spot for misel ;
For it's gettin' weel known as a notable place,
Wheer 'th Liberals an' Tories can meet face to face ;
Wheer 'th Fylde politicians can have a good feight ;
Wheer disputes can be settled, an' wrongs be made reight ;
There's no wonder this place yo' call Eccleston's Great,
When we think o' th' grand sturrin's yo'n had here of late !

What a meetin' that wur 'at yo' had th' other neet !
Aw should think yo're noan short o' political leet.
Let's hope Mr. Gladstone hasn't yeard what yo're doin'—
'At yo' charged him wi' bringin' this nation to ruin—
Or that saviours o' th' nation are stumpin' through th' Fylde—
Or the "Grand Old Man" will go very near wild !
Aw can fancy aw see him rise up in his place,
Wi' a look of alarm plainly seen in his face,—

An' knockin' his papers abeawt in a fuss,
He commences a sort o' soliloquy thus :—
" Great Eccleston ! bless us, why, wheer can this be ?
It certainly seawnds like a new place to me."
Then, turnin' to Randolph, he asks, with a sneer—
" Does Great Eccleston join up to Woodstock ? or wheer ?
If so, aw'll give up to thee, Randy—th' game's thine !
This has settled th' whole business—here's th' reins, aw'll resign.

What a sad an' momentous affair that would be !
An' yo' folks at Great Eccleston th' cause, do yo' see ?
If yo' care to save th' country fro' bloodshed an' riot,
Yo'll have to be careful, an' keep these things quiet.
Yo' may argue for ever o'er figures an' facts—
Or criticise Gladstone's an' Beaconsfield's acts—
But yo' musn't name Jesus, or th' Vicar o' Copp
Will threaten to close th' theological shop.

Well, we've met here this evenin' to get thro' some wark,
An' enlighten yo' foalk 'at are gropin' i' th' dark.
Yo'n had th' Tories here lately, an' we're here to-neet ;
When boath lots have sceawred yo', yo' owt to look breet.
No deawt th' Tories tow'd yo' 'at th' Liberals are bad,
An' wouldn't object to enfranchise th' Owd Lad ;
While the Liberals would tell yo' if th' Tories had peawr,
They'd ruin this country i' less nor an heawr.

Which is th' nearest to th' truth it's for yo' to decide ;
At there's been some strong language it won't be denied.
If Gladstone's as black as he's made to appear
By one or two Bees 'at's been buzzin' reawnd here,
Then th' Great Eccleston foalks owt to give him a sign
That he's noan fit for office, an' owt to resign ;
But if yo' should find 'at these charges are lies—
'At his foes have been tryin' t' fling dust i' yore eyes,—

Remember these matters, an' mak' a few notes
To refer to when th' Tories come reawnd for yore votes.
We, as Liberals, invite yo' to prove what we sen ;
We appeal not to ignorance, but truth-seekin' men.
English history's before yo', i' print on yore shelves ;
Ole yon getten to do is to read for yourselves.
If yo' find the Conservative principles seawnd,
Then give 'em yore votes when th' elections come reawnd ;—

But if yo' should think 'at we Liberals are reight,
An' have made a moor worthy an' streightforrud feight,
Then, men o' Great Eccleston—growers of oats,
Give th' Conservatives th' sack, an' give us yore votes.
Neaw, aw dar say yo'll fancy it looks rayther queer,
'At we should leov Blackpool, an' come treawnsin' here ;
But it just comes to this—th' Blackpool Tories have been,
An' towd yo' some very strange tales, as we've seen ;

So it seemed only proper 'at we should come too,
An' give yo' good foalk here a bit ov a doo ;
Th' result will be—we shall get th' breetest an' best,
An' th' Conservative Patriots are welcome to th' rest.
If there's one thing i' th' world 'at one's sick on, it's cant !
Neaw, look here—what yo' men o' Great Eccleston want
Is what we, yore best friends, come to give yo' to-neet,
But what th' others keep from yo'—political leet !

What have th' Tories done for yo ?　They'n plundered an' fowt ;
An' what have yo' farmers to thank 'em for ?　Nowt !
Neaw, if ever a Tory goes in for reform,
It'll be when th' sun's cowd, an' ice becomes warm !
When each idiot 'at scribbles shall lay deawn his pen,
An' poike up a hommer—but never till then ;
An' when th' Liberals attempt to do out o' this mak',
Tories move ole creation to keep these things back ;—

For they know that if once we enfranchise a mon,
Their influence o'er that chap is just abeawt gone.
What do th' Tories want here, wi' their meawldy ideas ?
Do they think they can handle yo' just as they pleos ?
If they do, let 'em try, an' aw'll bet my owd hat
They'll be rarely dropped on for their pains—they will that ;
For th' Clerical peawr, 'at's bin wielded i' th' past,
Appears to be gettin' i' danger at last—

Or they'd ne'er come an' threaten to close up their schoos
When th' Liberals illustrate moor rational views.
But it just favvers th' Tories—does this—to a tee ;
One may see throo their game, if he's blind o' one e'e !
It's a new way o' arguin' 'at's lately come eawt,
'At suits these young Bees 'at are buzzin' abeawt ;
At Blackpool they formerly argued wi' stones,
But lately they've altered to hisses an' groans.

They suit 'em much better—do these sort o' acts —
Nor botherin' their noddles wi' hard-yeaded facts ;
Still, we ought to excuse 'em ole ever we can,
For no deawt they'll mak' use o' th' best weapons they han.
But aw'll drop it, an' let somb'dy else talk a bit,
'At may deal i' less sarcasm, an' rayther moor wit.
So, Great Eccleston people, aw wish yo' good-neet,
Feelin' certain yo'll do what yo' know to be reet.

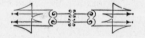

JOE AN' ALICE.

A W yeard a chap tell a good tale th' other neet,
    An' aw think it's to' rich to be kept eawt o' th' seet ;
    Iv yo'll lend me a minute or two o' yor time,
    Aw'll try an' repeat it i' Lancashire rhyme.
Well, a couple i' Yawshur—at least so it's said—
After coartin' awhile, made it up to get wed ;
But there's nowt abeawt that oather strikin' or queer,
It's nobbut what's done bi th' young folk abeawt here.

Heawever, accordin' to th' tale aw've yeard towd,
In a year or two they'd a young stranger i' th' fowd ;
A noice little dowter, wi' bonny blue een ;
It' mother said, " Th' noicest 'at ever wur seen."
Neaw this couple lived reet up at th' top ov a moor ;
It wur seldom a stranger e'er darken'd their door ;
But one day an owd fellow co'd Solomon Crook
Went marchin' i' th' heawse wi' a register book.

He said " I've been told by a man I've just met
That you've got a young child—have you christened it yet ?"
" What's that yo' sen, Maister, yo' token so fawn ;
Is it sum'at abeawt this new babby o' mawn ? "
" Has the baby been christened ? that's what I would know."
" Whaw, aw am no reight suir ; but aw'll sheat o' yaar Joe."
" Oh, there's no need of troubling your husband, good dame ;
Tell me this—Has this youngster of yours got a name ?"

" A name : Oh, a name ! Now—at least aw think so ;
Heigh ! aw say ; does ta yer up i' th' choamber theer, Joe ?
There's a felley fro' Lunnon or sumwheer, just called,
An' he's wantin' to know iv we'n kersun'd yaar chawld !"
" Well, now, lass, its nivver been kersun'd, aw think ;
Slip i' th' cellar an' fotch him a pot-full o' drink ;
An' then, when he's supped it, just ass him to look
An' see iv he's toathry nawce names in his book.

So hoo gete a quart pitcher, an' fot him some ale—
Or rather some greawt, for it looked dreadful pale ;
" Neah, Maister," hoo said, " there's a cheer, sit yo daan,
An taste o' yaar drink, there's nowt lawk it i'th taan ;
An' then, when yo'n done, iv yo'n getten a mawnd,
Yo' shall see if yo'n toathry nawce names yo' can fawnd."
So to pleos her he supped a few drops o' this greawt ;
But when Alice wurn't lookin', he squirted it eawt.

" Well, Misses," he said, " I will read a few names ;
There's Albert, John, Edward, Charles, William, and James ;
Augustus, Emanuel, Christopher, Duke,
Cornelius, Jonathan, Isaac, and Luke."
" Stop, Maister, there's Awsuk ; that seands varry nawce ;
Aw've seen that i' th' Bawble, aw think once or twawce.
Heigh, Joe ! dusta yer ? stop that weighvin' a bit ;
There's Awsuk, here, dusta think Awsuk ull fit ?"

" Oh, ah ! varry weel, varry weel, that'll do ;
Iv aw am no' mista'en, it's a Scriptur' name too."
" It is," said owd Crook, " and I'm proud of your choice ;
I am sure the name Isaac will sound very nice."
" It will, mun, it will ; soa yo'll just put it daan ;
Guid day to yo, Maister, aw reckon yo're baan ;"
Well, th' name wur put deawn, an' th' chap off eawt o' th' door,
He'd ne'er come across folk loike these were afoor.

Neaw he hadn't bin gone eawt o' th' heawse very long,
Afoor Alice bethowt her they'd happen done wrong,
Soa hoo bowted to th' bottom o' th' steers, an' hoo bawled,
" What thinks ta—is Awsuk th' reight name for yaar chawld ?
It seands varry mich lawk a lad's name to me,
An' this babby o' yaars is a lass, dusta see ?"
" Well, Alice, it does seand lawk one o' that mack ;
But, ne'er mawnd, it 'll do, aw'd ne'er cole on him back."

TO MY FRIEND, EDWIN WAUGH.

DEAR Waugh, aw must say aw feel sorry
    To see 'at tha'rt poorly, owd friend;
    But awm glad to read th' pappers this mornin',
    An' find 'at tha'rt likely to mend.
Get on wi' thi mendin', owd songster;
    It's noa time for deein' i' th' spring,
When th' hedge-rows burst forth into beauty,
    An' th' birds are beginnin' to sing.

Do get eawt o' th' hands o' thoose doctors,
    For tha'll ne'er do no good while i' bed;
Let th' pills 'at tha tacks be steak dumplin's,
    Then tha'll get weel i' th' spite on 'em, Ned.
Aw've been badly misel' this last winter—
    Lumbago, an' ole macks o' ills;
But awm happy to tell thee awm better,
    Notwithstandin' their blisters an' pills.

Tha'd see that description o' Brierley's,
    Wheer awm pictured as nearly ole yead;
Well, it's certainly noan very flatt'rin',
    Tho' mi friends think it true what he said.
But aw'll care nowt abeawt it, would theaw, Ned;
    It's nobbut their fun, one can see;
It's a very good joke, an' quite harmless;
    They're pleased, an' it doesn't hurt me.

But we'll get back to th' subject—tha'rt poorly;
    An' awm sorry theaw art soa, owd mon;
An' this is th' advice aw shall gie thee—
    Get better as soon as tha con;
For there's nowt could to me be moor painful
    Than to goa to a funeral o' thine;
Except it wur this (heaw outrageous),
    Seein' thee at a funeral o' mine.

Well, Ned, thee get whoam to New Brighton,
    Wheer aw hope tha'll enjoy thisel' long ;
An' when thar't again i' good fither,
    Pipe eawt a sweet Lancashire song.
" Too owd," does ta say ? nowt o' th' sort, mon !
    It's true theaw may have a grey yead ;
But tha'rt one o' thoose strangely strung craturs
    'At live when they're thowt to be dead.

But why should aw trouble thee neaw, friend ;
    Just neaw, when there's gall i' thi cup ?
Well, for this—an' for no other reason—
    Tha'rt deawn, an' we're wantin' thee up.
Is it likely a chap can feel happy,
    When, i' lookin' o'er th' pappers, aw see
'At my friend Edwin Waugh's lyin' badly,
    Witheawt tryin' t' cheer him ?   Not me !

An' awm noan bi misel' i' this matter,
    For there's theawsands o' hearts leap an' beawnd—
O'erjoyed wi' th' good tidin's 'at reach us—
    'At tha'rt in a fair way to come reawnd.
Well, Edwin, owd crony, God bless thee !
    This may seawnd rayther strangely fro' me ;
But, 'mong ole mi good friends an' dear kindred,
    There's none aw like better nor thee !

An' neaw, Waugh, ta-ta for the present,
    Aw shall think on thee kindly tha'rt sure ;
An' tho' we're booath owd, an' nowt worth mitch,
    Awm hopin' to see thee once moor.
Keep thi pluck up, be cheerful an' hopeful ;
    An', Edwin, don't worry an' fret ;
A chap at's so honoured as theaw art,
    Should dee noan—at leost not yet.

DICK O' TH' MERRYDALE.

ADS, poo off thoose caps for a minute or two,
    While aw try to unfold a tale
  Of a warm-hearted friend 'at e'en God couldn't mend,
    Known as " Dick o' th' Merrydale."

He're a farmer wur Dick, an' a doctor as weel,
  Conversant wi' ole macks o' ills :
He'd churn milk an' ham collops for th' hearty an' hale,
  An' for poorly foalk plasters an' pills.

Dick's fame as a doctor wur very weel known,
  But moor soa i' th' country parts ;
Thoose 'at fractured a limb would go limpin' to him ;
  He're famed too for bunions an' warts.

Th' last time aw wur theer, th' wife wur brewin' yarb-beer,
  An' th' new milk stood i' th' pantry i' mugs ;
At th' back side o' th' heawse, piled up on some drawers,
  Wur pill-boxes, bottles, an' drugs.

But he's gone is th' owd chap, an's neaw tackin' th' last nap
  Wheer there's nowt to disturb his long rest ;
One's had mony a good friend, an' dear chums witheawt end,
  But th' owd doctor aw rank among th' best.

MI GRONNY.

HOO'S turned eighty-one—mi gronny is neaw,
    An' yet for her age hoo's reet clever;
    An' her silvery locks spread abeawt o'er her broo
    Macks her look just as bonny as ever.
Aw wur theer t' other neet, an' aw thowt to misel'
    God bless her! hoo's farantly lookin'!
An' it wur a grand seet, as wi' tears in her een,
    Hoo sat readin' her Bible an' smookin'.

Hoo wur browt up i' Yorkshur, 'mong fields an' fleawers,
    An' drank wayter pure fro' th' spring;
An' hoo loved to get up when th' sun geet up,
    An' hearken th' cuckoo sing.
Th' owd foalk had a farm, an' they'd lots o' milk,
    An' hoo geet it warm fro' th' ceaw;
An' it did her good, an' nourished her blood,
    Or hoo metn't ha' lived till neaw.

Hoo's a widow, an' has been for th' last forty year,
    Soa hoo hasn't a bad husband to bother;
Hoo's a dowter 'at hasn't said "I will" yet,
    An' hoo tarries awhoam wi' her mother.
Neaw this dowter an' hur they baken an' done,
    An' sell potates, boath English an' foreign;
An' other odd matters i' th' grocery loine,
    Sich as sceawerin'-stones, candles, an' herrin'.

Neaw, mi Gronny's a Christian, aw'd ha' yo' to know,
    Says her prayers at th' bed-soide every neet;
Gies her customers measure an' weight for their brass,
    An' as fur as hoo knows hoo does reet.
Soa God bless mi owd Gronny, God bless her, say I;
    May that heart o' hur's never grow cowd
Till hoo's baked ole her fleawr up and sowd ole her bread,
    An' getten a hundred year owd!

COCK-COCK-AW-LAID.

WELL, well, tha's no 'casion to mak' o' this bother;
  If tha's laid it's o' reet, an' it needs nowt no moor.
There's nowt very strikin' abeawt thi performance,
  One's yeard o' hens layin' an' swagg'rin' befoor.
Howd thi noise theaw young beggar, an' get back to th' hen-cote,
  Or tha'll wacken ole th' nayburs i' th' yard awm afraid.
Tha'rt becomin' a bore, an' a regular noosance,
  Wi' thi clatterin nonsense, thi cock-cock-aw-laid!

Why, layin' an egg or two's nowt to get wild o'er;
  Do we ever get "brag" fro' a cawve-breedin' ceaw?
Do birds when they've laid ever publish their actions,
  Annoyin' their nayburs? If not, why should theaw?
We're bothered enuff here i' th' neet time wi' tom cats;
  But their hideous noises are thrown into th' shade,
And aren't worth namin' wi' th' cock crowin' noosance,
  An' thy silly clatter, thy cock-cock-aw-laid.

An' th' cock—what has he got to do wi' 't aw wonder,
  Are to beawnd to tell him every time tha may lay?
If theaw art it's a case, an' aw do hope to goodness,
  Tha'll let him ha' th' news in a quieter way.
For to sleep after dayleet is quite eawt o' th' question,
  Wi' th' noises 'at thee an th' owd tom cats have made;
An' aw shouldn't be surprised if there's folk i' th' asylum
  'At's been sent theer throo list'nin' to cock-cock-aw-laid!

Neaw, aw mack nowt o' boastin' i' men or i' poultry ;
   There's follies an' frailties i' th' breetest an' best ;
An' what appears great may turn eawt very little,
   If eawr actions are properly put to a test.
An' it strikes me a hen should be humble an' modest,
   An' not ole her little achievements parade ;
But to me it seawnds very like bluster an' swagger,
   Does "cock-cock-cock-cock-cock-cock-cock-cock-aw-laid."

When a chap goes to bed its wi' th' object o' sleepin',
   But what does it matter what plans may be laid,
It theaw cocks thi yead up as soon as its dayleet,
   An' sings th' tune 'at th' ceaw deed on—cock-cock-aw-laid.
Thee tak' my advice, an' when next tha's done layin',
   Go quietly back to thi perch, an' theer sit
Like a fowl 'ats just finished a brilliant achievement ;
   In short, like a hen 'at lays claim to some wit.

TO TH' OWD DERBYSHIRE BARD, JOSEPH COOPER.

SUPPOSIN' one felt a desire for a stroll,
  An' happened to wander as fur as Eaves Knowl,
  Would he find an owd Bard ceawrin' quietly i' th' nook
  Enjoyin' hissel wi' his poipe an' his book?
He's very weel known i' that quarter o' th' globe
As an ardent admirer o' th' Patriarch Job.
On th' owd veteran's virtues he glories to dwell,
Tho' its seldom he puts 'em i' practice hissel'.
He's a garden at th' front, an' another behind,
Wheer he reckons to ceawer a bit—when he's a mind;
While his friends are delighted to visit these beawers,
An' sniff the sweet fragrance 'at comes fro' his fleawers.
He's a widower—that is he hasn't a wife,
Nor no childer to harrass, or sweeten his loife.
He's a member o' th' School Board, a Guardian o' th' poor,
An' aw think he's some moor posts; but am no' quite sure.
He gets thro' his wark without mackin' mitch din;
He's a foine flowin' beard hangs at th' end ov his chin.
They coed him "Joe Cooper" when dabblin' i' th' drink,
But neaw he's teetotal, its "Joseph" aw think.
He's past middle age, walks abeawt rayther slow;
Some say he's some "brass," he's some heawses, aw know.
He's a horse, an' a trap 'at he rides in sometimes,
When he isn't in his cot manufacturin' rhymes.
Aw think he's a kind ov a "Ranter" bi trade;
But, of course, i' religion he's noan to a shade;
He's a chap 'at believes i' good *livin'*, noa deawt,
But good *deein'* he never says nowt mitch abeawt.
It's been said—tho' it hasn't been proved as a fact—
That he's loike other Bards—he's a little bit crackt.
If yo' meet wi' a chap wi' a slit in his yed,
'At's wider nor th' shop wheer he munches his bread—
An' yo' see there's some 'bacco abeawt it 'at's reechin'—
Send me word, if yo' pleos, for that's th' chap at awm seechin'.

CHEER UP IRISH BROTHERS.

CHEER up a bit, poor Irish brethren,
 Tho' it's hard wark to do so awm sure ;
One's surprised yo'n kept up as yo' have done,
 Wi' th' hardships yo'n had to endure.
What wi' soldiers, police, an' coercion,
 Imprisonment, buckshot, an' fines ;
An' land agents sneakin' areawnd yo',
 Yo'n certainly very hard lines.

Well, try to hold on a bit longer ;
 Stand firm, neaw 'at help seems so near ;
We're feightin' yo'r battles i' England,
 An' shall win 'em, yo'n no need to fear.
Let me tell yo' we're gettin' on grandly ;
 We've some rare intellectual fights ;
Morley, Sir William Harcourt, an' others,
 Are battlin' reet hard for yo'r rights.

We're aware what yo'r patriots are sufferin'——
 What vengence is piled on their yeads ;
Heaw they're treated as murderers an' felons,
 Thrown i' prison, wi planks for their beds.
But, tak' heart, mi poor sufferin' brothers,
 There's room e'en for th' Tories to mend ;
When they'll stoop to go steal a chap's breeches
 They must be abeawt at th' far end.

It's a queer game for statesmen to play at—
    A mean sort o' business, for sure ;
But it needn't cause very mitch wonder,
    We've been guilty o' stealin' befoor.
Eawr Tory friends call it "annexin' "—
    A rayther fine sort ov a name ;
An' yet, when one looks at th' job fairly,
    It's thievin', pure thievin', ole th' same.

We're noted througheawt ole creation
    For convertin' black niggers an' Jews ;
We mak' 'em respect us, aw'll tell yo' ;
    Or "pepper" those weel 'at refuse.
We've been tryin' that game on i' Ireland—
    For eighty long years, an' moor ;
But, someheaw, this treatment doesn't suit yo—
    It's a med'cine 'at doesn't seem t' cure.

God help yo' ! an' may yo' have patience ;
    For it's certainly very "hard cheese "
To be treated as yo'r bein' treated,
    Wi' vain, heartless men like these.
Well, tho' they're so clever at braggin',
    Yo'll think they're abeawt at th' last shift
Neaw they've stolen yo'r pigs an' potatoes,
    Burnt yo'r hovels, an' turned yo' adrift.

Yo'n long been i' th' wilderness, weepin',
    An' mournful an' sad's been yo'r song ;
But leet's breakin' forth at th' horizon,
    An' th' sun will be up before long.
Get yo'r harps, 'at have long lain i' silence,
    An' prepare for a merrier tune ;
For th' daisies will oppen i' th' spring time,
    An' there's sure to be roses i' June.

THANK GOD FOR O THESE BONNY FLEAWERS!

THANK God for o these bonny fleawers
 'At grow abeawt one's feet;
  For th' silv'ry moon, an' th' million stars
   At shine aboon at neet.
For rain an' dew, for sun an' shade,
 An' th' stormy winds 'at blow;
For rays o' hope, an' snacks o' bliss,
 An' drops o' grief an' o.

Thank God for wealth, still moor for health,
 That boon o' priceless worth;
A blessin' moor to be desired
 Nor th' breetest gems on earth:
Beawt this, what's peawer, or influence?
 What's fame, or pomp an' show?
Or life itsel'? Why, bless yo', foalk,
 They're just worth nowt at o!

Thank God for friends, kind hearts an' true,
 'At everywheer abeawned,
Dispersin' sorrow, leetnin' care,
 An' spreadin' joy areawnd.
For lovely woman, Heaven's best gift,
 Sent deawn i' human form;
For ever lovin', allis th' same,
 I' sunshoine, or i' storm.

Thank God for o these bonny fleawers,
  'At grow abeawt one's feet ;—
For th' silv'ry moon, an' th' million stars,
  'At shine aboon at neet ;—
For rain an' dew, for sun an' shade,
  An' th' stormy winds 'at blow ;—
For rays o' hope, an' snacks o' bliss,
  An' drops o' grief an' o !

Thank God for little childer, too—
    Thoose " bonny brids " o' eawers,
Thoose " olive branches " 'at we love,
    Thoose cherished garden fleawers!
Let's thank him for these " hungry gifts,"
    An' may he send us moor ;
A mon 'at 's blest wi' lots o' these
    Can never say he's poor.

Life's sweeten'd, too, wheer childer are—
    They keep one's heart i' tune ;
They're gowden links connectin' us
    Wi' th' angels up aboon.
Besides they ease life's burdens, too ;
    They keep one's pockets leet ;
An' iv there's ony traycle cakes—
    They'n side 'em eawt o'th' seet.

It's quite a treat to see 'em o
    Come trailin' in at noon ;
They'll walk o'er every mat i' th' heawse
    An' never wipe their shoon.
One youngster's torn his trousers leg ;
    Another says he hurt ;
A third comes plaster'd up to th' een,
    Wi' wadin' through some durt.

Aw'm wed, an' th' woife says hoo is, too ;
    An' childer ! bless mi soul !
Why, we can hardly ceawnt 'em o !
    We han some noise i'th' hole !
Eawr Dick comes into th' heawse an' says
    He's tumbled off a wo' ;
Eawr Billy's perched o'th' table top,
    An' singin' " Not for Joe."

Thank God we'n each a spoon a-piece,
  An' summat for 'em t' do!
We'n everyone a porritch pot,
  An' plenty o' porritch, too.
An' tho' eawr childer need so mich,
  We mooastly get enuff;
We seldom clem for th' want o' meat,
  Unless we're short o' stuff.

" Ah, well," says some owd bachelor,
  " Yo'll rue i' toathry week."
What's he agate on do yo' think?
  He's warmin' th' bed wi' breek.
To-morn he'll have his stockin's t' mend,
  An' dress his geawty tooas;
Th' day after that, mop eawt his cote,
  An' air his Sunday clooas.

Thank God aw'm noan a bachelor,
  Beawt whom, an' all forlorn!
An' iv aw wur, aw'd choose a mate,
  An' go be wed to-morn.
Aw would, indeed!   Another thing,
  My conscience says aw'm reet;
Neaw, what think yo' abeawt it foalk?
  Just weigh it o'er.   Good neet.

TH' QUEEN'S VISIT TO LIVERPOOL, TO OPPEN TH' EXHIBITION.

SOA th' Queen's been to Liverpool, bless her;
    An' after a rayther long spell
  O' mournin' her loss i' retirement,
    Hoo's fairly come eawt of her shell.
Sin' " Albert the Good " wur ta'en from her,
  Her surroundin's—'at once wur so breet—
Have often been darkened wi' sorrow,
  An' hoo's kept a good deal eawt o' th' seet.

E'en Queens have their troubles an' trials;
  Royal hearts have oft cause to be sad;
Beside losin' husband an' dowter,
  Queen Victoria has buried a lad.
An' parents 'at's lost their dear childer
  Know well what sich parents must feel;
An' it's th' same booath i' th' cottage an' th' palace,
  An tho' th' Queen, hoo's a mother as weel!

It's true we'n been rayther impatient,
  While th' lady's bin mournin' her loss;
But we little know th' wearisome burdens
  O' thoose 'at are bearin' their cross.
An' before we come forrud as judges,
  Or proneawnce ony verdict as true,
It's needful to learn by experience,
  An' study a bit i' that schoo'.

Con we think any worse o' th' dear widow,
  For mournin' i' secret so long?
Shall we blame a poor heart-broken singer?
  If sadness is mixed wi' her song?
Nay, rayther let's cherish these feelin's,
  An' do all 'at ever we con,
To soothe wounded hearts 'at are mournin',
  An' frettin' for thoose 'at are gone.

Queen Victoria's a woman, God bless her !
    An' tho' hoo's an Empress an' Queen,
Hoo isn't ashamed 'at her subjects
    Should see her wi' tears in her een ;
An' yet, hoo's a keen sense o' humour ;
    Heaw hoo took everyone bi surprise,
When hoo beckoned o' th' Mayor to kneel deawn theer,
    An' then said, " Sir David, arise !"

Wurn't that a grand piece o' sly fencin' ?
    Wurn that a mooast wonderful sight ?
A Queen—as if actin' by magic—
    Transformin' a Da' to a K(night) ?
It's a womanly act, there's no deawt on't ;
    A queenly act too, an' that's moor ;
An' one 'at will long be remembered
    Bi Sir David Radcliffe, awm sure.

Aw wish hoo'd come see us at Blackpool ;
    Eh, but wouldn't we do the thing grand !
We'd everyone meet her at th' station,
    Wi' th' Lifeboat an' th' Fishermen's Band.
We'd have a review o' th' Artillery,
    An' shew her heaw battles are fowt ;
Hoo should ride on th' Electric Tramways,
    An' all this free gratis for nowt.

Talk a' wayter ! why Liverpool's nowheer !
    They'n no sea 'at's worth namin' eawt theer ;
Thoose 'at want to see grand exhibitions,
    Should pack up their traps an' come here.
What ! compare th' bit o' th' Mersey to Blackpool !
    Why, th' idea would amount to a sin ;
It's plain we could lick 'em quite hollow,
    Wi' th' Thames up at Lon'on thrown in !

Neaw, aw dunno like braggin' or boastin',
    But aw think aw may say this as true,—
That if th' Queen would come see us at Blackpool,
    Hoo'd have no occasion to rue ;
For hoo'd get sich a noble reception,
    An' find it soa pleasant a shop,
That aw'll venture to prophecy this much,—
    Hoo'd want to tack rooms here, an' stop.

R. R. BEALEY'S FURST CHOILT.

(AUTHOR OF "AFTER BUSINESS JOTTINGS," &c.)

HAT! has theaw th' bonniest lad i' th' world;
    Theaw's never seen eawr Jack;
    Or theaw'd ha' to whistle another tune,
      An' co that sentence back.

Noa deawt theaw thinks thi babby's nice;
  That's just becose it's thine;
If aw'd thy specks for lookin' throo,
  Aw met say th' same o' mine.

A choilt a miracle to see!
  Well, well, theaw art a dunce;
Why, bless thee, mon, at eawr heawse here
  We'n had 'em two at once.

A greater miracle to me,
  A stranger thing bi' th' hawve,
Would be to have a strappin' ceaw,
  'At didn't breed a cawve.

Eh dear! my wife did carry on!
  " Him th' noicest choilt!" hoo said;
" Th' conceited puppy 'at he is;
  He must be wrong i' th' yed.

Thee write, an' say eawr little Jack's
   Three toimes as noice a lad,
As ony Bealey has i' stock,
   Or owt his mother had ! "

Theaw says theaw'rt preawdest fayther, too,
   'At lives 'neath English skies ;
Nay, hang it, Bealey, do shut up ;
   Theaw knows tha'rt telling lies !

Does breedin' childer allis tend
   To stur up pride i' men ?
If so, aw've reason to be preawd,
   This woife o' moine's had ten.

Well, come, ne'er mind ; wire in, owd brid,
   Theaw's made a daycent start ;
Aw wish thee luck i' th' breedin' line ;
   Aw do wi' o' mi heart.

Get hawve a dozen little chicks,
   To frisk abeawt th' owd hen ;
An' clamber on their daddy's knee,
   An' theaw may swagger then !

TO WILLIAM EDWARDS.

(IN REPLY TO HIS "WORDS OF WELCOME.")

WELL, Edwards, awm certainly very weel pleased,
    'At tha's held eawt a welcomin' hond;
    Tha'rt one o' th' kind souls 'at would leeten foalks cares,
    As we travel this wearisome lond.
Mon, aw didn't expect to be noticed at ole;
    But there's one spied mi pearch eawt aw see;
An' it seems 'at aw haven't been labourin' i' vain,
    For there's one 'at's been pleased, an' that's thee.

Well, aw've done what aw could i' mi own humble way,
    To help a poor brother along;
Sometimes it's been done wi' a few kindly words,
    Or it may be—a bit ov a song.
An' Edwards, tha knows 'at there are a few hearts
    At respond to some soul-stirrin' strain;
An' we scribblers must feel very thankful to find,
    That we haven't been toilin' i' vain.

As to settlin' i' Owdham—well, sometime aw may;
    But it won't be at present aw fear;
There's to mitch filthy language made use of for me;
    Yo'n to mitch "bloody-hellin'" done here!
Neaw, awm noan on for preachin' up Puritan cant,
    Or turnin' up th' white o' mi een;
But awm gradely disgusted wi' th' language aw've yeard,
    An' th' sickenin' seets at awve seen!

Wheer are th' teachers o' morals! Can nothin' be done
    To sweep this vile noosance away?
Have th' newspappers tackled this damnable vice?
    Have th' parsons got nothin' to say?
Is th' constable peawrless? Has th' law no effect
    To stem this vile blot on yore teawn?
Is there no way o' stoppin' this scandalous slang,
    Nor no way o' puttin' it deawn?

Aw'd often yeard tell o' yo're " roughyeads " an' " clogs,"
　　An' yo've got a few of 'em aw see ;
But, Edwards, if th' truth mun be honestly towd,
　　Owdham's worse than aw thowt it to be.
After ole, mon, there's much 'at a chap con admire ;
　　For yore very warm-hearted aw find.
Yore awkard an' ruff i' yore manners it's true,
　　But yore nayburly, honest, an' kind.

When one comes to reflect on a matter like this,
　　It macks him feel deawncast an' sad ;
To think 'at sich praiseworthy traits should be mixed
　　Wi' language so filthy an' bad !
Brids are singin' i' th' trees, makin' vocal th' breeze,
　　An' primroses bloom deawn i' th' dell ;
An' has man nothin' better to give to his God
　　Than the nasty words " bloody " an' " hell !"

That face, neaw so bloated, an' dreadfully marred,
　　Wur once healthy-lookin' an fair ;
Thoose lips, neaw the medium for curses' an' slang,
　　Wur once towt to utter a prayer.
Aw wish th' foalk i' Owdham would think o' these things,
　　Like intelligent women an' men ;
Put away filthy language 'at only degrades,
　　An' resolve not to use it ogen.

Excuse me, friend Edwards, for, bless thee, owd mon—
　　Aw've wandered fro' th' subject aw find ;
But aw felt aw'd a duty aw had to perform,
　　'At aw could'nt dismiss fro' mi mind.
Accept mi best thanks for thoose lines 'at tha's sent,
　　For they show tha'rt a warm-hearted brick.
Aw shall never forget thi kind, welcomin' words—
　　Nawe, never, so long as awm wick.

MARY AN' BETTY.

ELL, aw've certainly heard some queer tales i' mi time,
'At aw've often felt tempted to put into rhyme ;
Here's one which aw've nobbut just lately been towd :—
　　Two women had met i' Tom Shackleton's Fowd,
An' after conversin' abeawt former days,
The followin' strange bit o' plain talkin' took place.
"Well, Betty, owd creetur, an' yaa does ta feel ?"
"Oh, awm middlin' lawk, Mary ; are taa varry weel ?
"Well," said Mary, aw ail nowt, except a sore tooa,
An' that's varry painful ; but yaa's yore owd Jooa ?"
"Eh ! bless thee," said Betty, " yaar Jooa's noan here ;
His place is neah vacant i' yond arm cheer !"
"Well," said Mary, " tha fairly astonishes me !
But yaa did it happen, lass, yaa did he dee ?"
"Well," said Betty, " awm troubled, an' hardly can tell ;
But he deed witheawt doctor, he deed ov hissel'.
He're asleep in his cheer, wi' his hat on his yead,
When he wackened awm sooary to say he wur dead !"
"Come," said Mary, " don't fret, dry th' weet off thi face,
An' tell me yaa long it is sin' this took place."
Said Betty, " aw have it choked daan i' mi churn—
He'd have been dead a month iv he'd lived till to-morn."
"Eh ! dear-a-me, Betty, mi lass, yaa tha says !
Aw never yeard th' marrow i' ole mi born days !
To-day thoose we doat on are safe wi' us here,
An' yesterday gooan—ah—nob'dy knows wheer !"

SECOND VISIT TO QUALITY ROW.

ELL, aw've bin reawnd ogen, wi' mi basket an' poke,
    An' drawin' another rough sketch o' th' foine foalk;
    But aw'm warned to be rayther moor careful this
        toime,
An' keep certain characters eawt o' mi rhyme.

There's one or two chaps rarely pottered aw know
Cose they fancy *they're* livin' i' Quality Row;
Neaw it's true, an' they'n threat'nd to kick me some day,
When they happen to leet on mi goin' that way.

Aw spoke th' other Friday to one o' these chaps,
But he wouldn't speak back; he'll speak next toime, perhaps;
Iv he doesn't, it's reet, aw con happen get through,
Aw shall only ha' rayther less talkin' to do.

Iv th' cap doesn't fit 'em, they'n no need to wear it,
But aw'm freetn'd they'll stretch it so fur till they'll tear it.
Eh! there has bin some pooin' an' frabbin' for sure!
Sich measurin' o' yeads as aw ne'er seed afoor!

They're woiser than I am, a deal, if they know
Wheer there is sich a place as a Quality Row;
It's nobbut a picture i' th' brains ov a bard,
A bit of a contrast to " Bowton's yard."

Heawever, aw think one can see pretty clear,
'At they aren't ole angels 'at's livin' up theer;
For aw foind when aw'm reawnd wi' mi basket an' poke,
'At they'n vices an failin's, just loike other foalk.

An' bein' up heigher they'n further to fo',
Nor thoose 'at are livin' i' th' heawses below ;
For, spoite o' bow windows, brass knocker, an' bell,
They'n their trials an' sorrows as weel as one's sel' !

Eh ! aw've seen one poor mother goa very near mad,
Becose hoo had t' bury her dear little lad ;
An' o' her foine things couldn't give her relief,
For hoo ceawered upo' th' sofa, yond, nursin' her grief.

There's owd Mester Jones lives at heawse number ten,
Yo met think him abeawt one o' th' happiest o' men ;
Whenever one sees him, he's allus weel drest,
An' a gowd Albert cheon hangin' deawn at his breast.

But look at him gradely, an' iv yo're noan blind,
Yo'll see 'at he's some mak o' care on his mind ;
It's true, he's some heawses up yonder, at th' Glent,
But what use are these, iv he conno get th' rent ?

Then look at Miss Goldthorp, at number eleven,
As fair as an angel just dropt eawt o' heaven ;
An' talk abeawt brass—why hoo's rowlin' i' wealth,
But cannot enjoy it, because hoo's bad health.

Well then, there's th' owd lady 'at's livin' th' next dur,
But aw haven't mich toime neaw to write abeawt hur ;
But fro' what aw could yer th' other day, it appears
Hoo's a poor helpless cripple, an' has bin for years.

Well, come neaw, what's th' lesson for me an' for yo,
'At owt to be larned eawt o' th' Quality Row ?
This—there's two or three things we should prize aboon wealth,
They're a contented mind, a cleon breast, an' good health.

‡·‡·‡·‡·‡·‡·‡·‡·‡·‡·‡·‡·‡·‡

SAM BAMFORD.

TH' owd veteran brid's toppled deawn fro' his pearch,
 He'll charm us no more wi' his singin';
 His voice has been hushed i' th' melodious grove,
 Wheer feebler voices are ringin' !
He sang in his youth,—in his green owd age ;
 An' he sang when i' monly prime ;
Then, loike other warblers, he meaunted aloft,
 To a fairer an' sunnier clime.

He sang fifty year sin', ere some o' us brids
 Had managed to creep eawt o' th' shell ;
An' sweetly an' grandly he poiped i' thoose days,
 As th' owd Middletonians can tell !
Unloike other warblers an' songsters o' th' grove,
 He ne'er changed his fithers, nor meawted ;
For th' longer he lived, an' th' harder he sung,
 An' faster these ornaments spreawted.

He wur dragg'd fro' his nest once, at th' dead-time o'th' neet,
 An' him an' his mate had to sever,—
But it ne'er made no difference to him—not a bit,
 For he sang just as sweetly as ever.
He warbled his notes in his own native shire,
 When his pearch wur surreaunded wi' dangers ;
An' he ne'er changed his tune when he'rn hurried away,
 An' imprisoned 'mongst traitors an' strangers.

Owd Sam seldom flattered wi' owt 'at he wrote,
 But for truthfulness allis wur famed ;
When he feawnd there wur owt needed smitin', he smote,
 An' cared nowt whoa praised or whoa blamed.
An' they wur songs, wur his,—not that maudlin' stuff,
 Would-be poets spin eawt into rhyme ;
There's a genuine ring i' what great men sing,
 Summat sweet, summat grand, an' sublime !

He warbled when Waugh wur a fledglin' i' th' nest,
 An' had ne'er had a thowt abeawt meauntin';
An' young 'Lijah Rydin's had hardly begun
 To give us his " Streams fro' th' owd Fountain."
Th' owd loom heawse i' Middleton rang wi' his notes,
 An' his shuttle kept toime to his songs,
Ere he led up his nayburs to famed Peterloo,
 To deneaunce what they felt to be wrongs.

He sang when his mate drooped away at his side,
 Not a song o' rejoicin' or gladness,
But a low, plaintive dirge, softened deawn an' subdued,
 Wellin' eawt ov a heart full o' sadness.
He sang, too, when th' spoiler bore off his lone lamb,
 Tho' his heart wi deep sorrow wur riven ;
Still he didn't despair, for he'd faith to believe
 'At his dear ones had gone up to heaven.

He sang when th' breet sunshine illumined his path,
 An' th' fleawers wur ole bloomin' areawnd ;
An' he sang, too, when th' storm-cleawds coom sweepin'
  along,
 An' threatened to crush him to th' greawnd.
He sang when his een had grown tearful an' dim,
 An' his toppin' turned thin an' grey ;
An' th' muse never left this owd veteran bard,
 Till Death coom an' took him away.

Thus he sung till he deed, an' his soul-stirrin' strains,
 Never failed to encourage an' bless ;
For he loved to rejoice wi' thoose hearts 'at rejoiced,
 An' sorrow wi' thoose i' distress.
God bless him, an' iv there's a spot up aboon,
 Where dwell th' noble-minded an' pure,
Wheer th' songsters are gathered to strike up a tune,
 Th' owd brid's perched amongst 'em we're sure !

READ AT
TH' "BONNY BRID'S" WEDDING PARTY,
8TH NOVEMBER, 1886.

WELL, Schofield, tha'rt welcome to Hannah;
   Tho' awm troubled a bit, as tha'll see;
But if there's one moor nor another
   'At th' lass will be safe wi', it's thee.
For twenty-three year, or near on it,
  Aw've had th' pleasure o' callin her mine;
But tha's 'ticed her away fro' my brid-cage,
  An' coaxed her to go into thine.

Well, bless her! aw've done th' best aw could do,
  An' noa deawt tha intends to do th' same.
Let's hope 'at hoo's made a good bargain
  I' changin' her cage an' her name.
When hoo gets to her whoam at New Moston,
  May her nayburs eawt theer be as kind
An' as anxious to mak' her feel happy,
  As thoose 'at hoo's leavin' behind.

Neaw, it's pleasant to ha' one's good wishes,
  An' these yo'll tak' with yo', awm sure;
An' what is there moor to feel preawd on,
  Than a hearty "God bless yo'!" fro' th' poor.
A lovin' an' good mother's blessin'
  Is o' far greater value nor gowd;
Yo may find human natur i' th' crescent,
  But yo'll find a deol moor on't i' th' fowd!

Two year' sin' tha sought my acquaintance,
  An' admired oather me or mi song;
At least tha pretended to do so;
  But aw saw throo thi game ole along.
We had eawr nice walks in a mornin',
  An' mi company then wur o reet;
But there's one little matter aw noticed,
  Thi een wur on th' brid-cage at neet!

It's o very weel to be laffin',
  But youth allis did laff at age ;
Tha'rt desarvin' a reet deawn good thrashin'
  For stealin' my brid eawt o' th' cage.
Well, ne'er mind ; iv tha'rt suited tha'rt welcome ;
  Aw've noa deawt but thi motives are pure ;
So aw'll not ha' thee ta'en up for robb'ry
  If tha'll promise to do it no moor.

These presents fro' friends an' fro' nayburs
  Are expressive o' love an' good-will ;
They're ole very pratty an' useful,
  An' some on 'em samples o' skill.
When they get to " Rose Cottage," New Moston,
  They cannot but serve to remind
O'th years 'at yo' spent here at Blackpool,
  Wi' thoose 'at your leavin' behind.

We shall think an yo' kindly an' often,
  Altho' yo're away eawt o' th' seet :
We shall miss Hannah's footsteps on th' threshold ;
  We shall miss, too, her well-known " good neet."
Well, yo' go wi' a father's good wishes ;
  Yo're united for better or worse ;
Yo'll booath ha' to draw i' one harness,
  An' join at one bed, an' one purse.

An' neaw—just one word to those present—
  Awm fairly surprised, aw must own,
At th' manner yon treated th' young couple,
  An' th' good naybourly feelin' yon shown.
Yon flung a few fleawers i' life's pathway,
  An' Royalty couldn't do moor ;
These presents, kind words, an' good wishes,
  Will long be remembered, awm sure.

FORTY-EIGHT.

ORTY-EIGHT ?   Where's th' lookin' glass ?
Eh, dear ! awm gettin' grey, bi th' mass !
An' yet it seems but yesterday,
Sin' aw'rn a little lad at play.
One must ha' calculated wrong ;
Aw've hardly bin i' th' world soa long ;
Besides, aw foind awm middlin' streight,
An' yet aw must be forty-eight.

Where's th' Bible ? that'll tell mi age ;
Oh, here it is, on th' title page.
Here's Abram's name, an' Betty's too—
Two little things aw never knew.
An' here's mi brother John's aw see ;
He's o'er two year' a-head o' me,
An' here comes moine, it must be reight,
Awm forty-eight, ah, forty-eight.

Heaw toime does jog along for sure !
Does t' year, lass ; someb'dy's punsin' th' door.
Eh ! Jim, owd lad, heaw's theaw got here ?
Come forrud mon, poo up that cheer.
Owd brid, aw do feel some an' glad !
But, eh, theaw art some altered lad !
Tha'll stop an' have a cup o' tay,
Awm forty-eight year' owd to-day !

It's forty-year' sin' thee an' me
Geet thrashed for climbin' th' apple tree.
Tha'll recollect that Friday, too,
When ole us lads ran off fro' th' schoo'
To goa a catchin' fish i' th' river—
Awst ne'er forget that Friday—never.
Aw've noan forgot bein' strapped i' th' fowd
Altho' awm forty-eight year' owd.

Let's see—what age will theaw be, Jim ?
Owd brid ! theaw looks i' daycent trim ;
But then—there's this in't, doesta see—
Theaw hasn't bin wed as oft as me.
Perhaps tha'll think aw've been to' soft,
An' wed a toime or two to' oft.
Well, theer it is lad, wrong or reight ;
There's foolish foalk at forty-eight.

An' mon, there's ups an' deawns i' loife,
An' will be, whether a chap's a woife
Or livin' beawt one, same as thee ;
There's single foalk worse off nor me.
An' it isn't allis thoose 'at's brass
'At's th' happiest, is it, Sarah, lass ?
Well, come, owd wench, let's have some tay,
Awm forty-eight year' owd to-day.

TO MY OWD FRIEND, THOMAS KENWORTHY,

THESE strokes come thick an' heavy, mon;
But bear 'em bravely iv tha con,
    Brother Bard.
    Tha's had thi share o' grief, aw know,
An' fowt loife's battles here below
    Long an' hard.

That yead o' thine is gettin' gray;
Aw see it's lateish on i' th' day
    Wi' thi, lad.
But come, cheer up, mon, things ull mend,
Aw dunno loike to see a friend
    Lookin' sad.

One's had their cares as weel as thee;
Tha's noan had mony moor nor me,
    That awm sure.
But, then, tha knows there's nob'dy beawt,
So th' ills we conno get witheawt
    Let's endure.

O sickness, death, want, grief, an' care,
There's some foalks get a biggish share—
    Moor than's sweet.
It's noan so pleasant kissin' th' rod;
But come, mon, put thi trust i' God,
    He'll do reet.

Tha's noan so fur to tramp, owd friend,
Tha's welly reached thi journey's end,
    Trudge along.
Thi fiddle's mony a toime bin strung,
An aw've noa deawt but what tha's sung
    Mony a song.

But, neaw, owd mon, thi days are few,
So iv there's owt tha has to do,
    Do it soon.
An' th' bit o' toime tha has to stop,
Get ready for another shop
    Up aboon.

WHAT! ANOTHER CRACKED POET!

WHAT! another cracked poet! bi thi mass, Jim, owd lad,
    Aw thowt we'd enoo o' this mack;
    An' iv tha'll alleaw me to say what aw think,
      Tha desarves a good stick to thi back.
Aw'll tell thee what, lad, tha'll be awfully clemmed
    Iv tha'rt thinkin' to live bi thi pen.
Iv tha wants to get on, get some porritch an' milk,
    An' some good cheese an' bread neaw an' then.

Neaw, aw've had some experience i' this mak' o' wark;
    Aw've bin thirty odd year i' this schoo';
An' what have aw managed to larn does ta think?
    Well, aw've managed to larn awm a foo'!
Tha'll find 'at this scribblin's a very poor trade,
    An' tha'd ger along better bi th' hawve,
Iv tha'd start as a quack, wi' a tapeworm or two,
    Or a few decent pills an' some sawve.

Iv tha still feels determined to turn eawt as bard,
    Aw'd advise thee to let nob'dy know,
Or tha'll rue it to th' very last day 'at tha lives,
    Tha'll wish tha'd kept quiet—tha will so!
Iv Betty o' Bowsers at th' bottom o' th' lone
    Happens t' lose an' owd favourite cat,
Very loikely th' furst body tha chances to meet
    Will ax thee to write abeawt that.

Iv a couple gets wed, or a chap licks his wife,
    Or some scamp in a train steals a kiss,
Aw'll warrant th' furst gossip tha meets 'll say, " Jim,
    Tha'll spin us a rhyme abeawt this."
Tha'll be loikely to feel a bit flattered at first,
    An' think it a stunnin' good trade;
But let me impress just one fact on thi mind,
    It's this, Jim, tha'll never get paid.

Iv tha's ony opinions 'at doesn't just square
  Wi' thoose 'at are held bi thi friends,
They'll look on thee coolly, as iv tha'rn a thief,
  An' turn thee adrift till tha mends.
Iv tha knows heaw to flatter, an' wink at men's wrongs,
  Tha may manage t' get on very weel ;
But, tackle their habits, expose their mean tricks,
  An' they'll shun thee as iv tha'rn the de'il !

Well, aw've towd thee mi moind, tha can do what tha loikes,
  Go on rhymin', or let it alone ;
Iv th' latter—thi friends may provide thee a fish ;
  Iv th' former—they'll give thee a stone.
An' what abeawt sellin' thi poetry, Jim ?
  Neaw, tha'll foind that a job aw can tell ;
Iv tha'rt treated loike other poor Lancashire bards,
  Tha'll ha' to go sell 'em thisel' !

Heaw would t' loike goin' reawnd wi' a bag full o' books ?
  Heaw would t' loike to go hawkin' thi brains ?
Or, when tha's bin tryin' to do some kind act,
To be towd tha'rt a foo' for thi pains.
Aw can tell thee this, Jim, it's aboon twenty year',
  Sin' aw wur set deawn as a foo' ;
An', tho' it's a charge at one doesn't loike to own,
  Awm beginnin' to think 'at it's true.

Thee stick to recitin'—tha'rt clever at that ;
  In fact, there's few loike thee i' th' lond,
An' booath i' th' pathetic an' th' humorous vein
  Tha'rt reckoned a very good hond.
But aw'll drop it, owd friend, for awm gradely fag'd eawt ;
  Booath mi brain an' mi hand 'gin to tire ;
Iv tha loikes tha can stick these few lines i' thi book ;
  Or—iv tha prefers it—i' th' fire.

A TRIBUTE TO THE DROWNED.

LADS! doff yo'r hats, an' gether reawnd,
  An' listen to mi song,
  Mi subject's rayther painful, so
  Aw'll not detain yo' long.
Yon' happen heard o' th' wreck we'n had,
  So near this stormy coast,
O th' sad mishaps to th' lifeboat crews,
  An' th' precious lives we'n lost.

It's bad enuff to hear these tales,
  Or read what's put i' print;
But what must be th' effects o' th' storm
  To thoose poor chaps 'at's in't:
When seated cosily i' th' nook,
  It's little we can know
O' th' foamin' billows meawntains high,
  Or th' stormy winds 'at blow!

Eh, bless yo', lads! aw mind that neet,
  That fatal neet to some;
Aw're sit deawn readin' th' *Evening News*,
  I' this mi sea-side whoam,
When th' woind i' th' chimney 'gan to roar,
  At length it blew a gale;
An' th' windows fairly rattled, lads,
  Wi' th' peltin' rain an' hail.

Aw looked at th' woife, who, just at th' toime,
  Sat knittin' in her cheer,
An' said, " It's gettin' fearful, lass;
  There'll be some wrecks, aw fear!"
Yo' know the result—th' bad news 'at coome;
  Th' next mornin' when aw woke,
Aw're hauve prepared to hear th' sad words
  Mi sorrowin' naybors spoke :—

Heaw two brave crews had faced that sea—
    Ah, one o' th' stormiest known—
An' tryin' t' rescue other lives
    Had sacrificed their own !
Sad news wur this !   As th' day wore on,
    It only proved too true ;
Saint Annes and Southport boats wur lost
    An' th' biggest part o' th' crew.

While these sad scenes wur takkin' place
    That stormy neet i' th' dark,
Th' brave Lytham crew wur eawt, an' proved
    Successful i' their wark.
Ah, these brave fellows put to sea,
    An' fowt booath wind an' waves,
Till every man on th' Mexico
    Wur saved fro' watery graves !

Well, th' next we yeard wur—Coxs'n Bob
    Wur launchin' th' Blackpool boat ;
An' th' Samuel Fletcher, wi' her crew,
    Wur very soon afloat.
They went as close as they could think
    To wheer th' sad wreck had been ;
But, as yo' know, lads, all wur vain,
    No boats or bodies seen.

Aw'll say no moor ; yo' know the rest,
    Heaw widows grieve an' mourn ;
An' little childer cry for th' dads
    They'll never see return.
Heaw aged parents mourn their sons,
    An' social ties are rent ;
Heaw the nation's moved fro' end to side,
    At this mooast sad event !

Well, lads, aw've done, put on your hats,
    Yo'n heard mi plaintive lay ;
It's th' saddest song aw've had to sing
    For many and many a day.
Aw've pleaded th' boatmen's cause before,
    Aw'll plead it once ogen ;
For God hasn't made ow't nobler yet,
    Than these brave Lifeboat Men !

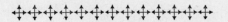

TO GEORGE HARRY BARDSLEY, ON HIS EIGHTEENTH BIRTHDAY.

O tha'rt eighteen year' owd to-day, arto, mi lad ?
    Well, unless time should play thi some tricks,
If tha lives eighteen longer, an's moderate good luck,
    Tha'll be somewheer abeawt thirty-six.

After ole, mi dear lad, a mon's character here,
    Isn't made up o' days, or o' years,
But i' th' way 'at one battles wi' th' troubles he meets,
    An' his struggles wi hopes an' wi' fears.

Some live i' this world till they're eighty or moor,
    But heaw have life's battles been fowt ?
Or what have they done i' humanity's cause,
    Or for th' country 'at's nurtured 'em ?   Nowt !

Dunno thee be loike these are—dead weights upo' th' state ;
    Do thi duty i' th' world, loike a mon ;
Scorn to live loike a drone ; earn moor nor tha eats,
    An' a little bit moor iv tha con.

Tha'rt eighteen year' owd, a nice time to begin
    To carve for thisel' a good name ;
An' let me assure thee 'at goodness endures,
    Far longer than mere empty fame.

Get thi wisdom fro' thoose 'at are known to be wise,
    An' for strength look to thoose 'at are strong ;
Let thi feyther be th' pattern tha goes by, an' then
    Tha'll never get very fur wrong.

But tha'll want noan o' this mak' o' preitchin' aw'm sure,
    So aw'll drop it wi' what aw've neaw said,
Or tha'll come to th' conclusion 'at others have done,
    'At poets are wrong i' their yead.

" 'SIXTY-SIX."

OOD-BYE, owd Sixty-Six;
  Tha's welly played us o thi tricks;
  We'n seen thi smoiles, an' felt thi kicks,
    So neaw we'll say good-bye.
    Tha's seen us sick an' sad;
Tha's seen us hearty, weel, an' glad—
Dancin' and singin' here loike mad;
    Tha's known some on us t' cry.

Bring in that poor owd form
'At's standin' shiverin' theer i' th' storm.
Wilt have a drop o' sum 'at warm
    To cheer thee, 'Sixty-Six?
    Come in, an' sit thee deawn,
It's noan yet toime to goo—not it;
Come, warm them shanks o' thine a bit,
    An' tell us wheer tha'rt beawn.

Tha coom here when tha'rn young,
An' eh! heaw noicely th' singers sung!
To mak' thee welcome th' bells wur rung;
    An' neaw tha'rt beawn to goo—
    Owd friend, tha'rt beawn to goo.
Well, come, there's sum'at here to sup;
Ger howd o' th' pot, an' drink it up;
    Drink th' New Year's health—neaw do.

That's reet—neaw rest thisel',
For one can see tha'rt noan so well;
Hast ony good owd tales to tell?
    Iv so, let's have 'em neaw,
    It's latish on i' th' day.
It's after eight o'clock, owd friend;
Tha'rt gettin' near thi journey's end,
    Tha's noan so long to stay.

He's faintin', dear a me!
Bring him some wayter in a cup;
Let's raise his yead, an' let him sup;
    He's very bad, aw see;
    Give him a drop o' wine.
We munno go an' let him dee
Till th' New Year comes to set him free;
    Th' church clock's just strikin' nine.

Three heawrs ull see him off,
Poor thing! he's getten a weary cough;
It racks him up, altho' he's tough;
    It shouldn't use him so,
    Th' owd mon's i' pain, aw know.
He'll noan be with us here so long;
Then let's strike up a farewell song,
    An' sing it soft an' slow.

Then leov him to hissel',
He's happen sum'at on his mind
He'd loike to try and leave behind—
    Hush! Hush! yond's th' owd church bell,
    Biddin' th' Owd Year farewell.
O listen, friends! heaw soft an' sweet,
An' yet heaw sad it seawnds to-neet!
    Toll on, toll on, church bell.

He's deein' neaw, be still;
Heaw thick an' short he takes his breath;
He's lyin' neaw i' th' arms o' Death,
    Beyond eawr care an' skill,
    Good-bye, owd 'Sixty-Six.
Tha's played thi pranks, and done thi tricks,
We'n seen thi smoiles, and felt thi kicks,
    So neaw, old year, good-bye.

ISAAC BRADSHAW.

WD Isaac Bradshaw keeps a shop
 Th' next dur to Nancy Wood's ;
He's carrots, turnips, apples, eggs,
 Red cabbages, an' spuds :
He's scrubbin'-brushes, idleback,
 Mop yeads, an' wooden pails ;
He's besoms, ladin' cans, an' mugs,
 Oil, candlesticks, an' nails.

He does a bit i' th' quackin' line,
 An' mendin' broken limbs ;
At curin' th' toothwartch he's a brick ;
 He's cured mi Uncle Jim's.
Aw'll tell yo heaw th' owd covey does,—
 Yo'll think he's fawse no deawt ;
He sets a pair o' pincers on,
 An' poo's th' beggars eawt.

One day mi feyther hurt his thumb,
 Wi' helpin' t' kill a cawve ;
Owd Isaac cured it in a week,
 Wi' some o' his green sawve.
It's true ; iv onybody deawts,
 Go ax mi Uncle John ;
He're wi' mi feyther when he went,
 An' saw him put it on.

He's yead-wartch pills—owd Isaac has,
 An' pills for purgin' to' ;
He says they'll oppen " Chatwood's Safes ;"
 But that'll hardly do.
Aw dunna think he lies so mitch,
 Or cheats his dullest friends ;
Unless bi doin' so he finds
 'At it suits his private ends.

He tricked one fellow nicely once,
    'At he met at th' " Risin' Sun ;"
But he didn't intend to hurt th' poor chap,
    It wur only done for fun.
Joe Brown once went an' bowt some sawve
    For a corn 'at hurt his toe ;
Ike towd him t' rub some on his nose,
    An' eat a bit an' o.

A rare good doctor Isaac is,
    Just reet for ailin' folks ;
For thoose 'at dunno like his pills.
    Are sure to like his jokes.
Aw coed at' th' shop one Friday neet,
    An' axed iv he wur in ;
Well, Isaac yeard me, so he bawled—
    " Nawe, he's gone eawt, long sin ! "

Well, are yo wantin' owt he has,—
    Mop-yeads, or besom stails ;
Mugs, ladin' cans, or idleback,
    White sond, or wooden pails ;
Or do yo want some good yarb pills,
    For curin' pains i' th' back ;
If so, he keeps a stock on hand,
    An' he says they're good to tak' !

He's lately ta'en a patent eawt,
    For a dodge he claims as new ;
It's this—when shiftin' pain away,
    He shifts his patients to !
Well, neaw, it's time aw stopp'd this rhyme,
    An' aw've said enuff to show
Wheer pills an' fun together run,
    So gie th' owd chap a co' !

OWD FOGEY.

OWD Fogey lives i' Turner's Fowd,
　　Near Matty Wilson's Schoo' ;
An' everybody knows him theer,
　　Becose he's sich a foo'.
Last week he pawned his Sunday clooas,
　　An' sowd a favourite tit ;
An' neaw he hasn't a haupney left,
　　He's drunk it every bit.

He took their Johnny's Testament
　　To Barney Logan's sale ;
An' th' bit o' brass he geet for that,
　　He spent o' gin an' ale.
He made away wi' lots o' things ;
　　He's drunk his pig an' cote ;
An' any profit th' poultry brings,
　　Goes deawn his thirsty throat.

There's nowt o' ony value left,
　　Except poor Jane, his wife ;
An' hoo's so knocked abeawt i' th' world,
　　'At hoo's weary ov her life.
An' nobbut th' week before they're wed,
　　He took her on his knee,
An' swore he'd allus treat her weel ;
　　But has he done ? not he !

His garden's covered o'er wi' weeds,
　　An' th' fence is brocken deawn ;
He used to have as nice a plot
　　As ony chap i' th' teawn.
He took a pride i' th' business then,
　　He're in it every neet ;
But neaw yo'd hardly give a groat
　　For o' he has i' th' seet.

Last year he'd lots o' collyfleawers,
   An' beans, an' peas, an' o ;
He'd twenty furst-rate gooseberry trees,
   An' celery sticks to show.
He built a heawse for growin' plants,
   An' spent a peawnd o glass ;
But this he sowd to Farmer Jones,
   An' had a spree wi' th' brass.

A pig he had, worth thurty bob,
   He sowd for seven an' six
To someb'dy deawn i' Kinder Lone ;
   It's just like o his tricks.
He's reckless what he says or does,
   An' when he's soaked his clay,
He cares for nowt, nor nobody,
   He'll give his things away.

A month sin' some o' th' nayburs here
   Sowd off their poultry stocks ;
Owd Fogey went an' bowt 'em o,
   He'd twenty hens an' cocks.
Next day he went to th' " Gapin' Goose,"
   At th' bottom end o' th' teawn,
An' sowd o' th' lot to Boniface,—
   For what ?   A hawve a creawn !

He ceawered theer drinkin' grog an' stuff,
   Till twelve o'clock at neet ;
But when he reached his whoam th' next day,
   Weren't he a bonny seet !
His cooat wur daubed fro' top to tail
   Wi' slurrin deawn a broo ;
But nob'dy pitied him, becose
   He's sich a silly foo' !

TO SUPERINTENDENT JAMES BENT.

W'VE read th' book tha gave me, an'—flattery aside,—
At some things aw've laughed, an' at others aw've
cried;
One's amused at th' smart tricks tha's performed i'
thi time
When huntin' poor beggars suspected o' crime.

Why, Bent, mon; tha must ha' been made o' good weft,
For tha's worn weel, an' yet there's a lot of thee left!
Tha's stood some hard usage, an' knockin' abeawt;
But it's happen this thumpin' 'at's made thee so steawt.

They tell us 'at th' best way to raise a low bump
Is to set to an' give it a rattlin' good thump.
Well, jokin' aside; tha'rt a wonderful brick,
An' it's really surprisin' to find 'at tha'rt wick.

But Providence seems to ha' guarded thi life,
When traps wur laid for thee, an' dangers wur rife;
An' neaw, when thi locks are just turnin' to gray,
An' tha'rt gettin' near th' end ov a long hard day,—

Tha'rt getherin' areawnd thee th' poor waifs an' strays,—
'At have run,—but have failed to win life's race;
An,' to my mind, this rootin' eawt dregs fro' th' ditch—
Is moor Christ-like nor swaggerin' i' pulpits so mitch!

Did Christ strut abeawt in a broad-brimmed hat ?
Not he ! he'd to' mitch common sense to do that ;
But he sowt th' poor an' needy, an' gave 'em a feed,
An' we must do th' same iv we want to succeed.

True, there's nowt very startlin', nor nowt very fine,
I' that Owd Trafford Soup Kitchen business o' thine ;
But tha'rt doin' a grand work among th' eawtcasts an' such,
'At th' ring-fingered, white-honded foalk daren't touch.

But this isn't what aw wur wantin' to say,
When this rap at bad tactics allured me away ;—
Aw wanted to tell th' Trafford Soup Kitchen cook
Heaw aw relished th' choice bits 'at aw feawnd i' his book.

There's noa gristle or paxwax 'at winno digest ;
But ole put before us seems th' choicest an' th' best ;
An' aw must ha feawnd th' book entertainin' tha'rt sure ;
When th' furst readin' cleared two hundred pages an' moor.

An' aw met ha' cleared th' lot, hadn't th' woman aw wed—
Sheawted " What arto readin' ? come on here to bed."
A hint to " move on " this, aw thowt, Mister Bent ;
So—after aw'd swallowed mi porridge—aw went.

TH' PULPIT AN' TH' PEWS.

EAR, dear, whatever's comin' next!
 It seems some parson's feawnd a text
 'At hints 'at God Almighty's vext
   At th' English race.
An' why? becose we haven't th' wit
To mourn o'er sins we don't commit;
An', what's still worse,—we haven't seen fit
   To seek His face.

Does th' sun e'er sulk, or vent its spleen,
Bi' blightin' every lovely scene,
Becose folk dunno lift their een,
   An' look at *it?*
Or does it freawn on goodly seed,
An' smile on useless tares an' weed
Throo jealousy? Not it indeed;
   Th' sun's moor wit!

It seems God's played on various strings,
An' vainly tried o macks o' things,
To get poor folk—an' even kings—
   To own His peawer.
Well, these aren't themes for paltry jokes,
Or even keen, sarcastic strokes;
Still, th' job looks strange to common folks;—
   It does for seawer.

It's said God plagued th' Egyptian kings,
Wi' sendin' locusts, lice, an' things;
But persecution seldom brings
   One nearer God.
There's lots o' folk t' be feawnd i' th' lond,
To grasp, or kiss some patriot's hond;
But th' number's very few 'at's fond
   O' kissin' th' rod.

Another strange suggestion's made,
It's this : th' Almighty's damaged trade ;
Th' chap's makin' statements aw'm afraid
   He conno prove.
What nasty filth some men con fling !
What serious charges these to bring,
Against a just an' righteous King—
   A God o' love.

We know, fro' what i' th' Book appears,
God's charged wi' causin' sighs an' tears,
An' laughin' at His children's fears !
   What fiendish acts !
But will this kind o' twaddle wash ?
Can we accept this balderdash,
Or treat sich silly, drivellin' trash
   As sober facts ?

God's ruined agriculture, too ;
Do those i' th' pulpit think this true ?
It seawnds like lies to us i' th' pew,
   It does indeed.
There's just one chance for parsons yet,
If they wouldn't ha' th' " preachin'-shops " to let,
There's one thing sure—they'll ha' to get
   A better Creed !

Heaw th' parson knows what God intends,
Bi th' wars an' plagues it's said He sends,
Unless they're varry chummy friends,
   Aw canno' see.
It's hard to grasp these knotty themes ;
They creawd one's mind as misty dreams ;
We know God ne'er lays bare His schemes,
   To sich as me.

Aw'm but a feeble earthly worm ;
What scientists might call a " germ,"—
Neaw moulded to a human form,
   An' slightly made :
An' yet, aw never feel aw'm mist ;
Aw needn't raise mi puny fist ;
Aw con let folk know aw still exist,
   Beawt spoilin' trade !

Mysterious deeds are these, an' dark;
An' it may be wrong to mak' th' remark;
But to me it looks mere baby wark—
           To ruin crops!
An' this is th' greawnd wheer th' parson stands!
An' th' trash is sent to foreign lands!
Why, they wouldn't employ sich 'prentice hands
           I' *earthly* shops!

We'll ha' noa truck wi' jealous gods,
'At preawl abeawt i' th' world wi' rods,
An' shut poor devils up i' quods
           They'll never quit.
We want a God 'at's better drilled;
Moor used to govern folk—more skilled;
One less inhuman, less self-willed,
               An' shows moor wit!

If these are pulpit thowts, try th' pews,
An' let's go in for nobler views,
Than thoose we get fro' ignorant Jews,
               Or priestly drones!
Let darkness flee! mak' room for leet!
Instead o' crutches, use yo'r feet;
An', while we've good, sound, honest meat,
               Why pick at bones!

God isn't a fiend, inventin' pains;
A tyrant, bindin' slaves i' chains;
Nor castin' blight i' fertile plains,
               Becose He's vext;
No! "God is good;" we see His peawers
I' woods, an' streams, i' fields, an' fleawers;
This pratty world we live in's eawrs,
               An' so is th' next!

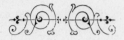

HEAW TO RAISE TH' WOIND.

AW tell yo what, foalk, it's surprisin' to think
What skeomin' there is to ger howd o' some drink;
It really astonishes one to see th' skill
Some o' th' women display to ger howd o' a gill.
Aw wur towd a queer sort ov a skit th' other neet
Bi a friend 'at aw happened to leet on i' th' street;
Iv yo loike aw con set to an' tell it ogen,
It'll be an heawer's practice or so for mi pen.

Well, a chap an' his woife wur once hard up for brass;
They couldn' booath muster up th' price ov a glass:
Till, one day, an idea coom into th' woife's yead,
So hoo turned to owd Robin, her husband, an' said—
"Thee rowl up them sleeves, an' away wi' thee eawt,
An' th' lon'lord at th' Swan ull be somewheer abeawt;
When he sees tha's thi cooat off, he'll ax wheer tha'rt beawn;
So tham tell him tha's let ov a job deawn i' th' teawn,

An' tha'rt just goin' to it a mackin' a start;
An' aw'll bet thee a hawpney he'll chalk thee a quart."
Well, Robin thowt that wur noan sich a bad plan,
So he acted at once on th' advoice o' their Nan;
An' he rowled up his sleeves, an' he went eawt o' th' dur,
An' spied eawt th' owd lon'lord, afore he'd gone fur;
So Robin pretended to be in a swat;
He pood a great napkin fro' eawt ov his hat,

An' wi' it he gated a woipin' his face,
An' hurried along at a very quick pace.
When he geet facin' th' "Swan," an' wur bowtin' past th' dur,
Th' owd lon'lord said, "Robin, owd lad, wheer are t' for?"
But Robin pretended he'd no time to stop,
An' towd him he'd let ov a stunnin' good shop:
"Well, come," said th' owd lon'lord, "aw'll trust thi a quart:
Aw'm fain 'at tha'rt gooin' a mackin' a start;

Folk 'at's workin' are th' best sort for me aw can tell,
Tho' aw'm noan very partial to workin' misel;
Come in, mon, an' have an odd quart moor to th' lot,
Tha can co in at th' reckonin' an' pay off thi shot."
Well, Robin went in, an' his ale wur soon browt;
Come, this hasn't bin badly managed he thowt;
So he swigg'd off his ale, laid his pitcher o' th' hob,
An' towd th' lon'lord he wanted t' be off to his job.

But th' owd fox turned his heels, when he geet eawt o' th' seet,
An' play'd for their heawse deawn i' Parliament-street.
Well, his woife wur at th' dur—hoo wur weshin' a pon;
So hoo started a axin' him how he'd gone on.
" Gone on," said Owd Robin, " the dule's i' that yead—
Why, everythin's happened just same as tha said;
This is th' best trick tha's played sin' aw'rn wed to thee, Nan;
We'n made a good thing eawt o' th' lon'lord at th' ' Swan ;'

Aw said aw'd a job, an' wur goin' deawn to start,
So he took me i' th' heawse, an' he fot me a quart,
An' said when aw'd brass, aw could co in an' pay,
So aw drunk off mi ale, an' aw bid him good day.
Wheer's mi cooat ? Aw'll go tell Sam o' Dick's what aw've
        done;
It'll just pleos him rarely, he's fond o' some fun."
" Wheer's thi cooat ?" said his woife. " Ah, mi coat, wheer's
        it gone?
Come, be handy, an' bring it, an' let's put it on."

" Thi cooat, lad, thi cooat ? Why, aw've put it up th' speawt;
Does t' think aw'st foind thee drink an' sarve misel beawt?"
Eh, aw wish yo'd seen Robin when th' woife towd him that;
He sprang eawt o' th' heawse witheawt jacket or hat;
Went leatherin' deawn th' street to an uncle o' mine,
An' said iv he'd find him a pledge card, he'd sign;
Th' woife had larnt him a lesson he'd ne'er larnt afoor;
So he signed pledge that day, an' ne'er touch'd drink no moor.

CURE FOR TH' TOOTH-WARCH.

I' this wonderful age ov invention we find
'At medical science is noan fur behind,
Tho' it seems 'at i' this field o' knowledge an' skill
Important discoveries are tackin' place still.
One o' th' latest an' th' breetest 'at's knockin' abeawt,
Bein' a safe an' chep method o' pooin' teeth eawt.
Neaw this is no second-hond, owd woman's tale,
Trumped up, same as mony a thing, merely for sale;
It's a fact, this, at least it's related as such,
One o' that sort 'at conno' be mended so much.

This discoverer, as fur as aw'm able to larn,
Wur a chap up i' Yorshur, they co'd "Joe o' th' Barn."
Like mony a poor sufferin' sinner beside,
He'd th' tooth-warch so bad he could hardly abide.
He went grinnin an' grumblin', an' slavverin' abeawt,
So th' naybours advised him to ger it poo'd eawt;
But Joe wur beawt brass—Joe had spent it o up
At th' "Fiddle an' Hayfork" o' sum'at to sup.

Time went on, an' Joe's tooth geet to warchin' so bad,
'At he stamped abeawt th' heawse loike someb'dy gone mad;
But a brilliant idea flashed upon him at last,
As is often th' case when a mon's gradely fast.
A foo' when he's put to 't, con mak' some good hits,
An' th' tooth-warch it seems help'd to sharpen Joe's wits.

While feelin' abeawt in his pockets he feawnd
A piece o' good bandin' 'at looked strong an' seawnd.
Well, one eend o' this he made fast to th' oon dur,
Th' other eend to his fang—(th' owd plague 'at it wur).
Then he geet howd o' th' poker, an' put it i' th' fire—
An act his friend Bob couldn't help but admire.
O this bein' done, an' proneawnced " very good."
Joe stepped back, an' made th' bandin' as tight as he could.
" Neaw then, lad," he said, " let's ger on wi' this job,
Look iv th' faur-poker's reight-daan red, wilta, Bob ?"
" Red !" said Bob, " ah, my word lad, aw think it is soa ;
What doest' reckon tha'rt wantin' to use it for, Jooa ?"
" Thee do what aw tell thee," said Joe.   " Well, neaw then ;
Touch maw nooaz wi' 't, as soon as ta yers me say *when*."
Bob expressed hissel willin' to do what he could ;
Iv it lay in his peawer to obleege him he would.
Joe at once sheawted " When !" Bob drew th' fire-poker eawt,
An' put it reet gently to th' eend o' Joe's sneawt.
Th' effect one may guess at—th' oon dur stood it greawnd,
An' th' band did it duty—it proved to be seawnd ;
So when Joe smelt at th' poker it made him start back,
When eawt coom his troublesome tooth in a crack ;
It seem'd rather vex'd, th' little pest 'at it wur,
For it flew like a bullet slap bang at th' oon dur.

Joe wur cured, an', believin' th' invention furst-class,
He's for gettin' a patent as soon as he's th' brass ;
I' th' meantime, he declares he shall mak' thoose repent
'At use his invention witheawt his consent.

CHEER UP, TOILIN' BROTHERS!

CHEER up, toilin' brothers! cheer up an' be glad;
　　There's breeter days for us i' store;
　　Things are lookin' more sattled i' Lancashire here,
　　Neaw 'at th' 'Merica war's getten o'er.
Th' long chimnies are smokin' as hard as they con,
　　An' th' machinery's wurlin' areawnd;
Owd shopmates 'at havn't bin seen for some years
　　Are o gettin' back to th' owd greawnd.

Billy Taylor—he's bin off at Bradford awhile,
　　Weavin' woollen for one Mester Hooms,
But he's brought hissel back to this quarter ogen,
　　An' he's peggin' away at th' owd looms.
Their Jack's bin i' Staffordshire one or two years—
　　He'rn somewheer tort Bilston, aw think—
He garden'd an' did 'em odd jobs abeawt th' heawse,
　　An' he'd twelve bob a week an' his drink.

An owd crony o' mine's bin at Halifax yond,
　　Sellin' trotters an' tripe an' ceaw heel;
I' winter he'd cockles an' mussels an' stuff,
　　An' he tells me he did rare an' weel.
When th' wayterworks started up tort Swineshaw Brook,
　　He wur th' gaffer awhile o'er some men;
But for some cause or other he's left 'em, aw see,
　　An' getten i' th' factory ogen.

Polly Breawn's bin i' sarvice for two or three year',
　　At a aleheawse o' th' name o' th' Bull's Yead;
An hur an' a waiter there is abeawt th' place,
　　They tell'n me, are beawn to be wed.
Eawer Lucy's i' sarvice up Huddersfield way,
　　Wi' some chap—aw've forgotten his name;
But, heawever, hoo says hoo shall leave in a month,
　　When they'n put her some wark in her frame.

Eh, we han done some knockin' abeawt up an' deawn,
    While trade's bin so bad abeawt here !
We could spin some rare yarns, some on us, aw know—
    We could tell some strange tales, never fear.
We'n had to set to an' do o sorts o' jobs,
    An' we'n bin among o sorts o' folks ;
There's theawsands i' Lancashire know what it is,
    To go reawnd o' beggin' wi' pokes.

A lot o' young chaps 'at aw know very weel
    Made it up t' go a singin' one day,
But th' very furst place 'at they sung at, aw'rn towd,
    They gan 'em a creawn t' go away.
Then they sung for a doctor, a bit further up,
    An' Bolus sent one ov his men
Wi' a shillin'—an' towd 'em he'd give 'em two moor
    Iv they'd sing him " Th' Shurat Song " ogen.

But come, lads, we'll say nowt abeawt this no moor,
    But try an' forget o 'at's past ;
It wur th' furst time we'd ever done owt o' this sooart,
    An' we're livin' i' hopes 'at it's th' last.
Let's be careful i' future o'th' bit we can get,
    An' pay off what debts we may owe ;
We'n had heawses to live in, clooas, tommy, an' stuff,
    'At's never bin paid for, aw know.

Let's be honest to thoose 'at wur friendly to us,
    An' show bi eawr actions we're men ;
There's nob'dy can tell what's before 'em i' th' world—
    We may happen want helpin' ogen.
Neaw yo'll kindly excuse ony blunders aw've made,
    For aw've written as weel as aw con ;
An' beg to remain, wi respect an' esteem,
    Yours truly, A Poor Workin' Mon.

Th' village pedlar's a jovial ovvd brick;
A merchant o' great local fame;
He goes trudgin' areawnd wi' his basket an' stick,

TH' VILLAGE PEDLAR.

TH' village pedlar's a jovial owd brick,
    A merchant o' great local fame;
    He goes trudgin' abeawt wi' his basket an' stick,
    An' a few useful things 'at aw'll name.
He's needles, an' bodkins, an' thread,
    An' buttons, an' bobbins, an' tape;
An' hair-pins, 'at girls use (before they get wed),
    To keep their hair nicely i' shape.

He's worsted a haupney a bo,
    Blue-peawder, an' furniture paste;
An' he's capital mustard i' packets an' o,—
    Well, he says thoose 'at deawt it con taste.
Neaw th' owd pedlar ne'er gets eawt o' tune,
    Tho' he's bothered wi' o sorts o' foalk:
If they vex him a bit, he forgets ogen soon,
    An' passes it off as a joke.

He's carried his basket so long,
    That it neaw seems to act as a charm;
An' he tells us he feels as if summat wur wrong,
    If he hasn't it hung on his arm.
E'en at church,—well,—at least soa aw'm towd,—
    When his mind should be free fro' sich cares,
He's ole ov a shiver, his arm feels so cowd,
    For th' want ov his basket an' wares.

He's a christian i' th' spite ov o this ;
   Oh, aw've often yeard th' owd fellow tell
'At he thowt he could boast o' moor genuine bliss
   Than even eawr Queen could hersel'.
Earthly jewels one sees up an' deawn,
   He will tell yo' must crumble to dust ;
But he's livin' i' hopes o' possessin' a creawn,
   'At 'll noather turn faded nor rust.

Owd pedlar, tha'rt happy aw'm sure,—
   Trampin' reawnd wi' thi basket an' wares ;—
Leavin' blackin' an' blessin's at everyone's door,
   An' tryin' to leeten foalk's cares.
When tha claps deawn thi basket to dee,
   There'll be some weet een aw'll be beawnd ;
For it's allus affectin' an' painful to see
   An owd favourite laid i' th' greawnd !

Th' little childer,—when th' daisies appear,—
   To that spot wheer tha'rt buried will throng ;
An' sadly they'll say " Th' dear owd pedlar lies here,
   So let's sing him a nice little song !"
Then they'll deck thi green grave wi' wild fleawers,
   Wi' th' idea 'at they're keepin' thi warm ;
An' say,—as they leave thee alone a few heawers,—
   " God bless him ! he's tackin' no harm !"

A LITTLE BIT O' BOATH SIDES.

PART FIRST.

HE'S just come whoam fuddelt ogen,
  An' flung hissel deawn on th' bed ;
One's sick o' such low drunken men,
  An' aw'm sure there's none worse nor eawr Ned ;
For he spends nearly o he con get ;
  What to do, aw'm as fast as a thief ;
Ole th' cubburts an' drawers are " to let,"
  An' eawr Jane's gone to ax for relief.

As for good decent clooas, we're o beawt,
  An' we've nowt to stond up in but rags ;
To tell th' truth, aw'm ashamed to turn eawt,
  If it's nobbut when swillin' th' flags.
An' he knows heaw we are very weel,
  But he's getten so hardened wi' th' drink,
That it's eawt ov his natur' to feel,
  An' get's madder nor ever, aw think.

When he's drunk he'll come in ov a neet,
  An' ceawer like a pig on th' floor ;
Then aw wish he'd get eawt o' mi seet,
  An' never come near me no moor.
Yo' may think me a hard-hearted wife,
  An' tell me aw'm sadly to blame ;
But aw think iv yo' lived my life,
  Yo'r actions would be abeawt th' same.

Look ! he ceawers wi' his yead upo' th' hob ;
  For a pillow, he's getten his cap ;
An' his face is as black as a cob ;—
  Dear-a-me, neaw ! whatever's yon rap !
It's lon'lord, he's comin' for th' rent,
  But we haven't a farthin' i' th' hole ;
Th' last three-haupence we had has been spent
  On a quarter ov a hundert o' coal.

" Howd on, lass, aw've summat to say
   Abeawt th' blame bein' thrown on to me;
Aw know aw've been drinkin' to-day,
   But it's ole on it owin' to thee.
Aw'm not th' only sinner i' th' place,
   Tho' aw'm willin' to own aw've done wrong;
Let me tell thee straight eawt to thi face,
   'At tha's done it thisel wi' thi tongue.

Tha knows at tha's scores o' times said
   'At a sup o' whoam-brew'd would do good;
Tha's made th' spot 'at should shelter mi yead,
   Well,—as mitch like a hell as tha could !
When aw come in at neets fro' mi wark,
   It's a job for me t' get in at th' door;
An' tha's th' heawse very often i' th' dark,
   An' th' wesh-tub an' th' clooas abeawt th' floor.

Aw know aw'm a bit ov a foo',
   An' aw know we've no bread up o'th' shelf;
But aw know this,—an' so does tha too,—
   Tha's been th' cause o' this misery thyself.
When aw took thi as bride fro' thi whoam,
   I' th' bonny breet month o' May,
Does t' think aw intended t' become
   Th' drunken sot 'at tha sees me to-day ?

Not I ! an' aw tell thee what, wife,
   This longin' for drink is so strong,
'At there'll soon be an end to mi life;
   Aw shall noan be i' th' road on thee long.
There's just one little favour aw crave ;—
   Aw hope tha'll be able to see
'At th' drunkard 'at's gone to his grave,
   Attributes his deawnfall to thee !"

A LITTLE BIT O' BOATH SIDES.

PART SECOND

HE'S just signed a pledge, has eawr John,
　　An' for once he's just done as he said ;
Why, to see him a reet decent mon,
　　Welly macks me feel wrong i' mi yead.
If th' lad brings o his wage wi' him whoam,
　　It will be a wonderful seet :
Heawever, aw want it to come,
　　An' wish it wur th' reckonin' to-neet.

Eh, aw wonder what th' nayburs 'll think,
　　When they see mi new bonnet an' cap ;
Aw con fancy aw see a sly wink,
　　'At may meon 'at aw've had 'em on th' strap.
They'll wonder what's up wi' th' owd lass,
　　Wearin' silk, wheer hoo once wore rags ;
Won't aw look at misel' i' th' glass !
　　But aw hear John's clogs on th' flags.

Well, tha'rt here, lad ; aw thowt it wur thee :
　　But, bless us ! theaw art some an' weet ;
Is it rainin' like that ? dear-a-me !
　　Get these warm carpet shoon on thi feet.
Aw'm just thinkin' heaw Skinflint 'll stare,
　　When aw co' at his shop for some beef ;
He'll say he's no bones he con spare,
　　For he'll think aw've co'd in for relief.

What's th' lon'lord at th' " Angel " to do,
　　Neaw tha's turned a teetotaller, John ?
They'll be gradely surprised deawn at th' " Q "
　　When they find eawt their customer's gone.
Won't thi grey-yeaded fayther be glad !
　　Ah, an' th' owd woman to', when hoo's towd ;
But awm sure tha'll be hungry mi lad,
　　Get thi baggin', thi tay 'll be cowd.

There's some nice buttered toast on th' hob,
    An' th' hawve ov a herrin' theer, see;
Aw browt it to pleos eawr Bob,
    But aw've saved a bit on it for thee.
Neaw, tha'rt owd enuff to get what tha needs;
    There's some celery, see, an' some salt;
An' some nice curran' loaf witheawt seeds,
    If tha'rt short it'll be thi own fault.

"There's plenty mi lass, an' to spare;
    An' aw'm sure it o looks very nice;
Tha's provided some capital fare,
    An' there's no need for axin' me twice.
Wheer's eawr lads?   Are they o gone to bed?
    Has t' put some warm bricks to their feet?
Aw feel rayther uneasy o'er Ned,
    But let's hope 'at he'll soon get reet.

Aw wish tha'd hond th' taypot this way,
    An' teem me a sope i' mi cup:
But there's summat gone wrong, lass,—eh!
    Whatever i' th' world is there up!
There's a waist button gone, by the mass!
    Why, aw must ha' been eatin' to' mitch:
Well, it cannot be helped neaw, mi lass,
    Get thi needle an' give it a stitch.

There's mi haliday shurt i' th' owd chest;
    Aw shall want it th' next Sunday, does t' know:
Tha mun mak' it reet nice abeawt th' breast;
    Starch th' neck weel, an' th' wrist-bands an' o;
For owd Turner, an' young Jemmy Burch
    Are callin' for me an' eawr Ned;
Tha may stare, but we're o beawn to th' church;
    Bless me, lass, aw ne'er been sin' we'rn wed!"

PRAYIN' JEMMY.

AS aw're passin' by th' corner o' th' church th' other
  day,
  Aw popp'd on a lad 'at wur tryin' to pray ;
  In his own simple words he wur tellin' the Lord
'At He hadn't been faithful an' true to His word.
His complaint wur soa childlike aw couldn't but smoile,
As he said, " Mi poor fayther's been deod a great whoile ;
Mi poor sister Elizabeth's deof an' dumb,
An' mi mother's a bustion at th' end ov her thumb ;
Hoo's lapp'd it wi' rags, an hoo's rubbed it wi' sawve,
But sin' these wur put on it, hoo's worse bi' th' hawve.
Aw happened to touch it one neet wi' mi yead,
An' tha would ha' been capp'd iv tha'd yeard what hoo said.
Hoo sometimes starts singin', at other times sighs ;
An' then hoo sits deawn in her cheer an' hoo cries.

Well, awm sorry to see her, but what con aw do ?
So aw creep eawt o' th' heawse an' then aw cry to'.
When we get ony meat, sich as bacon or pork,
Eawr Alice has t' have it, to help her to work.
Tha says tha'll a fayther to th' faytherless be,
But tha must be forgettin' eawr childer an' me.
We'd some broth th' other day 'at eawr Sarah had given,
But this wur to' *thin* to ha' come deawn fro' heaven!

Aw've brocken mi slate, an' th' copy-book's filled
At Ann Jones browt me in when their Isaac wur killed.
Mi trousers want mendin', mi jacket's i' holes;
We've no fire, nor no brass to go buy ony coals.
We've porritch i' th' mornin' an porritch at neet;
We've no candles, nor nothin' to give us a leet.
It's a fortnit to-day sin' aw tasted o' bread;
An' aw haven't a cap to put on to mi yead.

When awm pickin' up cinders an' sticks i' th' lones,
Th' lads coe me ragg'd Jemmy, an' pelt me wi' stones.
Before mi poor fayther wur put i' yond hole,
Aw'd no need to do this, for we'd allus some coal.
Mi prayer may seem childish, an' even absurd,—
But tha couldn't let mi fayther come, could ta, good Lord?
Eawr Ben wants his hair cuttin' badly aw see;
If it isn't done soon, he'll be botherin' me;
An' mi poor mother's thumb would get better awm sure,
Could hoo look on th' dear face o' mi fayther once moor.
If he's wanted t' sweep heaven eawt, or owt o' that mack,
Aw've not the least deawt but he'd go wi' thee back."
Aw could stond this noa longer, soa graspin' his arm,
Said—" Come on wi' me, lad, an' get summat warm."
So aw took him t' eawr heawse, an' aw gav' him some pie,
An' towd him to coe every time he went by;
But didn't th' poor lad cock his face up an' grin!
Then thanked me, went eawt, an' aw've ne'er seen him sin'.

EAWR JIM.

AW hardly know what we're to do wi' eawr Jim,
    For he's drunk every neet ov his life ;
    He's crackin' a skull, or breaking a limb,
        An' often ill-usin' his wife.
He's as mad as a bull when he's drink in his yead,
    An' he gabbles an' talks like a foo' ;
An' it's every word true what mi gronny's oft said,—
    That iv th' drink isn't abandoned he'll rue.

They've a nice little cherry-faced thing ov a brat,
    'At aw've met deawn i' th' lone as aw've come ;
Aw bowt him some parkin off owd Betty Platt,
    An' towd him t' be sharp an' get whoam.
If his fayther 'd some wit, an' would put it to use,
    He'd buy th' lad a pair o' new clogs,
But he'd rayther be spendin' his time on at th' " Goose,"
    Makin' matches wi' pigeons an' dogs.

It pains me to look at his poor patient wife
　　'At wur once so good-lookin' an' fair :
Sich a harrasin', wretched, an' comfortless life
　　Must drive her to hopeless despair.
We wur talkin' this o'er i' eawr heawse th' other week,
　　Eh, but heaw mi poor mother did cry !
Big tears trickled deawn her pale furrowed cheek,
　　An' mi fayther's an' mine weren't dry.

It's seldom my een are mich troubled wi' weet,
　　But mi feelin's aw couldn't restrain ;
Let's hope 'at th' big tears 'at escaped us that neet,
　　Won't be shed altogether i' vain.
Well then,—there's wife's parents—owd Dinah an' Dave,
　　Livin' deawn i' th' thatched cottage below ;
This worthy owd couple are hastenin' to th' grave,—
　　Full o' trouble o'er Mary aw know.

Th' owd chap's often talked ov his troubles to me ;
　　It wur only last Setterday neet ;
'At he said he could lay his grey yead deawn an' dee,
　　If eawr Jim would be sober an' reet.
What gloom an' depression this drink can create,
　　Wheer once nowt but sunshine were seen ;
An' heart-broken friends sit lamentin' their fate,
　　Wi' big scoldin' tears i' their een !

GOOD-BYE, OWD YEAR!

GOOD-BYE, Owd Year; tha'rt goin' soon, aw reckon :
    Well, one thing's sure,—tha's been no friend o'
      mine ;
      Soa go thi ways to thoose tha's treated better ;—
  Thoose tha's supplied wi honour, wealth, an' wine.
Aw've watched thi marlocks ever sin' tha coom here,
    An', that bein' so, aw couldn't help but see
Tha's had thi friends, an' these tha's nursed an' petted,
    While tryin' t' throw cowd wayter on to me.

Be off! an' leov thi reawm for somb'dy better ;
    An' tak' thi pampered favourites wi thee to';
Clear eawt ole th' hangers-on theaw has abeawt thee,
    An' give us th' chance o' tryin' summat new.
What! me ungrateful! here, neaw, just one minute ;
    Doest meon to tell me 'at aw owe *thee* owt ?
Neaw, here's a plain, straight-forrud question for thee :—
    Come, shew me what tha's oather sent or browt.

Well, let that pass ; aw bear no malice, mind thee :
    Tha'rt clearin' eawt, an' one thing's very sure,'—
'At when we hear th' church bells ring eawt at midneet,—
    Tha'll tak' thi hook, an' trouble me no moor.
Still, one thing rayther plagues me, neaw aw think on't ;—
    Heaw wilta get fro' Blackpool, 'Eighty-Nine ?
We've noa trains leov as late as twelve o'clock ; but,
    P'raps tha meons to walk, as th' neet's so fine.

At onyrate,—sit deawn, an' warm thi shanks weel;
    Tha's getten twenty minutes yet to stop.
Sarah, bring up another cob o' coal, lass,
    An' bring this pilgrim here a sope o' pop.
Wheer are thi friends to-neet,—thoose pets tha's favoured?
    They're dinin' off a goose at th' Queen's Hotel.
There isn't *one* to shake thi hond at partin';
    Aw've ole these kindly acts to do misel'.

Neaw, sup that pop, an' eat this bit o' parkin;
    Tha's far to goa, an' noan mitch brass to spend.
Shove him a moufin in his pocket, Sarah;
    He'll need it ere he gets to th' journey's end.
Aw'm noan a very *bad* sort, after ole, mon;
    A chap may love his enemies, tha sees.
Aw think he'll find that moufin rayther dry, lass;
    Tha'd better let him have a bit o' cheese.

Neaw wheer does t' find tha's met wi' th' nicest treatment?
    At th' sea-side cot? or 'mongst thi wealthy friends?
Well, never mind; but get thi cooat an' hat on;—
    Two minutes moor, an' then eawr campin' ends!
Neaw what's to do? Come, come, tha'rt cryin' arto?
    Aw've touched thi feelin's, have aw? Well, o reet!
Tha met ha feawnd thi *friend* eawt twelve months sooner:
    But time's neaw up! Well, 'Eighty-Nine, good-neet!

EIGHTEEN' NINETY.

THA'RT here, arto, Eighteen' Ninety?
    Does ta come as foe, or friend?
    Wilta treat us weel or badly?
       Heaw's thi twelve months' stay to end?
Summat same as th' last, aw reckon; —
    After servin' th' peawers that be,
An' tha'rt pumped as dry as peawder,
    Tha'll come sneakin' here to me.

True, i' th' past aw've been to' lenient,
    Been a little bit to' soft;
Still, it's possible mi temper
    May be roused up once to' oft.
Anyheaw, aw'll tell thee plainly,
    If tha leovs me eawt i' th' cowd,
Tha's no need to come here spongin',
    When tha gets worn eawt an' owd.

Choose thi favourites, iv tha pleases;
    But aw want thee just to see
I, for one at least, shall never
    Let 'em wipe their shoon o' me!
Th' world's a ring: aw meon to wrostle;
    Life's a race: aw meon to run;
Trot us eawt a worthy champion,
    Then yo'll see a bit o' fun.

If there's ony goals to tackle,
    Bring thi men, an' bring thi bo';
Clear us th' field, an' aw'll soon show yo'
    Aw con kick a bit an' o.
Pike thi crew eawt, Eighteen' Ninety;
    Leov me eawt, if tha's a mind;
For no deawt there's somb'dy waitin'
    'At's an axe or two to grind.

Let 'em play ; aw'll stond an' watch 'em ;—
  Watch 'em kick, an' dodge, an' tup ;
Then *aw'll* strip,—play " centre-for'ards,"—
  An' we'll see whoa collars th' cup !
Favourite-mongers, praise yo'r pets up ;
  Slash at my wark hip an' thigh ;
Aw con do a bit i' that line ;—
  Onyheaw, aw meon to try.

Aw'm on th' warpath, Eighteen' Ninety ;
  Mon, aw've held mi peace to' long ;
What's th' result ? this—other scribblers
  Wear mi honours,—steal mi song.
Isn't it time to speak eawt plainly,
  When one sees sich tricks as these ?
Whoa con show th' most claim to th' honey ?—
  Idle drones, or workin' bees ?

Mix wi' th' gentry, iv it suits thee ;
  Join 'em in their mirth an' wine ;—
Shun true worth, an' worship Mammon,
  Same as th' owd year, 'Eighty-Nine :
But,—an' this tha'll pleos remember—
  Iv tha turns thi back o' me
Till tha'rt ragg'd, an' starved, an' hungry,—
  Aw shall be noa friend to thee.

What, tha'rt sulkin' at me, arto ?
  Vexed or pleosed, it's ole the same ;
Do thi own ; but let me tell thee,—
  Aw shall watch thi little game !
Treat me weel, or treat me badly ;
  Gie me kisses, gie me blows ;
" Tit for tat " shall be my motto ;—
  Neaw, tha hears me ;—off tha goes !

JOHN BOOTH AN' TH' VICAR.

CERTIN owd Vicar, noan fur fro' this spot,
Among other folk he looked after, had got
A chap coed John Booth—he'rn thowt rayther queer—
Everybody knew John when he'rn livin' on here ;
An' tho' it wur said he wur noan gradely reet
He'rn sharper nor lots 'at aw know, a fine seet.
Neaw th' Vicar ax'd John to do o 'at he could
To bring him some news, so he promised he would.

Well, one neet, as John lay fast asleep in his bed,
He'd a very strange dreom coom to bother his yead ;
An' it seems when he wacken'd he didn't intend
To keep it so long witheawt tellin' his friend,
For soon on i'th' mornin' to th' Vicar he hied,
As it happen'd, th' owd fellow wur'n smookin' eawtside,
So he see'd John come leatherin' away very fast,
Reet cromm'd full o' news, as iv ready to brast.

" Well, John," said the Vicar, " how are you to-day ?
But you seem to have something important to say ;
What's the news ? let us have it at once, if you please,
Then no doubt you will feel rather more at your ease.
" Well, then, iv yo pleos, sur, last neet, when i' bed,
Aw'd a sort ov a dreom loike coom into mi yead ;
Aw thowt aw'rn gone up to heaven, dun yo' know ? "
" Just so," said the Vicar, " I hope you *will* go :—

" But how did you like the place ? how did you fare ?
And what did you see in your rambles up there ? "
" Well, sur, iv yo pleos, aw went straight up to th' dur,
But when aw geet theer couldn't ger ony fur ;
So aw started an' punced it wi' one o' these shoon,
For aw yeard they wur singin' some mak' ov a tune,
An' thowt iv aw didn't mak' a middlin' big din
Aw should never be yeard, an' they wouldn't let me in.

"Well, sur, as aw stood theer, as white as a cleawt,
Peter oppen'd a window, an' bobb'd his yead eawt;
An eyein' me o'er fro' mi yead to mi feet,
He ax'd what aw'rn wantin' at that time o'th' neet
(Aw think it wur then abeawt hauve-past eleven),
So aw towd him aw wanted to go into heaven.
Then he ax'd wheer aw lived at, an' what aw wur co'ed;
But he'd no need t' ax that, for aw'rn certain he know'd.

"Well, aw said aw'rn livin' i' Smoshaw just then,
Wi' a uncle o' mine they co'ed 'Slavverin' Ben.
Then he ax'd wheer aw went to o'th' Sundays when theer;
So aw towd him to th' church, when aw went onywheer;
Then he ax'd me to give him a bit ov a prayer;
But aw towd him aw couldn't—aw'd getten nowt t' spare.
Eh, heaw he did sceawl at these owd clooas o' mine!
Aw dar' say he'd think aw're noan donn'd up so fine.

"Well, he poo'd his yead in, an' he bang'd th' window deawn,
An' then, sur, my hopes wur o very nee fleawn;
Aw ceawered at th' eawtside till aw'rn getten weel starved,
An' aw felt rarely pottered at th' trick aw'd bin sarved;
For aw didn't think Peter wur'n sarvin' mi reet,
To let me ceawer waitin' so long wi' cowd feet:
Aw thowt one were hampered an' clemm'd enough here,
Beawt goin' a clemmin' an' starvin' up theer.

"Heawever, at last Peter oppen'd me th' dur;
An' eh, what a foine-lookin' manshun it wur!
'Come forrud,' he said, 'aw'll reach thee a cheer,
But aw met as weel tell thee *tha'll know nob'dy here*;
We'n had plenty fro' Owdham, fro' Royton, an' Lees,
Bur there's nob'dy fro Smoshaw no moor nor tha sees.
Aw'll tell thee what, John, tha may think it seems queer,
But tha'rt th' furst 'at th' owd Vicar's e'er sent us up here!'"

A TRIP TO GRIMSBY.

 LOVELY Sabbath morn it wur, tort th' eend o' last
July,
 An' scarce a cleawd wur seen to pass across the clear
blue sky ;
Th' young larks wur warblin' up i' th' air, dew lay like pearls o'
th' greawnd,
An' oh, one couldn't help feelin' pleased wi everything areawnd.

Well, me an' two or three moor chaps—we thowt we'd have
an eawt ;
An' so we geet some bits o' things we couldn't weel do beawt ;
We took some pipes, an' 'bacco, too, some umbrell's an' sticks,
Steered off to th' station,—took a train 'at seet off eawt at six.

But furst—afore we started eawt, wi o insured eawr lives ;
Thinkin' iv owt should happen us, there'd be some brass for
th' wives.
It was a splendid morning, as I have said before,
(Excuse the Sunday travelling, an' we'll do so no more) ;

The sun shone brightly in the east, the fields were clad in green,
And, oh, our hearts were gladdened, as we gazed upon the scene.
Jones poo'd his poipe an' bacco eawt, an' said he'd have a smook;
Owd Pincher crossed his arms an' legs, un' perch'd hissel i'th'
nook ;

Young Dawson had no poipes wi' him, nor wanted none he said ;
He'd summat better, a rare foin seet,—a lump o' noice pig's
yead ;
An' while some smooked their poipes an' did, he crashed away
at that :
He says he's fond o' sich like stuff, it makes him strong an' fat.

K

He says iv he wur t' drink like some, an' let his stomach clem,
He'd very soon be pale an' leon, an' look as ill as them.
At length our journey's end was reached,—it was the service
    hour ;
The Sabbath bells were pealing sweet from many a time-worn
    tower ;

And christian people, young an' old, were wending on their way,
To worship God in his own house, upon that holy day.
We gauped an' stared abeawt us theer, loike chaps noan gradely
    reet ;
They eyed us o'er above a bit—did foalk we met i' th' street,

But we ne'er cared heaw much they stared,—they'd ne'er seen
    us afoor,
An' aw dar bet a haupney top they never will no moor.
At last we geet to Grimsby Docks, an' looked reawnd theer a
    while,—
Afoor us th' German Ocean lay stretched eawt for mony a mile.

We gathered shells upon the shore, inhaled the healthful breeze,
So bracing, so refreshing, too, to feeble frames like these ;
And, if we did not worship God, with those who humbly knelt,
Our hearts were full of gratitude for all the joy we felt.

Well,—as we'rn ceawered bi th' side o' th' " Snipe," smookin'
    an' eatin' pie,
Jones said, " As Peter walked on th' say, let us go have a try ;
But, lads, heaw are yo off for faith ? for that wur Peter's crutch ;"
Says Pincher, " Iv its loike thy brains, aw deawt we hanno
    much ;

Iv tha's a mind to try it on, tha'll find it safe, aw think,
For iv thi body's loike thi yead, tha'rt certain not to sink."
Well, Jones wur vexed, an' so he said, " Come, lad, aw'll let
    thee see,
Ivt' doesn't howd that tongue o' thine, an' let a chap a be."

The sun was sinking in the west, the clouds seemed tinged with
 gold,
And oh ! I think a grander sight we could not well behold ;
For nature once more closed her eyes in sweet and balmy sleep,
Spreading her evening mantle o'er the bosom of the deep.

We went an' geet a sope o' tay, at one o' th' huts close by ;
Owd Pincher said he'rn hungry, so he'd have a piece o' pie.
Them other chaps had beef an' bread, an' curran' cake an' stuff;
So when we'd drunk an' etten till we thowt we'd had enuff,—

We went to th' station, geet on th' train,—Jones had another
 smook,—
Owd Pincher crossed his arms an' legs, an' reared hissel i' th'
 nook,
We sung th' Owd Hundred, Evening Hymn, French, Job, an'
 toathry moor,
An' th' foalk declared they'd never yeard sich harmony afoor.

An' we believed 'em what they said,—we didn't think they had,
We sung 'em every one to sleep, an' that wur noan so bad.
No doubt the landscape all around was beautiful to see,
Still, with a sense of shame I own it had no charms for me ;

For while the clear and sparkling dew did o'er the flow'rets
 weep,
I, overpowered with Nature's gifts, had fallen fast asleep ;
An' so had Jones an' Pincher too,—we slept one hawve o' th'
 way,
An' this wur th' road my friends an' me thowt fit to spend that
 day.

JACK O' TH' NOOK AN' T' LAN'LOARD.

OWD Jack o' th' Nook—a Yorkshire chap—
    Fuil that he wur—ud used to swap
        His wage for muddy watter;
            But changed, an' spent his brass o' bread,
This made th' owd lan'loard scrat his yead,
    An' wonder what wur th' matter.

He kindled th' faur up ivvery neet,
An' made it vary nauce and breet,
    An' th' bar wur cheerful lookin';
A few gret blusterin' chaps went in,
To kear an' drink whot ale an' gin,
    Or waste their toime wi' smokin'.

They used to wonder yeah it wor
Jack noather went nor said what for;
    Soa made it up to as' him.
They waited full two yaars one neet,
To get to see him go up th' street,
    But couldn't come across him.

Well, Jack kept on i' th' temperance lawn,
An' suin began o' donnin' fawn—
    His childer, too, looked smarter.
One day, when extra nawcely drest,
Black cloath, kid glooves, an' ole the rest—
    He went past th' "Jolly Carter."

An' just as luck would have it then,
   Th' owd lan'loard—nick-named " Burley Ben "—
   Wur keard at th' durstead smookin'.
" Hey, Jack ! " he said, "an' is that thee ?
Wau tha'rt a stranger, neah, to me ;
   Bless us, heah weel tha'rt lookin' !

" Wheer as to been so long, owd lad ?
Eh mun ! aw do feel some an' glad
   To see thi weel an' hearty !
When arto bean to fill yon cheer ?
We're olèz fain to see thee here,
   O' th' Sunday or o' th' warty.

" We han some rare good ale in neah,
Tha'll cole an' have a pawnt, choose yeah,
   Tha'll find it nawce an' warmin'.
An' then yaar Jane's come whoam to-day,
Hoo's been six months a leornin' t' play ;
   Come, yer her mun—it's charmin'."

" Not aw," said Jack, aw've leorn'd moor wit,
Thaw toak ull noan catch me—not it.
   Aw've gien up all this drinkin'.
Aw must ha' bin a stupid fuil,
To send thaw lass to th' booardin' skuil—
   At least—that's what aw'm thinkin'.

" Aw've lots o' burds come every day,
They"ll sing a bit, then goa away—
   An' never mention payin'.
An' rare good music, too, tha maunds,
Better nor any lan'loard fawnds—
   Not lawk some jackass brayin' !

" Aw've crickets singin' ivvery neet,
There's sich a neighse abeat mi feet,
   An' ole their music's gratis.
They'll kear i' ony sooart o' hoils—
Strawk up a tune i' th' cowks an' coils :
   It's cheppish music, that is.

" Aw'm rare an' weel off, neah tha sees ;
For what wi' crickets, birds, an' bees,
   Aw get enuff o' singin'.
We han a neighsey yaas for suir !
Music indeed ! aw want no moor,
   Yaar hear'ston's olez ringin.'

" It's noice to kear bi' th' sawd o' th' faur,
An' hearken th' woife an' th' youthful kwaur,
   An' gie one's leg a rest, mun.
Aw'll tell thee what aw loike a deol—
Aw lawk to yer yaar piggins squeol,
   That's th' music aw lawk best, mun.

" Aw've gien o'er feedin' pigs o' thawn ;
Tha sees yon dean i' th' loin—they're mawn ;
   Aw've two rare fawn uns, sithee ;
They'n booath bin bowt wi' th' brass aw've saved,
Sin' aw gav' ovver gettin' shaved
   At thaw confeanded smithy.

" Tha'll ha' to pool that coit off neah,
An' try to keep thiseln—someheah—
   Aw've cleon gien ovver givin'.
So dunnot thee depend o' me,
'Cose iv tha does tha'll ha' to dee,
   As sartin as tha'rt livin'."

ADAM AN' MARY.

ON th' borders o' Scotland, a long toime ago,
    Lived a chap an' his wife, an' their names, yo
      mun know,
    Wur Adam an' Mary—good foalks i' their way,
But fond o' their whisky, aw'm sorry to say.
Neaw th' neighbourin' parson used to go theer,
To talk o' religion, an' taste o' their beer;
He wur summat loike th' parson 'at lives eawr way—
He could oather pretich, wrostle, drink whisky, or pray.

One mornin' as Adam an' th' woife sat i'th' heawse,
Watchin' th' cat play her pranks wi' a newly-catch'd meawse,
Ole at once summat coom into owd Mary's yead,
An' turning reet sharply to Adam, hoo said—
" Aw say, Mr. Bell may be comin' to-day,
An' we'n getten no whisky : go fetch some aw pray ;
Tak' th' bottle an' th' brass, and be sure to make haste,
An' see 'at tha doesn't poo th' cork eawt to taste."

Well, Adam set off, an' soon landed i' th' teawn,
But his woife's gentle warnin' appears to ha' fleawn ;
For, findin' his bottle wur rayther to' smo,
He thowt to hissel ther'd be no harm at o—
Considerin' 'at th' day wur so stormy an' cowd—
I' drinkin' what th' bottle wurn't able to howd ;
Well, he drank it—an' just as drink had done afoor,
It gan him th' idea 'at he wanted some moor.

As Adam wur trudgin' tort whoam i' great haste,
He felt rayther dry, an' wur tempted to taste ;
But remember'd what woife said afoor he set eawt ;
If he'rn fuddle't th' owd lass ud go on he'd no deawt ;
He knew if he tasted their Mary could tell ;
Heawever he thowt he met just hav a smell ;
He poo'd th' cork eawt, an' did so, an' then yo' may think,
Heaw th' poor foolish chap ud be tempted to drink.

Well, he tasted an' tasted, then took a good swig,
Till at length th' silly chap wur as "drunk as a pig."
As he'rn goin' tort whoam, the'rn a great pile o' stones,
'At soon coom i' contact wi' poor Adam's bones ;
For trudgin' along, at a moderate pace,
Wi' his e'en welly shut, he fell slap on his face.
"Oh, dear, dear !" said Adam, "aw'm very near killed,
An' aw've brocken my bottle, an' th' whisky's o spill'd !"

Theer he lay, wi' his face welly covered wi' blood—
Aw wish aw could draw yo his likeness, aw would ;
Heawever, th' owd chap wur a pitiful seet
When he londed at th' dur ov his cottage that neet.
When th' woife fun' it eawt 'at ole th' whisky wur gone,
There wur a rare noise i' that auction, bi' th' mon !
Just then, as hoo're turnin' her yead o' one soide,
An' glancin' deawn th' meadow th' owd parson hoo spied.

Well, hoo did carry on !   Hoo stamp'd wi' her feet ;
An' bawled eawt to Adam, "Be off, eawt o'th' seet !"
Th' owd parson wur in in a minute or two,
An' could see plain enuff there wur summat to do ;
Soa thowt it his duty to give her a slice
'At he culled fro' th' owd Book—namely—spiritual advoice ;
"Can you tell me," he ax'd, "how it was Adam fell ?"
"Well, aw could do," hoo said, "but aw'd rayther not tell."

Th' owd mon wur reet capp'd at a answer loike that,
An' shapin' for goin', geet howd ov his hat ;
"Well, Mary," he said, "since you don't choose to tell
Your spiritual guide how it was Adam fell,
I am sure you could tell me—at least, if you tried,
Where the guilty transgressor attempted to hide."
Mary, neaw fairly pinn'd, to her husband did sheawt,
"Mon, he knows ole abeawt it, tha'll ha' to come eawt !"

THINKS I TO MISEL'.

AS aw're ceawered bi mysel' here a bit th' other day,
 Mi muse bein' unshackled an' havin' fair play,—
 Aw wur lookin' abeawt on these fruits an' fleawers,
 So tastefully placed reawnd this " Bethel " o' eawrs,—
Thinks I to mysel' neaw there's summat wrong here ;
Th' theologians have made some sad blunders, aw fear.
Is th' God 'at provides us wi' ole these grand things
Th' same God 'at we read of i' Numbers an' Kings ?

It's hard to imagine a Bein' 'at's good
Takin' pleasure i' spillin' pure, innocent blood ;
But they had some queer notions, had th' Jews, aw must say ;—
In fact, one or two on 'em have to this day.
I' their hearts they'll pull deawn a just God fro' His throne,
An' i' th' place on Him fix up a god o' their own.
Thoose 'at glory i' war, an' think it foine sport,
Someheaw manage to meet wi' a god o' th' same sort.

If they happen to meet wi' one rayther to' good,
They set th' Roman rabble to yeawl for his blood.
It's th' same here, i' Blackpool, there's men to be feawnd
Who i' doctrine an' dogma are perfectly seawnd ;
But as for good morals, pure lives, or good works—
They're as innocent, bless yo, o' these things as th' Turks.
If yo try to do reet, they peawnce on yo' an' yell—
" Good works never yet kept one soul eawt o' hell !"

Of course, sich a doctrine must mack us feel sad,
For it seems, to be saved, we shall have to be bad.
An' men 'at are hearty, an' seawnd, an' can kick,
Have no need of a doctor, it's thoose 'at are sick.
Th' Unitarians are wrong if they trust to good deeds ;
Th' Trinitarians are too, wi' their dogmas an' creeds.
They may sprinkle their childer —a doctrine long towt—
Or dip 'em o'er th' yead, it'll ole come to nowt !

It's thoose 'at are sinners 'at God deigns to bless,
An' th' righteous will find their poor selves in a mess.
Wheer's th' use ov a barber, if nob'dy needs shavin' ?
Or wheer's th' use o' a Saviour, if nob'dy needs savin' ?
What's to come o' th' Owd Book, wi' ole th' shadows an' types,
An' ole thoose grand words sich as " healin' " an' " stripes "—
If we're ole on us perfect, an' needin' noa Saviour ?
Aw must tell yo, to my mind, this seems bad behaviour !

Just think what a task it would be to th' owd scribes,
Arrangin' th' " burnt offerin's " an' ceawntin' up th' " tribes,"
Gettin' ole things i' order fro' th' furst to th' last day,
An' us mackin' light o' their wark i' this way ;
Mackin' merry, an' lookin' as happy an' breet
As if we imagined sich conduct wur reet :
Stickin' mottoes on th' walls wi' sich beautiful words
As " Our God will provide," " The earth is the Lord's."

Aw'm surprised at yo' crackin' yo'r jokes o'er yo r tay,
An' pamp'rin' yo'r preawd sinful tastes i' this way !
It would look better on yo t' clear eawt ole these things
'At wur only intended for priests an' for kings—
An' get a young kid into th' chapel—an' kill it !
Never mind abeawt th' blood bein' innocent—spill it !
An', if yo're noan sinners, turn sinners at once,
An' gi'e th' sacred writers a bit ov a chance.

Yo may fancy yo'r reet baskin' here i' these beawers,
Surreawnded wi' cabbages, onions, an' fleawers ;
Alleawin' yo'r time to glide smoothly away ;
But, as sure as yo're livin', yo ll catch it some day !
Away wi' yo whoam, an' get deawn on yo'r shanks,
An', instead of insultin' high Heaven wi' yo'r thanks
For beawntiful harvests, an' good tasty dinners,—
Get some sackcloth an' ashes, an' tell God yo're sinners.

GOOD TEMPLARS' WAR SONG.

A S Good Templars we're met once ogen,
　　Ah, met here to plan an' to work,
　　An' so long as there's owt to be done
　　　We're determined noa duty to shirk.
When we don on this armour o' eawrs,
　　It's a sign 'at we're rigg'd eawt for feightin';
An' there's plenty o' wark for us ole,
　　There's a vast deol o' wrongs 'at want reightin'.

Neaw, we're noan here to look at—not us;
　　Nor these trappin's aren't worn for a show;
An' eawr Order's no childish affair,
　　Though there are foalk 'at think soa, we know.
We'n a far grander object i' view,
　　An' th' lon'lords know that, never fret;
God bless yo', we'n summat else t' do
　　Nor be playin' at babheawse just yet.

When th' drink shops have ole bin shut up,
　　When th' woives o' poor drunkards can smile,
An' their poor little children are fed—
　　Well, then, we may play us awhoile.
But soa long as th' drink traffic exists,
　　An' so mony are perishin' thro' it,
We feel 'at there's work to be done,
　　An', God helpin' us, brothers, we'll do it.

There's some hundreds o' theawsands i' th' field,
　　Sworn foes to this enemy, drink;
An' we're noan very likely to yield,
　　Chus what some may say or may think.
Eawr opponents may turn eawt their " chaff,"
　　An' treat us wi' second-hand wit;
They can just do an' say what they loike,
　　But we'll oppen their een in a bit.

We're soldiers! an' trained up to feight
   Wi' owd England's deadliest foe;
An' eawr swords shall ne'er rest i' their sheaths
   Till we'n laid this great enemy low.
Eawr warfare is God-like an' fair;
   Eawr cause one o' justice an' right;
We're aimin' a terrible blow
   At selfishness, meanness, an' might.

Eh, there would be some stock o' foalk pleased,
   If this drink could noa longer be had!
There would be some tears woiped away,
   Some hearts leetened up 'at are sad!
As Good Templars let's do what we con
   To bring ole these good things abeawt;
Heaven ull bless us i' work o' this sort,
   An' give us success, there's no deawt.

Neaw there's nowt 'at needs cause ony shame
   I' this great undertakin' o' eawrs,
For we're rootin' eawt poisonous plants,
   An' in th' place on 'em plantin' fair fleawers.
Isn't this a grand work to engage in?
   Need we wonder at th' glorious success
Attendin' eawr Heaven-inspired efforts?
   Nay! we cannot expect nowt no less!

Some object to us wearin' these badges,
   But th' objections are noan "worth a fig;"
Do we sin ony more nor a parson
   Or a barrister wearin' a wig?
Don't th' Oddfellows wear their regalia—
   Their aprons, their sashes, an' things?
Don't widowers wear mournin' hatbands?
   An' don't married women wear rings?

This is th' armour we put on to feight in,
   An' we've never yet stained it wi' blood;
We feight not to kill foalk, but save 'em,
   Not to injure, but do people good.
We con ax for God's blessing on eawr cause,
   An' while we're at war we con pray;
We con feight wi' clear consciences, brethren—
   Con eawr enemies do so?   Not they!

We're Good Templars, and moon to defend
 This glorious owd country o' eawers
'Gainst a traffic 'at's blighting her hopes,
 An crushin' her loveliest fleawers.
" Vested interests " we've nowt to do with ;
 Foalk are free to invest what they loike ;
Thoose 'at feel discontented con " shunt,"
 Or else do same as colliers do—" stroike."

Haven't we vested interests an ole ?
 Are these lassies an' lads o' eawers nowt,
These scholars we've paddled to th' schoo',
 An' toiled for, an' prayed for, an' towt ?
" Vested interests," indeed ! oh, for shame !
 Let that drop, for we've had quite enuff,
Lest th' owd lad should claim damages too,
 For investin' i' brimstone an' stuff !

We can do wi' a fair honest trade,
 Wheer th' articles dealt in are good,
But this traffic i' drink we abhor,
 As ole thowtful and sober men should.
As Good Templars an' lovers o' right,
 Let's be faithful an' true to a mon ;
An' wherever these plague-spots exist,
 Let's shift 'em as soon as we con.

We're right, mi dear brethren an' sisters,
 God smiles on eawr work from above ;
Let's go on moore determined than ever,
 I' this labour o' mercy an' love.
Eawr country's i' danger—let's save it ;
 We've peawer enuff, let it be felt ;
An' keep on agitatin' this question
 Until justice is honestly dealt.

Till owd England shall rise in her greatness,
 An' shake off her deadliest foe ;
Till Rachel feels safe wi' her childer,
 An' flings off her trappin's o' woe ;
Till the dram shops no more shall disfigure
 This bonny, dear island o' eawrs ;
Until sorrow is turned into gladness,
 An' thistles are changed into fleawers.

JIM LEE, AN' TH' POOAST OFFICE CLERK.

WHAT strange foalk we have i' this world, to be sure
    Aw've yeard tell o' ignorant numbskulls befoor,
    But one's hardly prepared to have such a display
    O' what we cole "greenhorns" at this toime o' th' day.
Well, a fellow fro' somewheer i' Smoshaw, aw think,
'At had muddled his reasonin' tackle wi' drink,
Went into a post office near to th' teawn end
Wi' a sooart ov a letter he'd getten to send;

An' not bein' up to these pooast office ways,
He said to a clerk 'at wur writin' i' th' place—
" Does theaw know a young chap they co' Abrum Lee?"
" Not I," said the clerk, " Why do you ask me?"
" Well, nowt o' mich consequence; only aw thowt
Aw should loike thee to send him this letter aw've browt.
Aw've a sister i' Owdham 'at's hurt her big toe,
An' aw thowt aw should just loike eawr Abrum to know."

" Now, just look you here," said the clerk in amaze,
" Put a stamp on your letter, and then go your ways;
You silly old goose, I should just like to know
What I have to do with your sister's big toe!
Get your hat, and be going, you ignorant elf,
And keep your weak heads and sore toes to yourself;
I cannot be bothered with fellows like you,
So get out of this office, whatever you do."

Lawst,—oather to-day, or else sometoime to-morn,
As pratty a babby as ever war born ;

Aw'm sorry," said th' chap, " iv aw done owt amiss,
But there's no need at ole ov a rumpus loike this.
Aw should think theaw may see aw'm no angel wi' wings.
What should aw know abeawt sendin' letters an' things ?
Ole aw wanted wur this—'at mi brother should know
'At mi sister at Owdham had hurt her big toe !
Iv there's owt wrong i' that—well, aw'm sorry aw've come,
An' aw'll poike up mi letter, an' tak' it back whoam."

" Do make yourself scarce here, you silliest of men,
And pray never darken this doorway again.
What with letters unstamped, saucy words, and sore toes,
And rubbish like this—why, Heaven only knows
What I have endured since you entered in,
With your ignorance that almost amounts to a sin.
Now let me advise you before you depart,
To endeavour to get just one lesson to heart :—

" That lesson is this—never trouble another
With matters concerning a sister or brother ;
Go join the Mechanics', and spend a few pence
On that much-needed article called " Common Sense ; "
Take that pipe which I see sticking out of your breast,
And fling it away as a nuisance and pest ;
Take that nose, which appears to have been in a plight,
To the temperance folks to be doctored.   Good night."

" Good neet to yo, mestur.   Aw'll toddle back whoam ;
But alleaw me to tell yo aw'm glad 'at aw've come.
Yo're reet i' th' remarks yo'n bin makin', aw think,
For Ignorance is often th' twin sister to Drink.
Aw've been a great foo up to neaw, to be sure,
But nob'dy's ne'er shown me mi folly befoor.
Henceforth an' for ever aw'll try to do reet.
No drinkin' nor smookin' i'th' future.   Good neet."

TH' OWD BELLMAN.

THEY may talk o' Tum Breawn bein' as "soft as a
cawve,"
But aw'll warrant th' owd Bellman t' be softer bi th'
hawve;
Scarce a day passes o'er but he's pooin' his face,
An' bleth'rin an' "cryin'" all up an' deawn th' place.
Th' other day Snuffy Bet ud bumbailys i' th' shop,
Gettin' ready for sellin' her besoms an' pop ;
An' among other sundries wur th' owd woman's cat :
Well, aw'm blest, iv th' owd softy didn't "cry" abeawt that.

He "cried" when Dick Whiteside sowd off at his farm ;
Aw met him th' same day wi' his bell on his arm,
Soa aw ax'd heaw it wur he wur bawlin' so loud,
Iv th' things belonged him 'at wur beawn to be sowd.
"Nowe, indeed 'em," he said, "cryin's part o' my trade,
An' aw dar say tha'd yeawl a bit, too, if tha're paid."
"Well," aw said, "there's no tellin' what one may ha' t' do,
Aw know aw once cried o'er an onion or two."

A day or two sin aw' wur goin' deawn th' street,
On a bit ov an errand, when whoa sbould aw meet,
But owd Jammie wi' th' bell, so says I, "What's up neaw?"
"Oh, nowt, nobbut Jonathan Smith's lost a ceaw,
An' he's gan me a shillin' to go reawnd an' cry;
Aw'm on duty, tha sees, so excuse me—good-bye."
"Stop a bit, mon," aw said, "as aw've nowt mitch to do,
Iv tha'll gie me th' tone hawve on't aw'll cry a bit too."

"Not to-day," Jammie said ; aw con manage misel,"—
Tong-tingle-tum, tingle-tum, tingle-tum-dell !
"Law-st a ceaw, 'at belongs unto Jonathan Smith ;
Thoose 'at foind it mun bring it to th' bellman forthwith,
At number nineteen, Betty Singleton's yard,
Wheer th' foinder ull meet wi' a han'some reward.
Neaw, yo chaps, here's a job, mak good use o' yo'r een ;
Foind Jonathan's ceaw ogen.   God save the Queen !"

Well, aw see'd him ogen, a week after or so,
He wur plasterin' some mack o' bills on a wo ;
" Oh, Jammie," aw said, " what becoom o' that ceaw ?
Wur it feawnd th' other day, when tha cried it, or heaw ?"
" Feawnd ! aye, to be sure ; mon aw knew wheer it wur ;
Aw'd had it ole th' toime hud at eawr back dur ;
When aw'd done goin' reawnd aw went whoam wi' mi bell,
Took th' ceaw, said aw'd feawnd it, geet th' brass for misel."

" Eh, theaw rascal !" aw said, " to do tricks sich as these ;
Wheerever does t' think tha'll ha' t' goa when tha dees ?
Here, aw think, aw con manage to foind thee a job."
Soa aw towd him aw'd lost one o' th' childer—eawr Bob ;
An' aw gan him a papper o' what he had t' say,
An' a shillin' or two, an' then sent him away ;
Th' furst corner he coom to he up wi' his bell,
Tong-tingle-tum, tingle-tum, tingle-tum dell !

" Law-st, oather to-day or else sometoime to-morn,
As pratty a babby as ever wur born ;
It has cheeks like red roses, two bonny blue een,
Had it's meawth daubed wi' traycle th' last toime it wur seen ;
It's just cuttin' it's teeth, an' has very sore gums,
An' it's getten' a habit o' suckin' it's thumbs ;
Thoose at foind it may keep it, there's nob'dy ull care,
For thoose 'at han lost it han lots moor to spare !"

Eh, there wur some rare laffin' when Jammie had done ;
Some o' th' women reet skreomed, they thowt it sich fun ;
But th' chap wur some mad, he threw th' papper on th' floor,
An' swore he'd ne'er " cry " o'er lost childer no moor.
Sin' that toime he's tried hard to keep eawt o' my seet,
Still aw neaw an' then drop on him somewheer i' th' street ;
An' aw allis inquire iv he's wantin' a job,
Iv he is, he can go reawnd a seechin' eawr Bob.

A "SMART" WAY O' CURIN' DRUNKARDS.

THERE'S a capital tale comes across the Atlantic,
 An' aw think aw shall hardly be doin' owt wrong,
Iv aw put it i' some mak o' form for recitin',
 Or—iv yo prefer it—a Lancashire song.
Neaw aw hardly need tell yo 'at th' Yankees are clever;
 They're " cuter " nor English foalk are a foine seet ;
One reason is this—there's less drinkin' amongst 'em,
 An' aw've not the least deawt that's a lot to do we't.

Well, Tom Jones an' Miss Sharp, bein' weary o' coartin',
 An' ceawerin' eawtsoide till their noses wur red,
Bethowt 'em they'rn fools to go starve theirsel's this way,
 An' they'd stand it no longer, but goo an' get wed.
So they went an' they stood before th' Rev'rend John Fleeceum,
 Who, wi' th' aid ov a book or two teed 'em reet fast.
When they'd paid him his charges they went away singin',
 " We're cured a cowd feet an' cowd noses at last."

Neaw one neet Tom stayed eawt rayther later nor usual,
 But at length woife beheld him come staggerin' in ;
An' at th' furst when hoo saw him hoo thowt he wur poorly,
 But soon feawnd it eawt he smelled strongly o' gin.
Well, it pained her to foind her dear Tom wur a drunkard,
 An' hoo said to herself, " I must cure him of this.
You are ill, my dear husband, lie down on the sofa ;
 Oh, whatever's to do, love ? whatever's amiss ? "

" Jane, run off for old Doctor Bell, and be handy ;
 And ask him to bring a few pills and his lance ;
And tell Widow Thompson to come with her leeches,
 For my husband must have some assistance at once."
When th' sarvant had gone hoo geet howd o' some mustard,
 An' plaistered it weel o'er his honds an' his feet.
Neaw, aw dar' say yo'll some on yo call out " Poor fellow!"
 While others will laugh, an' say " Just sarves him reet."

Well, th' doctor soon came, an' th' chap's pulse wur examined,
  An' he soon made th' discovery 'at th' fellow wur "tight;"
" Let him lie here," he said, " until ten in the morning,
  And I think you will find he will then be all right."
Oh, no ! " said his wife. " Sir, you must be mistaken ;
  I am sure my dear husband is dangerously ill ;
You must shave him his head, sir, and then apply blisters,
  Or else I shall send for a doctor who will."

So they shaved him his yead weel, an' then it wur blistered,
  But still ole their efforts to rouse him wur vain ;
For he kept snoorin' on until dayleet i'th' mornin',
  When he wackened, an' seemed to be conscious o' pain.
" What does this mean ? " he said, as he felt his bald cranium.
  " You are sick," said his wife, " and must lie very still."
" You're mistaken," said th' husband; "yes, greatly mistaken;
  Now I ought to know best, and I'm sure I'm not ill."

" You are rambling, my dear. You have got the brain fever;
  The doctor and I have been working all night."
" I should think so," said th' husband, "by what I can gather—
  I seem to be left in a very sad plight.
What's to do with my feet? " groaned aloud the poor victim.
  " Why, I've never been this way before in my life !
Oh, how I am punished with mustard and blisters !
  Do take all these plaisters away from me, wife !

" And if ever I get in this way any more, love,
  Don't send for a doctor, or trouble a bit."
" Oh dear ! but I shall—I should feel so much frightened.
  I am sure you would die in an apoplex fit ! "
Neaw yo women, 'at's husbands 'at mack theirsel's poorly,
  Yo set to an' give 'em a dose o' this mack ;
An' moind yo, aw dar' bet mi loife to a hawpney
  Yo'll never be plagued wi' a second attack.

JOHN BULL AN' HIS TRICKS!

OH, forshame on thee, John! forshame on thee, John!
  The murderin' owd thief 'at theaw art :
Tha'rt a burnin' disgrace to humanity, mon,
  Tho' theaw thinks thisel' clever an' smart.
Tha'rt a beggar for sendin' eawt Bibles an' beer,
  An' calling it " Civilization ; "
While thee an' thi dear christian countrymen here,
  Are chettin' an' lyin' like station.

Thee tak' my advoice, John, an' get a good brush,
  An' sweep well abeawt thi own door ;
An' put th' bit o' th' lond at tha's stown to some use,
  Ere theaw offers to steal ony moor.
An' let th' heathens a-be ; for tha's no need to fear
  'At they're loikely to get into hell :
My opinion is this—if there's onyone near
  A place o' that mack – it's thisel'.

It's thee 'at aw meon, John, theaw hypocrite, theaw ;
  Wi' thi Sundayfied, sanctified looks ! ·
Doesta think 'at ole th' milk comes fro' th' paps o' thy ceaw!
  Is ole th' wisdom beawnd up i' thy books !
An' what abeawt th' mixture o' cotton an' clay,
  'At theaw thrusts on thi unwillin' nayburs ?
Eh John, tha'rt a " Cure," but tha'll catch it some day,
  When tha's ended these damnable labours.

Tha may weel tell the Lord what a wretch theaw art, John,
  For tha pulls a long face on a Sunday ;
An', to prove what tha says, tha does o' 'at tha con
  To rob thi poor nayburs on th' Monday.
What business has theaw to go battin' thi wings,
  An' crowin' on other folks' middin ?
Doesta think thi black brothers sich mean cringin' things
  As to give up their whoams at thy biddin' ?

An' tha's th' cheek to thank God, when tha meets wi' success,
    As iv He stooped to sanction sich wark!
Neaw one would ha' thowt 'at tha couldn't ha' done less
    Than to keep sich loike actions i' th' dark.
Iv tha meons to go on wi' committin' these sins—
    Sins tha'll ne'er get weshed eawt or forgiven—
Tha should try to keep matters as quiet as tha con,
    An' ne'er let em' know up i' heaven.

Tha wur allus a bullyead, i' thi best o' thi days,
    An' this ole thi nayburs must know;
An', tho' tha seems pious, an' pulls a long face,
    They con manage to see through it o.
But when tha goes sneakin' an' tries to cheat God,
    It strikes me tha'rt goin' to' far.
Aw'm noan mitch surproised at thi impudence, John;
    Aw'm only surprised heaw tha dar!

What business has theaw to be sendin' eawt thieves,
    To steal slices off other foalks' bread?
It would look better on thee to rowl up thi sleeves,
    An' work for thi livin' instead.
Aw' tell thi what John—an' tak' notice o' this—
    Tha ne'er knew a nation to thrive,
Wheer th' bees preferred feightin' to good honest wark;—
    They're like drones stealin' honey fro' th' hive!

Iv tha's th' sense ov a jackass tha'll tarry awhoam,
    An' keep th' own garden i' fettle;
But tha'd rather be eawt wi' thi Bible an' gun,
    An' robbin' some other mon's kettle.
Neaw drop these mean tricks—this contemptible wrong,
    An' behave a bit more loike a mon;
Or aw'll gie thee another warm dose before long,
    For aw'm gradely ashamed on thee, John!

WHAT'S TO DO 'AT THA'RT LOOKIN' SOA SULKY, JOHN?

WHAT'S to do 'at tha'rt lookin' soa sulky?
    Are th' Radicals provin' unkoind?
    Tha seems very much eawt o' flunter,
      As iv tha'd some weight on thi moind.
Tha wanted these Tories to govern;
  They're governin' neaw doesta see;
Soa dunno thee run thi own wark deawn,
  Tha's sent 'em, so let 'em a-be.

The've mended thy sink-holes wi' " Science,"
  An' they want to mend other foalks' to';
They've th' Suez Canal to slutch yet, mon,
  An' then they've got Cyprus to do.
Look what millions o' foalk are i' darkness —
  Beawt Bible, beawt devil, beawt leet;
An' are we to leov 'em i' this way?
  Nay, nay, John, that wouldn't be reet.

It's wrong to be graspin' an' selfish,
  Soa John, lad, let's try to do fair;
Iv its only a devil we're blest wi',
  Let's goa an' tak' th' heathens a share.
They send us their rice an' their cotton,
  To keep these frail bodies i' tune;
Let's give them some peawder an' bullets,
  To prepare 'em for th' mansions aboon!

What ailsto? tha seems very restless!
  Oh, aw see, it's thi conscience at works;
Tha'rt thinkin' abeawt thoose Bulgarians,
  'At wur slaughtered bi' th' Russians an' th' Turks.
Neaw, why should theaw bother o'er these things?—
  Look here—keep thi heart up, owd brid;
Tha never encouraged these butchers
  To goa an' to do as they did.

Thee be easy ; tha'll live a deol longer;
   Dunno fret abeawt th' wrongs 'at tha sees ;
For tha connot get roses fro' thistles
   Iv tha bothers thisel' till tha dees.
There's evil i' th' world, an' there will be ;
   An' it's folly thee crackin' thi brains ;
For ole tha con do will be useless,
   An' tha'll only get kicked for thi pains.

What's th' use o' foalks botherin' their noddles
   Or bein' at th' trouble to think,
So long as there's plenty to stur on,
   I' th' shape o' meyt, bacco, an' drink.
Look heaw grogsellers fatten an' flourish ;
   Look heaw th' brewers are macking their " tin ;"
Neaw they never get favoured i' this way,
   When th' Radical government's in.

Look what toimes workin'-men con have neaw, mon;
   What lockeawts, an' turneawts, an' stroikes !
Iv tha's sense tha'll keep things as they are, John,
   For a chap can do just as he loikes.
Thee keep goin' on as theaw has done ;
   Never argue thi principles eawt ;
But up wi' thi' fist when tha'rt tackled,
   An' fot thi opponents a cleawt.

It's noa business o' thoine to be thinkin' ;
   Leov that job to thoose 'at have brains ;
Thee get on wi' thi workin' an' drinkin',
   Worship th' tyrant at' forges thi chains.
Shoot thi nayburs, to mak 'em respect thee ;
   Never mind abeawt doin' what's reet ;
Tha connot booath serve God an' Mammon,
   So tha's no need to try, mon.—Good neet.

SHUT UP! YO LIBERALS!

NEAW, then, what's this grumblin' an' growlin' abeawt?
Yo Liberals are gettin' ungrateful aw deawt.
Iv this nation gets led on to honour an' glory,
What matters whoa leads it—a Liberal or Tory?
Th' owd spirit's still in us—th' leaf envyin' th' fleawer;
A few discontented one's graspin' for peawer!
Forshame o' yo'r face, goin' on as yo' do;—
Tellin' th' Tories they aren't ole honest an' true!

Callin' Dizzy a "trickster," an' Salisbury a "tool,"
An' sendin' th' whole "bag o' tricks" to the dule!
Why, it's shockin' aw'm sure; aw'm surproised heaw yo dar',
An' them blessin' th' country as mitch as they are!
Neaw yo Liberals had better moind weel what yo'r doin',
Or yo'r actions may soon bring this country to ruin;
Yo'd better shut up, an' be quiet for awhile,
Till th' Tories have finished enlargin' this isle.

Yo'd ne'er ha' no pleasure i' office aw fear;
Men 'at's troubled wi' consciences shouldn't go theer.
Foalk are givin' o'er botherin' their brains abeawt hell,
An' th' motto to-day is—"Look after yo'rsel."
Why, this age 'at we live in thinks nowt ov a mon,
Iv he hasn't th' good sense to get howd when he con;
Fair play an' square deolin' are ole reet enuff,
For thoose 'at have laid in a good lot o' stuff;

But a chap 'at's th' bad luck to be honest an' poor,
Should lay conscience aside till he's got summat moor.
Just look what grand wark th' English nation's bin doin';
Why, bless yo, this world wur fast hastenin' to ruin,
But th' English—reneawned througheawt th' world for good
    works—
Undertook to look after a lot o' th' bad Turks.
An' we did these kind acts wi' a neighbourly hand,
Tho', of course, we geet howd ov a slice o' their land.

Wheer would Cyprus have been when th' preawd Russians wur
    near,
But for Englishmen's guns, English bibles, an' beer!
Wheer would India's grand jewels an' camels have been,
Iv hoo hadn't had an Empress made eawt ov a Queen!
Then there's th' Zulus; it pains one to read their sad story,
But eawr breet English bay'nets can point 'em to glory.
Look at Ireland—that spot o' contentment an' quiet
Wheer there's ne'er sich a thing as a murder or riot!

Try to poike eawt a fault i' their laws iv yo dar ;—
An' look heaw contented an' happy they are !
Well, aw think yo'll admit 'at there's one thing quite clear—
That wheerever we've gone wi' eawr bibles an' beer—
Altho' we may vex foalk, an' stur up their blood,
We have only one object—to do 'em ole good.
Neaw yo Liberals could never convert foalk wi' th' gun,
But th' Tories can do it, an' think it rare fun.

Let 'em keep goin' on wi' these dignified labours,
Till we've getten a garden as big as eawr nayburs.
Look at th' lond 'at's belongin' to th' great Eastern peawers,
An' compare it with this puny island o' eawrs ;
But th' Tories 'll alter these things before long,
Iv Gladstone will nobbut just bridle his tongue.
So yo Liberals be quiet, an' let th' Tories a-be,
For ole nations are happy an' blest, as yo see.

Let Gladstone attend to his axe an' his fellin' ;
An' th' jingoes go on wi' their howlin' an' yellin' ;—
Let th' drink traffic blast us as mitch as it's able ;—
Kick Sir Wilfrid's pet Bill—an' him too—under th' table ;
Let Lord Beaconsfield rule us another six years,
Wi' ole th' lyin', an' murders, an' groanin's an' tears ;
An' iv this doesn't satisfy Gladstone an' Co.,
They're ungrateful, an' unpatriotic—that's o !

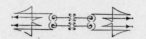

EIGHTY–SEVEN.

(SENT TO MR. JOSEPH LIVESEY, ON HIS 87TH BIRTHDAY.)

EIGHTY–SEVEN! A grand owd age;
   An' what a scene for history's page!
   Eighty-seven! What hopes an' fears;
   What ups an' deawns; what smiles an' tears.
Eighty-seven! Why, dear-a-me,
Teetotalers don't know heaw to dee;
Owd Bawsen Ben, 'at kept th' " White Bear,"
Has been i' th' grave o'er thirty year!

An' him an' thee wur born th' same day,
But tha'rt here yet, an' likely t' stay.
Heaw is it? Has t' insured thi life?
Or has t' a kind an' lovin' wife
'At tucks thee up, an' keeps thee warm,
An' sees tha'rt sheltered weel fro' th' storm?
Aw think a chap 'at's eighty seven
Should shut his een an' go to heaven.

It's time tha laid thi weapons deawn,
An' shaped for wearin' th' gowden creawn;
An' still we wouldn't be beawt thee, mon;
There'll be some cryin' when tha'rt gone.
Aw nobbut krow thee by thi name,
An' th' well-deserved an' spreadin' fame;
But still aw've often wished to sing
I' th' praise o' th' veteran Temperance King.

Aw've often read thi New Year's tracts,
An' feawnd 'em full o' sterlin' facts ;
But, then, a mon o' th' age o' thee,
Has had some painful seets to see.
Aw'm noan surprised 'at God sees fit
To let thee stop i' th' world a bit ;
For men like thee are hard to find—
They never faint or lag behind.

Tha comes to th' front, leads up i' th' van,
To bless an' save thi fellow-man ;
For fifty years tha's had to feight
An' try to set this country reight.
Ah ! wheer are thoose—aw'd like to know—
'At shared thi toils long years ago ?
Wheer's Anderton, that plucky bard,
'At rapped at drink so long an' hard ?

They're ole gone whom ; tired eawt, they fell ;
An' tha'rt left strugglin' here thisel' ;
An' yet tha seems to like thi shop ;
Tha'rt wheer tha'rt quite content to stop.
Tha never longs to plant thi feet
On deathless shore or gowden street ;
Tha'd rayther stop deawn here an' toil,
To mak' some drunkard's children smile.

Why, mon, it's plain enuff to see
'At heaven would be no heaven to thee,
If tha wur feastin' theer thisel',
An' ole thi brethren deawn i' hell !
Tha'rt eighty-seven, an' rich an' poor
To-day are throngin' reawnd thi door ;
An' these their kindly wishes bring,
To Joseph Livesey, th' Temperance King.

An', minglin' 'mongst this motley throng,
Is he who pens this humble song;
An' though we've never met on earth,
Aw've long admired thi genuine worth.
Accept this tribute, then, aw pray—
This simple, unpretendin' lay;
It's written wi' a good intent,
An' every word is kindly meant.

God bless thoose snowy locks o' thine!
They're ripe for th' harvest, same as mine;
Aw'm fifty-five, tha'rt eighty-seven;
Tha'rt nearer God, an' nearer heaven;
Tha'll soon have crossed death's gloomy tide,
Tha'll soon be safe on th' other side.
Thi friends have waited for thee long,
An' want thee t' help 'em sing their song.

An' so tha'll have to leave us soon,
An' join wi' th' ransomed up aboon;
Another scratch or two, and then
Tha'll have to lay aside thi pen.
There'll be some eyelids drenched wi' weet,
When Joseph Livesey says " Good-neet;"
An' mony a homestead wheer he's sat
Will miss his homely, friendly chat.

Accept o' th' best an' warmest thanks
O' one at feights i' th' temperance ranks;
Aw've long admired thi pluck an' skill,
Tha's fowt thi battles with a will—
Noa childish trucklin' wi' thi foes,
Tha deols straight-forrad, heavy blows;
Tha'rt one o' thoose at never shrink,
When battlin' wi' that monster Drink.

Go on, owd vet'ran friend ; tha'rt reet
I' tryin' to mak' dark homesteads breet ;
I' sowin' truth wheer ignorance dwells,
An' makin' heavens wheer once wur hells.
It's reet to bid men use their wings,
An' soar aloft to nobler things :
An' this tha's done for fifty years,
Wi' insults ringin' i' thi ears.

For teachin' people common sense,
Tha'd rotten eggs as recompense.
But things have changed ; i' th' place o' fear,
Tha's kindly help an' words o' cheer ;
An' neaw, when th' brunt o' th' battle's o'er,
An Bashan's Bulls have ceased to roar,
The name of Livesey's heard an' known
Fro' th' cotter's child to th' Queen on th' throne.

Eighty-seven ! still strong an' hale,
Can think an' feel, or tell a tale ;
A rare good lesson here, aw think,
For thoose 'at dreawn their peawers i' drink.
Ah ! Preston, tha may weel be proud :
Tha'rt rich i' men, if not i' gowd !
Eighty-seven ! can skip an' jump,
Wi' th' drink he gets fro' th' ceaw an' th' pump !

Eighty-seven ! well, vet'ran friend,
Tha'rt gettin' near thi journey's end ;
It will be grand, mon, wheer tha'rt beawn—
A happy change fro' th' cross to th' creawn.
Eighty-seven ! an' still tha'rt here,
An' nearer heaven nor me, aw fear.
Good-bye ; aw'll try to get i' tune,
An' meet thee somewheer up aboon.

TH' PEERS AN' TH' PEOPLE.

CLEAR us a ring, lads, an' let's have a feight,
    An' we'll soon have it settled whoa's wrong an' whoa's
        reight ;
    Th' People or th' Peers—which is it to be ?
Let's have a reawnd or two, then we shall see.

Must these preawd Peers tak' possession o' th' helm,
An' quietly say whoa's to govern this realm ?
Are th' Bees to eat th' lean, an' th' Drones to eat th' fat,
For ever an' ever ? we'll see abeawt that.

Widen that ring, lads ; neaw up wi' your sleeves,
An' we'll soon mak' short wark o' these lordlin's an' thieves ;
Lancashire lads can march up to their graves,
But can never be ceawards, or traitors, or slaves !

Comrades an' friends, shall we give up for nowt
That freedom for which eawr brave forefathers fowt ?
Nay, never, so long as these feet are well shod,
We'll oather win th' battle, or dee upo' th' clod !

But why talk o' deein', or have ony fears
While there's nowt i' eawr way but a hon'ful o' Peers ?
Let 'em only feel th' tips o' eawr famed wooden shoon,
An' they'll look for a road eawt o' th' field, an' soon.

Clear us a ring, then, an' let's have a feight,
An' we'll jolly soon settle it whoa's wrong an' whoa's reight.
Th' People or th' Peers—which is it to be ?
Let's have a tussle, an' th' world shall soon see !

From a Painting by George Barrett.   Photographed by D. Mitchell.

The Blackpool Lifeboat, "Robert William," going out to the Wreck of the "Bessie Jones," February 26th, 1880.

CREW :—: Robert Bickerstaffe (Coxwain), Jno. Parkinson (Bowman), Jas. Swarbrick, Wm. Rimmer, J. T. Fish, Richard Fish, Richard Parr, W. Owen, John Wylie, John Stanhope, and John Smith.

PROLOGUE :—

WRITTEN ON THE OCCASION OF THE PRESENTATION TO ROBERT BICKERSTAFFE, ON HIS RETIREMENT AS COXSWAIN OF THE BLACKPOOL LIFEBOAT, DECEMBER 5th, 1887.

TWENTY year' sin,—come th' furst o' next April
    Aw coom to reside i' this teawn ;
  A comparative stranger amongst yo',
    Unfavoured bi wealth or reneawn.
But one little circumstance happened,
  'At made matters rayther moor breet ;
There wur one bade me welcome to Blackpool ;
  That one is eawr guest here to neet ;

He said he wur happy to meet one
  'At he'd often yeard tell of befoor.
Well, this to a stranger wur cheerin',
  An' aw felt very thankful, yo'r sure.
An' fro' that day to this we've been friendly ;
  Yes, as friendly as brothers could be ;
At least aw'll say this much on my part,
  An' aw think he's th' same feelin's tow'rds me.

We've had mony a political battle,
  But there's been nowt but papper i' th' gun ;
A flash o' good wit, to please th' list'ners,
  'At ended i' nowt nobbut fun.
Aw pretend to be Radical,—aw do ;—
  Tho' aw'm but a poor hand at mi job :
Eawr guest seems to think he's a Tory ;—
  He's to' good to be either, is Bob !

His spurs have been won eawt i' th' Lifeboat ;
    An' he's won 'em mooast manfully too,—
I' shewin' true pluck when i' danger, .
    An' encouragin' on his brave crew.
If needed, they'd rush eawt to th' rescue,
    When Death seemed to be on their track ;
When we upo' th' shore have stood tremblin',
    For fear 'at they'd never get back.

Still, th' owd Coxs'n's been very reluctant
    To resign this position o' trust ;—
To sever himself fro' his comrades,
    But his health and his age say he must.
Well, he's got a good man to succeed him ;
    He's a brave-hearted fellow, is Will ;
An' noa deawt when he goes eawt to action,
    He'll show he's booath courage an' skill.

But we'll leave him, an' get back to Robert ;
    He's th' guest we're to honour to-neet ;
An' mak noa mistake abeawt this friends,—
    We're intendin' to do this job reet.
Why, we've talent enough i' this meetin'—
    That, when it get's fairly to work,—
Aw dar bet my hat to a haupney
    They'll hear us across at New York !

We've a portrait to give eawr friend, Robert ;
    An' it favvers th' owd Coxs'n soa mitch,
That when they're booath looked at together,
    Its vast hard to tell which is which.
We've other nice things here to give him ;
    But one aw may name among th' rest
Is a fine eighteen-carat gowd medal,
    'At th' booatmen will pin on his breast.

Neaw an action like this—to mi' thinkin'—
  Is one 'at's well worthy o' note :—
These are men 'at have shared in his dangers ;
  Been eawt wi' him often i' th' boat :
Been eawt when th' big waves o' th' owd ocean
  Have threat'ned to crush eawt their lives ;
While prayers have gone up for their safety,
  Fro' their poor anxious mothers an' wives.

Ah ! there's some o' these absent this evenin' ;
  Brave men who have met with us oft ;
They've ta'en their last look at owd Neptune ;
  Laid their oars deawn an' gone up aloft !
While amongst us, an' strugglin' as boatmen,
  Their lives wur oft toilsome an' hard ;
But they did their work nobly, an' neaw, friends,
  The're gone to receive their reward.

But, bless me ! aw'm gettin' too serious :
  Yo've come here to laugh not to cry ;
An' awm noan amongst yo' this evenin'
  To fill yo' wi' sadness ;—not I.
So we'll give eawr friend Robert these presents,
  For his services rendered so long ;
After that we'll keep on this grand meetin',
  Wi' speech, recitation, an' song.

As yo'll see,—we've got th' Fishermen's Band here ;—
  Smart lads these, an' allus i' tune ;
Give 'em plenty to eat an' to drink, an'
  They'll play fro' December to June !
Have yo' noticed Jack Fish, when he's playin',—
  Heaw he seems to put forth all his strength,—
When he's workin' th' trombone back an' forrud,
  An' tryin' to get it th' reet length ?

M

He s been tuggin' two year' at aw know on,—
    At what should be done i' two days ;
An' aw think if he's wise he'll get beawt it,
    An' try summat else in its place.
Neaw, I allus took Jack to be sharpish ;
    Eawtwitted an' beaten bi noan' ;
But if aw've ony skill abeawt music,
    He's bothered wi' that trombone !

But aw musn't go on any longer,
    For others have summat to say—
Moor important than my bit o' scribble,
    So aw'll drop it, an' get eawt o' th' way.
But aw couldn't sit still here i' silence,
    Or feel aw wur doin' what's reet,
If aw didn't tak' some part—tho' humble,—
    I' honourin' eawr friend here to-neet.

TH' OWD DUR SNECK.

HERE'S nowt very grand in an owd dur sneck,
    But its value lies here, do yo' see—
    It belongs to th' heawse dur wheer aw lived when
      a lad,
  An', of course, it's most precious to me.
Aw wur born i' that cottage, at least so they say,
    But can hardly remember th' event;
Aw didn't stur abeawt mitch for th' furst twothri days,
    For they kept me lapt up in a fent.

Aw've been thrashed i' that heawse, not becose aw'd done wrong,
    But becose aw'd noa peawer to do reet;
Aw'd two glarin' faults—gettin' hungry to' soon,
    An' wearin' mi clogs off mi feet.
But heaw could aw help mi owd clogs gettin' worn?
    Dunnot childer get hungry neaw?
These seem to be two o' th' " original sins "
    'At we connot shake off us, someheaw.

Whether Adam an' Eve wur to blame for this wark,
    Aw'm noan i' th' position to say;
But there's one thing we know—we 'at have it to find—
    There's a lot o' good meat thrown away.
Well, abeawt this owd sneck:—it's been middlin' weel worn
    Like mi naybur Tom Harlow's owd hat;
It's bin hondled an' rubbed abeawt th' edges a deol,
    But my thumb's helped to do some o' that.

Aw'm sorry th' owd heawse is unoccupied neaw,
    Still aw never goa past but aw co';
For it brings to mi mind childish acts an' events,
    Moor than onything else 'at aw know.
Th' bit o' garden's theer yet, but th' gardener's dead
    An' th' fleawers are ole gone to decay;
When aw look at th' dear spot, it brings tears to mi een,
    An' aw have to turn sadly away.

Soa aw value th' dur sneck as a relic o' th' past,
　　It's a sort ov a heirloom to me;
Seein' this, aw con live mi young days o'er again,
　　Kneel once more at mi dear mother's knee.
It wur deawn on that floor 'at aw lisped mi furst prayer;
　　It wur theer 'at aw sung mi furst stave;
But th' kind Christian parents 'at towt me these things,
　　Have long been asleep i' their grave.

They lie side bi side; brother Robert's theer too;
　　An' neaw there's but two of us left;
Aw'm like a knife-blade—gettin' worn deawn an' thin,
　　An ready to drop eawt o' th' heft.
Th' mainspring's gettin' cranky a bit, aw can feel,
　　An' th' rivets are ole workin' loose;
When aw've scraped a bit longer they'll fling me away,
　　Like a thing 'at's o' noa further use!

Aw'm rough abeawt th' edges, like other owd knives,
　　An' can " hack " a bit when there's occasion;—
An' it's needed at times, though it's dangerous wark,
　　Often endin' i' mortification!
But aw'm ramblin' away fro' mi subject aw find;
　　Still yon pleos to excuse me this time;
An' aw'll bring to a close these few triflin' remarks
　　'At aw've tried to work up into rhyme.

Aw shall value th' owd sneck as one o' thoose things
　　'At aw've hondled an' looked on when young;
An' shall store it amongst other treasures aw have,
　　Till mi very last song has been sung.
An' while Flora may value her jewels an' pearls,
　　'At so gracefully hang on her neck;
Aw'm content wi' a relic fro' th' home o' mi birth,
　　An' shall stick to mi owd dur sneck!

ALLIS TO' LAT'!

THERE'S a chap livin' somewheer on Huddersfield way,
'At's a very dry brick, though he's noan made o' clay.
Neaw, he's one strikin' feature—he's noated for that—
Wheerever th' chap goes to he's allis to' lat' !

He's fond o' his drink ; gets as "full as a fitch ;"
Soa one day, when he'd had hawve a gallon to' mitch,
One or two ov his chums—as aw've yeard 'em tell th' tale—
Took him into a shop wheer there'n coffins for sale.

Into one o' these coffins they crammed this owd chap,
Then left him to sowber hissel' wi' a nap ;
When he wackened he stared wi' ole th' een in his yead :
"Why, what's to do neaw ?   Aw'm surely noan dead ?

"It's a 'corker' is this ! but aw'm dryish, choose heaw :
Eh, wheerever i' th' world am aw getten to neaw ?
Aw'm to' lat' ogen, hang it !   Eh, dear, dear-a-me !
Aw'll be blest iv they aren't ole gooan but me !

"Eh, aw am some an' dry !   Is there nowt here to sup ?
Neaw they met just ha' nudged one, an' towd me t' get up ;
Wheer's this leet fro', aw wonder ?   It allis struck me
'At when one wur i' th' grave there'd be nowt mich to see.

But there must be a dayleet hole somewheer abeawt,
Or else heaw th' deuce han they ole getten eawt ?
Well, it caps me to see ole these coffins reared up !
But they must ha' crept eawt to get summat to sup.

" They'll happen be back in a minute or two,
When they'n bin on at th' ' Mitre ' an' had a good poo' ;
After ole's done an' said, it looks very unkind
On 'em ole to get up an' leov me behind.

" Still, aw know heaw it is 'at they'n left me, aw think,
Bein' a dry chap, they'd think aw should want ole th' drink ;
For they know aw could polish it off to some tune,
When aw're livin' an' hearty, i' th' world up aboon.

" Neaw, they've surely noan gooan off to heaven or to hell,
An' left me deawn here i' this hole bi misel' !
Has th' trumpet bin blown, an' aw've missed yerrin' that ?
Well, aw'm ' done ' iv it has ; but aw'm allis t' lat' !"

MASHERS.

SHUT up, yo political wranglers,
   Wi yo'r Ireland, " three acres," an' sich !
Are these childish questions worth raising'
   Bi th' fleawer o' owd England ?   Not mich.
It's o very weel to be patriots ;
   But it yo'd be noted for wit,
Yo'll provide a nice white pocket napkin,
   An' just show one corner a bit.

An' science—it's nowt nobbut humbug !
   Whoa cares abeawt th' structure o' plants ?
Or heaw this vast globe wur created ?
   What modern society wants,
Isn't th' meawldy ideas of a Darwin,
   Or th' author o' " Spoopendyke's " wit ;
But it's havin' a noice pocket napkin,
   An' showin' one corner a bit.

Eawr forefathers thowt they wur clever,
   But compared wi' us neaw they wur geese.
Need we wonder they're gropin' i' darkness,
   Wi' newspappers fourpence a-piece !
They'd no votes i' thoose days, had they Owdham ;
   Their dense ignorance kept 'em unfit ;
Their napkins wur made o' striped cotton,
   So it wouldn't do to show 'em—not it.

Do yo ax me what use they had for 'em ?
   Well, aw dar'say 'at some on yo know—
They used 'em when aw wur a youngster,
   For woipin' their noses—that's o !
They'd no rings on their fingers i' thoose days ;
   This shows 'at th' poor things had no wit ;
An' havin' noa noice pocket napkins,
   They didn't display 'em one bit.

Th' church parson wur th' " boss " fifty year sin' ;
    Poor foalk didn't think for theirsel !
But they paid their rich naybours to do it ;
    What th' result wur aw've no need to tell :
Th' landed gentry wur very near worshipp'd,
    An' th' poor wur set deawn as beawt wit ;
If they had a nice napkin i' thoose days,
    It wouldn't do to show one—not it.

Young men ! yo'n a future afore yo !
    A chance neaw for " sowin' wild oats ;"
They don't measure men bi their brains neaw,
    But bi th' colour an' th' cut o' their coats.
Don't turn up yo'r een, or look pious,
    For at this time o' th' day it won't fit ;
Yo look up a noice pocket napkin,
    An' just show one corner a bit.

Mack a plentiful use o' th' word " bloomin' ;"
    Embellish yo'r speech wi " Bi gads ;"
This'll show to the world 'at yo're clever,
    At yo'n getten moor sense nor yo'r dads.
Cock yo'r hats o' one side—just a trifle ;
    Yo'll find this a capital hit,
Along wi' a noice pocket napkin,
    Wi' one corner showin' a bit.

Slip a ring or two on to yo'r fingers,
    These'll help th' pocket napkins yo'll find ;
Get a pair o' noice silver-framed glasses;
    Ole " mashers " pretend to be blind !
Of course some may treat yo as " spooneys,"
    But ole sich as these have no wit ;
Yo'll be reet if yo stick to yo'r napkins,
    An' show up one corner a bit.

TH' STORM AT BLACKPOOL,

MARCH, 1876.

A W tell thee what, friend, tha's bin carryin' on strangely;
    Tha's bin on for a bit ov a " marlock," aw think,
An' tha seems eawt o' humour wi' summat or other,
    What's to do wi' thee loike ?   Hast bin havin'
      some drink ?
Tha's bin rayther " top heavy " lately, that's certain,
    An' they sen tha's bin " cuttin' thi capers" i' th' street ;
Aw know for a fact tha wur damagin' th' railin's.
    An' spoilin' us th' promenade rarely one neet.

Howd thi noise, for it's no use attemptin' t' deny it,
    For aw've catched thee agate o' this mischief misel ;
Tha wur busy one day pooin' th' hulkin' to pieces,
    Between th' new Aquarium an' th' Royal Hotel.
Aw saw thee, mon, rippin' an' tearin' away theer,
    An' squanderin' th' cobbles an' th' timbers abeawt ;
Tha made a rare hole i' th' sea fence, aw can tell thee,
    An' tha's made a fine hole i' my pockets, aw deawt.

T'other day aw turned eawt to admire thi performance,
    Intendin' to write a few lines i' thi praise ;
But tha quenched every spark o' poetical fervour,
    When tha wet mi best trowsers, an' spat i' mi face.
One loikes to be friendly an' gradely wi' strangers,
    When they come deawn to spend a few days wi' us here ;
But iv this is thy way o' returnin' a kindness,
    Tha'll have but few friends deawn at Blackpool, aw fear.

Before tha goes back aw've a job 'at wants doin'—
    It'll keep thee fro' mischief—at least for a day ;
Ther's a cart looad o' shingle tha's thrown on my doorstep,
    Aw'll thank thee to set to an' shift it away.
Aw've cleared it off twice, but tha's bin here i' th' neet toime
    (For tha conno for shame do thi tricks before men),
An' when th' lamps have bin eawt, an' tha thowt nob dy saw
      thee,
    Tha browt a great lot o' this rubbish ogen.

Aw'm fond o' that song " Sweep abeawt yo'r own doorsteps,"
    An aw've often ta'en th' brush eawt to sweep abeawt mine ;
An' aw'm still very willin' to side mi own rubbish,
    But aw connot just say 'at aw loike to shift *thine*.
There's nob'dy i' Blackpool mich fonder than I am
    O' seein' a regular stunnin' good storm ;
An' tha's certainly gan us some grand entertainments ;
    Still tha costs us a deol when tha comes to perform.

When a thing's really good we're quite willin' to pay for't,
    Though it's known 'at thy naybours are never so rich ;
We should loike thy excitin' performances better,
    Iv it wurno for one thing—tha charges to' mich.
Tha'rt clever, no deawt, an' a many 'at's yeard thee
    Have bin, loike misel, fairly melted to tears ;
But look what a while tha's bin howdin' thi concerts !
    Tha's been practicin' thy songs for theawsands o' years !

Tha'rt a very good sarvant, but shockin' bad mestur ;
    Tha'rt as harmless as owt while tha'rt kept within beawnds ;
But tha neaw an' then gets in a terrible passion ;
    An' tha maks weary wark when tha'rt havin' thi " reawnds."
Tha'll remember aw praised thee at th' furst when aw knew
       thee ;
    Then th' seawnd o' thi voice wur grand music to me ;
But aw've had rayther moor than aw've bargained for lately,
    An' we're nearer relations sin then, dusta see ?

Iv tha wants to be friendly wi' thoose 'at admire thee
    Tha'll have to set to abeawt mendin' thi ways ;
For tha connot expect a poor fellow to love thee
    Iv tha wets him his trowsers, an' spits in his face.
Well, my porritch is ready, so ta-ta, owd ocean ;
    Tha'd better be off, as it's gettin' so late ;
Iv tha finds it convenient to'ard th' end o' September,
    Slip o'er here, an' pay me my promenade rate.

BISPHAM.

ISPHAM here pratty?
　　Aw think it *is* pratty;
　　Foind me another spot
　　Lookin' soa "natty."
　Hedgerows are bloomin',
　　Ole the village perfumin',
An' garden beds put on their pleasantest looks.
　　Th' good childer's new weshed, love,
　　An' th' bad ones new threshed, love,
While th' dullards are kept to their slates an' their books.

　　Bispham here pratty?
　　Why, bless thi loife, Matty,
　　Thee on wi' thi bonnet
　　An' come here to-neet;
　　Throstles are singin',
　　　An' th' village bells ringin',
An' daisies are growin' reet under one's feet.
　　Fling away sadness, love,
　　Frettin' is madness, love;
Come thi ways here an' tha'll see a grand seet!

　　An' deawn on thi shanks, lass,
　　Return God thi thanks, lass;
　　We've never deserved
　　These dainties 'at's served.
　　Why, look up aboon,
　　At th' breet queenly moon,
Heaw grandly hoo pours deawn her silvery leet!
　　Look at th' stars creawdin' near,
　　Loike childer gone theer
To see their dear mother, an' bid her good neet.

Bispham here pratty?
Aw think it *is* pratty;
Then come thi ways, Matty,
An' see for thisel;
Come while it's May, love,
For th' fleawers fade away, love,
An' th' east winds may silence ole th' songsters i' th' dell.
Aw've tidied mi garden walks,
Shifted th' owd beon stalks,
An' dusted mi parlour, expectin' tha'd come.
Soa if tha's a bonnet, lass,
Look sharp an' don it, lass.
An' visit th' owd bard in his countryfied whoam.

LINES WRITTEN IN A VOLUME OF POEMS, AND SENT TO THE
REV. ROBERT COLLYER, AMERICA.

TO the once Yorkshire blacksmith—now parson—I send
This book, through a hint dropt by Elliot, our friend,
Who ventures to hope you may find in these rhymes
Some thought that may wake up old scenes and old
times.
You began at the anvil, and I at the loom,
Our pathway in those days was clouded with gloom;
But we toiled on in patience,—kept pushing along,
And now we're rewarded with sunshine and song.

TO MY FRIEND, ISAAC BARDSLEY.

' thoose lines 'at tha's sent,
    Which awm sure are well meant—
       Tha tells me I am no' to fret ;
    If aw'll follow thy plan,
An' attend th' inner man,
    Aw've other ten years to live yet.

Well, aw try o' aw con
To be cheerful, but, mon,
    Aw find it vast hard aw can tell ;
It's a terrible task,
An' awm tempted to ask,
    If tha's ever been poorly thisel' !

Mon, this owd neck o' mine
Isn't red, same as thine ;
    An' th' yeadwartch awm seldom witheawt.
An' tho' tha looks breet,
Wi' thi stomach ole reet,
    Tha'll know what that meons, no deawt.

It's hard wark to cheer up,
When life's bitter cup
    Is constantly under one's nose ;
But this looks like eawr doom ;
Some fade, others bloom ;
    One's a thorn, another's a rose.

After ole, mi dear lad,
One has cause to be glad,
    When he knows he's noan laboured for nowt ;
If aw've done as tha says,—
Cheered thi earlier days,—
    It's a grand an' encouragin' thowt !

Then tha calls me a Bard
Says mi song, " Bowton's Yard,"
   Has boath pleased folk an' mended 'em to' !
An' 'at Jammie wi' th' bell
Has made theawsands to yell ;
   Neaw that's just what aw meant 'em to do.

Then tha names other rhymes,
'At aw've published at times—
   " Bonny Brid," " Ode to th' Sun," "Thee an' Me;"
An' tha'rt bold to proclaim
These'll add to mi fame ;
   But that's hardish to tell—we shall see.

Th' next tha calls me a preacher,
A plain whomly teacher,
   Whose sarmons contain good advice.
Well, aw've tried, aw must say,
I' mi own humble way,
   To give yo' booath Med'cine an' Spice.

Then tha names lookin' back
Upo' life's rugged track,
   'An says it must cheer a chap's mind
To know what he's writ
Must have helped foalk a bit,
   An' thus leetened th' cares o' mankind.

Well, good neet, dear friend B. ;
An' aw'll try not to dee
   Till aw've finished mi wark here below ;
An' when yonder aboon
Aw strike up a new tune,
   Tha'll be somewheer abeawt me aw know !

TH' OWD PEDLAR'S GONE WHOAM.

TH' owd pedlar's packed up an' gone whoam;
    He'll go eawt wi' his basket no moor.
    Who is there 'at doesn't remember owd John
    Comin' reawnd once a week to their door?
An' whoa isn't sorry he's dead?
    Soa kind an' soa gentle was he!
Alas! it's too true what we've often yeard said,
    " Thoose we love th' best are oft th' furst to dee."

Thank God! he's neaw londed safe whoam,
    Wheer th' weary an' careworn can rest!
Wheer noa mack o' grief or misfortune can come,
    An' noa foe can disturb or molest.
Then let's noan to frettin' give way,
    Although there's nowt wrong in a tear;
We shall noan see his equal for mony a long day;
    He're a favourite amongst us when here.

When hearty he loiked a good joke;
    An' often he'd merrily chat;
But his dear lovin' partner drooped deawn at his side,
    An' he never looked reet after that.
He sawntered abeawt wi' his wares,
    An' tried to cheer up, as i' th' past;
But his sorrow wur moor than he're able to bear,
    An' he had to give in to 't at last.

Th' owd basket he carried so long,
    We'll carefully treasure as gowd ;
For th' arm wheer it hung, once nimble an' strong,
    Neaw lies by his side stiff an' cowd.
We've ta'en him an' put him i' th' grave,
    Wheer his dear wife an' childer are laid ;
There's noa stone to mark th' spot ; it's a green grassy
        meawnd,
    Happ'd an patted wi' th' owd sexton's spade.

Th' armcheer 'at he's ceawered in for years,
    We've carefully laid by i' th' nook :
An' oft are these een o' eawers wetted wi' tears,
    As on that dear relic we look.
For we loved that owd chap wi' th' grey hairs,
    An' he's missed bi ole th' nayburs i' th' street ;
For he'll come here no moor to exhibit his wares,
    Or bid us his well-known "Good neet !"

He're a honest owd creatur' wur John ;
    An' his bobbins an' thread wur furst-class ;
An' whoever had th' fortune to trade wi' th' owd mon,
    Geet plenty o' stuff for their brass.
But he's made his last bargain deawn here,
    An' there's just one indulgence we crave—
An' that is, to neaw an' then drop a warm tear,
    To moisten th' wild fleawers o'er his grave.

We allis meet abeawt one place,
 At th' end o' th' garden wo;
Hoo grins an' laughs ole o'er her face,
 Aw grin an' laugh an' o.

TH' COARTIN' NEET.

Part First.

I T'S time for me to leov mi wark,
    An' wesh an' dress misel ;
    Becose to-neet, at th' edge o' dark,
      Aw meet wi' Rosy Bell.
When leovin' th' lass o' Sunday neet,
    Aw took her hont i' mine,
Aw said, aw'd go iv o wur reet,
    An' th' weather midlin' fine.

We're rare an' nicely matched, us two ;
    That's plain enuff to see ;
For nob'dy could mak' moor ado
    Than Rosy does o' me.
We allis meet abeawt one place,
    At th' side o' th' garden wo ;
Hoo grins an' laughs all o'er her face,
    Aw grin an' laugh an o !

Her mother looked as shy as owt
    Th' furst neet aw went i' th' heawse ;
Aw dursn't speak, nor cough, nor nowt,
    But ceawered theer like a meawse.
Aw think hoo saw what th' visit meant,
    Before aw coom away ;
For, do yo know, th' next time aw went,
    Hoo axed me to mi tay.

An' neaw aw'm just as welcome theer,
    As ony lad i' th' teawn ;
They allis reach me th' two-arm cheer,
    An' tell me t' sit me deawn.
Th' owd chap's a horse worth twenty peawnd,
    Besides a lot o' ceaws ;
An' a bit o' rare good pasture greawnd
    Wheer th' sheep an' cattle breawse.

Neaw, dunno think aw'm after th' brass,
    For aw wouldn't thank for th' spot
Wi' th' pigs, an' th' ceaws, an' o he has,
    Unless aw'd *hur* i' th' lot.
But yonder Rosy comes, aw see,
    Hoo's just shut th' garden gate ;
An' neaw hoo's lookin' eawt for me,
    So aw musn't let her wait.

TH' COARTIN' NEET.

PART SECOND.

A W'VE made it up wi' Rosy Bell ;
    We've booath agreed t' be wed ;
But didn't th' lass have a cryin' spell !
    An' didn't her face go red !
Aw axed her nicely iv hoo wished
    Mi bed an' board to share ;
Hoo turned her yead aside an' blushed,
    An' said hoo didn't care.

Neaw, dunno let this secret eawt,
    Nor mention what aw've towd ;
Aw wouldn't have it talked abeawt,
    For fifty peawnd i' gowd.
Keep quiet, wait on patiently,
    Till th' rumour's made a fact ;
An' then aw meon to let yo see
    Heaw *aw* intend to act.

Yo'll noan find me like some ; for lo !—
    As soon as th' weddin's o'er,
There's sich a change—they're nowt at o
    Like what they wur before.
Aw'll turn mi hond to ony job,—
    Keep Johnny eawt o' th' durt,
Or sit bi th' hob an' nurse eawr Bob,
    While Rosy mends mi shirt.

Aw never wish to be admired
   For hondlin' broom or cleawt ;
But when aw see th' lass gettin' tired
   Aw meon to help her eawt.
Aw'll try an' save her o aw con,
   An' when hoo's noan so well,
Aw'll poo mi cooat off, like a mon,
   An' wesh an' bake misel.

So long as th' harston's cleon an' white,
   An' th' fender nice an' breet,
Aw shall allis feel it a delight
   To stop i' th' heawse at neet.
Aw'll ne'er put Rosy eawt o' tune
   Wi' daubin' th' parlour floor ;
But allis—when aw've durty shoon,
   Aw'll wipe 'em weel at th' door.

I' winter time, when th' neets are long,
   Aw'll ceawer me deawn i' th' nook ;
An', while th' wife sews, aw'll sing a song,
   Or read fro' th' Sacred Book.
Yo may co it vain, conceited pride,—
   But a chap 'at connot see
Nice pictur's at his own fireside,—
   Well, he's nowt akin to me !

EAWR POOASTMEN.

AS aw'rn sittin' one day i' mi cottage,
    An' runnin' things o'er i' mi knob,
  Aw saw a few wrongs needed tacklin' ;
    Soa aw buckled misel' to mi job.
Aw wur thinkin'—'mong other odd matters—
    Abeawt these big sal'ries we give
To theawsands o' drones 'at ne'er do nowt,
    While we've bees 'at have hard wark to live.

As an instance o' this—there's eawr pooastman—
    A very deservin' owd breek—
Well, aw'm towd 'at he tak's eawt ole th' letters
    For a paltry five shillin's a week.
Neaw, yo' couldn't ha' thowt it soa, could yo' ?
    But it's perfectly true as th' tale goas ;
An' further than this, aw can tell yo'—
    They don't even find him his clooas.

Neaw, aw've noa wish for gettin' up taxes,
    Soa dunno throw that i' mi face ;
But to think o' what taxes are paid for—
    Why, foalk, it's a burnin' disgrace !
Aw should just like to know heaw it happens
    That numbskulls wi' nowt i' their yead
Are up to their shoulders i' clover,
    While others are starvin' for bread.

Heaw is it 'at some men are honoured
    For bringin' us into disgrace,
While others are deein'—neglected—
    Real friends to their country an' race !
Can England believe in her Bible,
    An' at th' same time consider it reight
To starve an' neglect her real heroes,
    While we pay men to plunder an' feight ?

What does war do but bring want an' ruin !
   An' soa long as we've th' "piper to pay"
It's eawr interest, as well as eawr duty
   To sweep these dire evils away.
Whoa amongst us would harbour a greyhound,
   If it did nowt but worry an' bark ?
If we've sense wi shall pay nob'dy wages,
   But thoose 'at do good honest wark.

Let's clear eawt ole th' drones 'at are useless,
   An' get workin' bees into th' hive ;
An' let nob'dy eat th' honey 'at makes none,
   Then eawr commerce an' trade may revive.
But soa long as we keep public sarvants,
   To give us their time an' their aid,
Let's treat 'em as men should be treated,
   An' see 'at they're properly paid.

An' whoa's more desarvin' than th' pooastmen ?
   What a lot o' hard wark they get through !
An' yet, wheer are th' Government sarvants,
   'At get as ill paid as they do ?
Th' idea of a mon in his senses,
   Gooin' slpashin' thro' mire an' thro' clay,
Th' public sarvant for o' th' foalk i' th' village,
   For less than a shillin' a day !

Neaw, iv aw'd a noice seot at Saint Stephens,
   Aw'd regulate th' sal'ries, an' soon :—
Why, bless us ! a poor country pooastman
   May spend ole he gets up o' shoon !
But aw'll write up to th' Pooastmaister General,
   An' tho' aw know th' Government's poor,
Aw'll try if aw connot persuade him
   To give th' chap a " bob " or two moor.

CHARLES BRADLAUGH.

NOTHER comrade's said " Good-neet," an' left us ;
    Another warrior's laid his weapons deawn ;
He fowt life's battles bravely—won his laurels,
    An left behind a well-deserved reneawn.

He fowt 'gainst shams, 'gainst creeds worn out, an' musty ;
    He fowt 'gainst " beasts," as Paul once did of owd ;
He sowt not wealth ; refused to barter freedom,
    Or sell his birthright for a mint o' gowd.

Heaven's richer neaw ; but, oh ! we're vastly poorer ;
    A king 'mongst men has fall'n fro' th' ranks to day ;
His orders came to join th' great band o' martyrs,
    An', like ole soldiers, knew he must obey.

He'd won his battles ; friends were ole unitin'
    I' one loud song th' event to celebrate ;
But th' tired-eawt warrior heeded not their praises,
    His ears wur closed ; these honours coom to' late !

Men oft get wrong—mistakin' good for evil ;
    Imagine folly's wisdom, bitter sweet ;
But wheer eawr friend's gone ole these wrongs are reighted,
    An' tho' *man* fails i' justice, *God does reet !*

THANK YO', SIR!

ON RECEIVIN' A KESMUS GOOSE FRO' A PARSON.

AST Setturday neet, as aw'r nursin' eawr Bob,
An' runnin' a toothry things o'er i' mi nob,
Someb'dy pood at eawr bell, so aw went to th' front
  dur,
An' when aw geet theer some astonished aw wur,
When a young woman muttered some sort of excuse,
An' said " If you please, Sir, I've brought you a goose."
" Mi good woman," aw said, " yo're mistacken, aw fear ;
Aw think yo'll do wrong iv yo' leoven it here."

" I am perfectly right, I assure you," hoo said,
Soa aw stood toothry seconds theer scratchin' mi yead ;
An' this young woman stood theer quite fast what to do,
Whoile aw're lookin' sheepish, an' feelin' soa too.
At length aw said, " Well, iv it's eawrs bring it in,
But aw'm thinkin' it welly ameawnts to a sin,
For poor foalk loike we are to fare i' this style ;
It's eawt o' eawr way this bi monny a long mile.

" Sheep yeads, an' red herrin', an' that mack o' stuff
Are moor i' eawr loine, an' are quite good enuff ;
For one hasn't a desoire to be same as owd Peel,
'At dee'd th' other Sunday through livin' so weel,—
He ate so much cabbage an' mate o' that kind,
'At he didn't leov heawse-reawm enuff for his woind.
He'r a foine-lookin' fellow as ever one see'd,
Wur owd Mestur Peel ; it's a pity he deed."

Well, yo'r reverence, aw'm forty year owd—rayther moor,
But aw've ne'er seen a goose come i' eawr heawse afoor;
An' we dunno know heaw we're to cook sich like things,
Dun yo' eat ole the job lot—th' tail, fithers, an' wings?
Dun yo' roast 'em, or boil 'em, or fry 'em, or what?
Eawr Jack says he dar' say they're done up i' fat,
Same as fish, cowd potatoes, an' stuff o' that mack,
But aw neer tak noa notice at ole o' eawr Jack.

Well, mi thanks Mister Parson, for th' present yo'n sent,
An' aw hope 'at yo'll ne'er ha' no cause to repent
Havin' sent a poor fellow a goose to his dinner,
For it's one o'th' best ways o' convertin' a sinner.
Yo'r sermons, tho' good, aren't o hawve as mich use
For rousin' one up as a savery goose;
If yo'd mak' an impression on sich loike as me,
Yo'll ha' to appeal to eawr stomachs, yo see.

Neaw aw've noa deawt at ole but i' this sort o' weather
A goose spoiced wi' gospel would do weel together;
Eawr Saviour saw th' wisdom o' this, for we read,
'At He once gav' His hungry disciples a feed.
Well, aw'll drop it, yo'r reverence, aw've said enuff neaw,
An' aw've managed to get thro' mi tale o' sumheaw.
One met go on further, but then what's the use?
Ole aw want to say's this—Aw'm obliged for that goose.

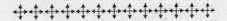

TO MY DAUGHTER BERTHA, ON HER 20TH BIRTHDAY.

BERTHA, mi lass, it's twenty year'
    Sin' theaw furst coom amongst us here,—
        Th' latest burd.
    Noa message left eawr humble whoam,
Proclaimin' th' glorious news tha'd come;
        Not a word.

We made no bother,—made no noise,
As iv we'd feawnd some valued prize,—
        Not a bit;
Nor did we ax foalk in to see
A miracle or owt:—not we,—
        We'd moor wit.

We'd seen sich " Miracles " before,
An' had to feed some hawve a score;—
        Clog 'em to'.
An', tho' we'd one moor meawth to fill,
Yo'r mother, wi' her care an' skill
        Made things do.

Th' sky, then, wur nobbut darkish, lass;
Like others, we wur short o' brass,—
        Friendless, poor.
But th' cleawds have partly pass'd away,
An' neaw we thankfully can say—
        Bread's moor sure.

It's true success wur dearly bowt,
But every foe wur fairly fowt,—
        Bravely met.
An', tho' th' remark may smack o' pride,—
We've ne'er done nowt we wish to hide,—
        Never, yet !

Well, tha's been with us twenty year',—
Seen mony a smile, an' mony a tear;
      Some tha's shed.
We've had a thorn for every rose;
There's links been severed, as tha knows;
      Two are wed.—

An' five frail fleawers have drooped an' died;
They're sleepin' yonder, side bi side,
      'Neath a yew!
We feawnd it hard wi' these to part,
An' moor nor one poor weawnded heart
      Lie theer to'!

Well, thoose we still have wi' us here,
Do ole they con eawr hearts to cheer,
      Neaw we're owd.
We value these dear, tender ties;
These kindly acts yo'r parents prize
      Moor nor gowd!

An' should it ever be yo'r lot
To have to leov eawr humble cot,
      May yo find
Yo'r future whoam's as snug an' pat,
An' every way as good as that
      Left behind!

An', here aw end mi humble lay;
Aw've getten nowt no moor to say,—
      Nobbut this :—
That, while tha roams thro' Nature's beawers,
We hope tha'll meet wi' lots o' fleawers,
      Lots o' bliss!

POOR PUSSY.

THEAW'RT one o' God's creatures—come in here, come
    in ;
  Poor Pussy !   Theau art hungry lookin' an' thin
  Eawr John's just bin tellin' me heaw tha's been used;
It's shawmful is th' way 'at he's seen thee abused.
Poor thing ! an' tha'rt nobbut a kittlin' aw see ;
An' yet th' nowty lads couldn't let thee a-be;
But tha's met wi' a friend at'll keep thee fro' harm,
So ceawer thee deawn here wheer it's cosy an' warm.

It's th' wrong time o'th' year to be takin' owt in ;
An' yet aw shall never be guilty o' th' sin
O' turnin' mi back on a creature i' need—
Iv it's nobbut a cat 'at awm able to feed.
Lie thee deawn close to th' hob, an' aw'll fot some moor coal ;
Tha shall join me at th' best 'at aw have i' this hole.
Wheer's thi mother, aw wonder ?   Well, that tha can't tell,
But tha'rt rayther to' young to turn eawt bi thisel'.

Neaw then, here's a sope o' warm milk in a plate ;
Lap it up, an' be sharp, for tha needs sum'at t' ate.
Here John, lad, thee slip into th' butcher's, th' next dur,
For a pennorth o' leets, an' say what they're for ;
He's a good-natured fellow is Alfred Maclure,
Iv he knows what they're for he may send rayther moor.
He's fond of a dog, is th' owd lad—he is that ;
Let's hope he can feel for a poor starvin' cat.

Here's John wi' his leets ; come an' have a " tuck in,"
An' we'll cure thee o' lookin' so famished an' thin.
Hasto getten nine lives ?   Some cats have, they sen ;
Well, stop here wi' me, an' tha'll happen ha' ten.
Come here, neaw—come here ; for tha mustn't go eawt,
Or tha'll get welly kilt wi' th' bad lads 'at's abeawt.
They think it foine sport to illuse sich as thee ;
Jump up, an' aw'll howd thee a bit on mi knee.

Poor thing ! an' tha'rt nobbut a kittlin' aw see,
An' yet th' nowty lads couldn't let thee a-be.

Well, it's th' way o' this world! When one's powfagg'd an'
    deawn,
An' friends 'at should care for us every one fleawn,
There's allis some ready—Tom, Harry, or Dick—
To hurl us still lower, an' give us a kick.
Like some hungry vulture 'at hovers areawnd,
An' fattens its carcase o' meat 'at's unseawnd—
So these, havin' passions degraded an' low,
Can feed upo' cruelty, revel 'midst woe!

Aw'd rayther this minute be clemm'd same as thee,
As friendless an' whoamless tha ceawers on mi knee,
Nor be cursed wi' mean actions, like some aw could name,
'At are soulless, an' heartless, an' " glory i' shame."
But tha pricks up thi ears, an' howds up thi yead
As iv t' understood every word 'at aw said:
An' theaw has as mitch sense—an' knows what to do wi't—
As that wretch 'at wur puncin' thee up an' deawn th' street.

Well, aw'm thinkin' we've summat t' be thankful for, John;
It's grand, lad, to do a kind act when we con;
Aw've towt thee a lesson aw want thee to heed,
Whenever tha meets a poor creature i' need.
Let's allis deal gently wi' th' sufferin' an' sad,
Then God will deal gently with us, mi dear lad;
An' iv ever, loike th' cat here, we get cast adrift,
There's no deawt but what someb'dy will give us a lift.

TO MY FRIEND, COUNCILLOR JOSEPH HEAP,
BLACKPOOL.

EXCUSE me, friend Heap, for intrudin';
 An' don't think me a troublesome mon;
For aw see tha looks sad, so aw'm wantin'
 To cheer thee a bit iv aw con.
Aw'm aware it may seem rayther foolish
 To attempt to give aid or relief
To a spirit 'at's bowed deawn wi' losses,
 Or a heart 'at's been smitten wi' grief.

Aw know what it meons to see cheeks fade;
 To miss th' childish prattle i' th' fowd;
Aw'm familiar wi' coffins an' graveyards,
 An' leovin' th' dear caskets i' th' cowd!
Mon, it cuts up a poor fellow's feelin's,
 An' gives to his nerves a rude shock;
When, i' lookin' areawnd on his homestead,
 He misses a lamb fro' his flock!

It's hard to see eyes growin' dimmer,
 Ah, eyes 'at so lately wur breet;
To miss th' merry ring o' their voices,
 When wishin' us ole " good neet!"
But away wi' this useless repinin';
 It's folly one's troubles to nurse;
Aw'm wantin' to cheer, not to sadden;
 To mak' thee feel better, not worse.

Look up, friend! for tho' it's neaw darkish,
 An' th' Spoiler's dismantled thi beawers,
We shall soon be made happy wi' springtime,
 Wi' singin' birds, sunshine, an' fleawers!
An' th' dear little childer 'at's left us,—
 Tho' they seem to be lost—they're feawnd;
They're neaw wi' their guardian angels,
 An' treadin' celestial greawnd.

TH' "BONNY BRID'S" BIRTHDAY.

IT'S thi birthday, mi love, come ger on mi knee ;
 That's a darlin'. Heaw owd arto neaw ? Let me see—
 Four year owd ! Is that o' ? Well, theaw art a foine
  girl !
An' this is thi birthday ! Well, give us a curl.
Run an' fot us some toffy, John, that's a foine lad,
Th' "Bonny Brid" shall ha' goody, to-neet, wi' its dad.
It is'nt so often yo get owt at's sweet,
But aw've made up mi moind 'at yo shall ha' to-neet.

Here he comes ! here he comes ! eh, what goody there is !
Neaw, what does't say for it ?   Come, gie me a kiss.
Oh, that wur a sweet un !   Another, an' then
Theaw shall poo thi dad's whiskers weel for him ogen.
Neaw, John, lad, come here, an' look after thisel',
For theawt'rt longin' t' have howd ov a bit aw con tell.
What ! eawt ov o' this is there noan theaw con spare ?
Neaw aw'm sure theaw owt t' let brother John have a share.

Come, let me divoide 'em. Neaw, then, let me see :
Howd thi hond, love, there's nuts, an' there's cumfits for thee.
Here, John, there's some humbugs for thy share, mi lad,
Theer, yo han 'em between yo, there's noan for yo'r dad.
Neaw, aw want yo t' be good, an' as still as yo con,
Whoile aw read a noice tale eawt o' th' Bible. Neaw, John ?
Art theaw tryin' to beg sister's cumfits, or what ?
Aw shall be very cross iv aw know theaw does that.

Oh ! dear, dear, my whiskers ! aw'll warm thee iv t' does ;
Theawt'rt allus i' mischief, theaw meddlesome puss ;
Leove off, do, this minute.   Oh ! dear-a-me, choild !
Here, aw'll put thee on th' floor, for theaw'rt gerrin' reet woild.
Aw con read noan to-neet, so aw've no need to try :
Here, Jane, tak' this book, lass, an' put it safe by.
Theaw'rt agate ogen, arto ? oh, dear, theaw art ruff !
Go an' poo' thi doll's toppin', aw've had quoite enuff.

There's a beggar at th' dur, John, go give him some bread ;
For he favvurs eawr poor little Robert 'at's dead.
Poor fellow ! he'rn allus so playful an' fond ;
But his mother an' him lie i' th' graveyard up yond.
Well, come, han yo done ? for it's toime to go t' bed ;
Misses Carter across is undressin' their Fred.
Here, Jane, lass, tak' Hannah, an' poo' off her shoon ;
An aw wish theaw'd just sing 'em some pratty hymn tune.

When their mother wur here to undress 'em at neet,
Hoo sung sich noice songs whoile they'rn warmin' their feet ;
Then they'd booath kneel 'em down, an' they'd lisp eawt their
        prayers ;
When they'd done, we used t' kiss em', an' tak' 'em upstairs.
Neaw, then, love, come here, it's thi birthday, is this,
So before theaw goes t' bed aw shall want one moor kiss.
What ! art luggin' ogen ?   Do give o'er, dear-a-me !
When theaw gets a bit bigger theaw'll catch it, theaw'll see.

Jane, rub 'em their faces an' honds o'er a bit,
An' then see iv that neet-geawn i' th' corner ull fit ;
It's one 'at their gron'mother browt tother neet ;
Aw dar' say theaw'll foind it to fit her o reet.
Come, neaw, kneel yo deawn, get yo'r prayers noicely said,
Then Jane shall leet th' candle, an' tak' yo to bed.
Amen.   Come this way, just one smack ; oh, heaw sweet !
Neaw then, away wi' yo.   God bless yo—good neet !

TH' STRICKEN STOKERS.

WHATEVER'S to do wi' yo Manchester way,
    Wi' yo'r stokers, dense fogs, and poor gas !
    One expects summat better nor this wordy fray,—
    This settin' o' class against class.
Neaw, aw'm noan goin' to argue whoa's wrong or whoa's reet,
    To sich wisdom aw'm layin' noa claim ;
Still, aw fancy iv facts wur browt fairly to th' leet,
    There'd be moor nor *one* party to blame.

But there's *one* point aw think on which ole will agree,
    There's a lot o' real sufferin' abeawt ;
An' must men keep starvin', an' are they to dee,
    Till we scribblers have done foin eawt ?
Come, let me appeal to yo, Tories or Rads,
    For we're ole made o' one sort o' clay,
Shall it ever be said 'at we Lancashire lads
    Treated th' helpless an' poor i' this way ?

Do yo say they're to blame ? well, well, granted they are,
    Whoa is there 'at allis does reet ?
Con we fairly expect men to walk o'er a snare
    Witheawt ever hurtin' their feet !
But that isn't th' question ; what we've got to do,—
    An' aw think we can hardly do less,—
Is to shew eawr owd mates we're for helpin' 'em thro'
    This painful, this sad distress.

We've Christmas near to,—that breet season o' mirth,
    When joy-bells will merrily ring,
Remindin' us ole o' that wondrous birth
    Of a brother, a Saviour, an' King.
Then mony a rich Dives will be feastin' off th' best,
    Drinkin' wine eawt o' vessels o' gowd ;
But whoa's to ax Lazarus in as a guest ?
    Is *he* to stop eawt i' th' cowd !

TO HENRY NUTTER, ON RECEIVING A VOLUME OF HIS POEMS.

EAR Nutter, accept mi best thanks for thi book;
An' aw tell thee what mon—tha'rt a capital cook,
Or tha wouldn't ha' had th' wisdom an' wit to invent
Sich a wonderful banquet as this 'at tha's sent;
An' th' man 'at can't sit deawn an' have a good feed,—
Well, he must have an awful bad stomach indeed;
Th' food's wholesome, an' easy to tak, an' what's th' best,
It winna lie heavy, it's sure to digest.

Like me, tha's employed a good deol o' thi time
I' treatin' thi friends to epistles i' rhyme;
But while theaw may be blamed for producin' bad verse,
Aw've been turnin' eawt stuff 'at's a theawsand times worse.
Well, tha writes wi' thi' heart quite as mitch as thi yead,
For tha's said a good word abeawt some 'at are dead;
Among others, tha mentions Job Hartley, aw see,
Abeawt whom tha seems t' howd th' same opinions as me.

Hast yeard owt o' Job sin' he left th' top o' th' teawn?
Poor Job! mon, he hardly knew wheer he wur beawn!
Let's hope he's arrived i' some happier sphere
Than ony he longed for, or sowt when here.
What a lot o' strange subjects tha's touched i' thi strain:
Eawr Matty will have it tha's "Burnley on th' brain."
There's birthdays, an' weddin's, an' dinners, an' trams,—
Ole come in for praise—there's not one 'at tha damns.

Tha's rhymin' epistles to young an' to owd :
Even drivers o' engines aren't left eawt i' th' cowd ;
While th' women,—'at oft change their mind,—as we see,
Are sure ov an able defender i' thee.
But this isn't what aw wur wantin' to say,
When these subjects tha's treated allured me away ;
Aw wur wantin' to thank thee for th' book 'at tha's sent,
Tho' thanks winno pay thee thi rates, nor thi rent.

Still, some foalk imagine 'at this is enuff ;
An' 'at poets con live upo' honour an' stuff.
Aw con tell thee aw've starved upo' that mak' o' cake,
Till aw'm gettin' to look like a donn'd-up rake.
Tha mentions poor Waugh, an' his funeral i' May ;
Mon, there wur some sad hearts an' wet een that day !
Ah, an' Nutter, owd friend, we feel th' loss on him still,
For a gap wur then made it's noan easy to fill.

Ben Brierley's here still, but it's plain enuff t' see
'At he's toddlin' tow'rd th' grave very fast, like me ;
A few moor unsteady scratches wi' th' pen ;
A few moor milestones to pass, an' then—
Two other owd Harps will ha' snapp'd a string ;
An' two other brids will ha' ceased to sing !
A few moor races may have to be run,
Then th' laurels will oather be lost or won !

"G SHARP" AN' TH' BAND OF HOPE ORGAN,

MESTUR Heditir, thank yo for th' "Onward" yon sent;
Aw connot weel send it yo back, for it's lent ;
A friend o' mine coom into th' heawse t' other neet
When this Band of Hope organ lay fair in his seet.
"Hello here !" he said, when he seed it, "What's this ?"
It's a number o' "Onward," lad, that's what it is.
It's a number o' "Onward," eh ? "Wheer is it fro ?"
So aw towd him fro' Lunnon, for owt as aw knew.

It's what they co'n th' Band of Hope organ is that ;
" Beg pardon, aw didn't just catch it—it's what ?"
It's th' Band of Hope organ—coom eawt yesterday.
" Oh, a organ o' some mack tha says—will it play ?"
Play ! aw think it will that ; tha should yer it awhile ;
When it's fairly on th' job it can play to some style.
" Well, well, lad," he said, " it's some bother, no deawt ;
Aw hope it's noan like that at Waugh tells abeawt ;

If it is, we shall do better beawt it nor wi' 't,
An' aw'd rayther not yer owt o' th' sort, a fine seet."
If tha'rt freet'ned, aw said, aw'll advise thee t' stand fur ;
That o' Waugh's wur a rum un, but this is far wur !
Th' church organ would stop when th' tunes wur o done,
But this has played on ever sin' it begun.
Well, this friend o' mine didn't tak it in aw wur chaffin' ;
An' mi wife, hoo wur very near splittin' wi' laffin'.

But aw giv' her a wink, when mi friend wurn't lookin',
For he'd poo'd a short pipe eawt, an' gated a smokin'.
Sit thee deawn, mon, aw said, it con do thee no harm,
There's not th' least danger or cause for alarm.
" Well, naybur," he said, theaw surproises me reet,
An' aw'm beawn'd to admit 'at aw'm puzzled to-neet ;
Aw've seen Owdham Church organ, but hang my owd hat
It's noan manufactured o' papper loike that.

Wind it up for us, mon, an' then set it a-goin',
An' let's see what th' new thing's calculated for doin'.
Wind it up, doesta say ? it needs no windin' up ;
An' th' players han nowt nobbut wayter to sup.
" Well, it's strange that," he said, " gradely puzzlin' to me ;
There's summat abeawt it aw connot just see.
Heawever, aw'll leov thee, it's neaw gettin' late,
An' co ogen t' morn, an' we'll have it agate.

Aw'll bring Robin Turner 'at lives i' th' next row,
For a thing o' that mack will just pleos him, aw know.
Well, aw'll bid thee good neet, at th' same time aw must say,
Aw shall be rarely capp'd if that thing theer can play.
So we booath said good neet, an' he off eawt o' th' dur.
Eh ! aw wish yo'd ha seen what a kitchen there wur !
Eawr Elizabeth laffed till hoo very nee split,
An' eawr Dick wur no better nor hur—not a bit !

" Eh, dear !" said my wife, " what a greenhorn, for sure,
Good gracious ! aw hope he'll ne'er come here no moor."
Howd thi noise, lass, aw said, a good laff ull do good ;
Aw'd have him i' th' heawse every neet iv aw could.
This is th' best bit o' fun 'at we'n had sin' we'rn wed,
Mack us toothery meal porritch, an' lets go to bed.
Well, neaw—Mistur Heditir, aw must give o'er,
For aw'm noan very weel, as aw towd yo before ;

Still, aw'll promise yo this—iv aw have no mishap—
Aw shall let yo know heaw aw go on wi' this chap.
If he comes again t' morn, aw shall give him a tune,
An' aw'll warrant he'll see what aw'm aimin' at soon.
Aw shall mack ole reet plain, iv he connot see that,—
Tho' his name be G Sharp, aw shall co him A Flat.
Well, good neet, for mi porritch is ready, aw'm towd,
An' aw met as weel eat 'em afore they get cowd.

"ONLY A POET."

"ONLY a poet," a schemer o' schemes;
A weaver o' fancies, a dreamer o' dreams;
Insanely eccentric, wi' long flowin' hair,
An' eyes strangely bright, wi' a meanin'less stare!
"Only a poet"—that's all, nowt no moor;
An', as every one knows, often needy an' poor;
Tho' that little fault may be remedied soon,
If th' minstrel could allis get paid for his tune.
Then look what a lot their strange yarns often cost!
Just fancy five sov'rins for "Paradise Lost"!
Why, for much less than that, there are theawsands o' men
Who would not only *lose* it, but *find* it ogen!

Neaw supposin' yo bowt some good clooas to yo'r back,
Some beef-steaks an' onions, or owt o' that mak';
These would bring yo some comfort, an' help yo to live,
But yo'll dee if yo'n nowt but what poets con give.
"Only a poet"—a gazer at th' moon,
Or soarin' aloft i' some mental baloon;
Ah, some of 'em wingin' their flight to God's throne,
An' seemin' t' forget they'n a whom o' their own,
Wheer a wife may be ceaw'red in an owd tattered geawn,
Very patiently waitin' till th' husband comes deawn.
"Only a poet," a spinner o' rhymes,
An' never caught worshippin' "dollars an' dimes."

"Only a poet"—a star-gazin' bard
'At met tell yo th' earth's distance fro' th' sun to a yard;
But question him closely on trade, or bank shares,
An' he'll soon show his ignorance bi th' way 'at he stares.
Wanderin' throo' country lanes all the day long,
Gabblin' strange jargon, or croonin' some song;
Pennin' grand thowts 'at may mak' a world stare,
Then die in a mad-heawse, like poor John Clare!
Only a poet"—ah! but what does that mean?
Bein' passed bi a naybur witheawt bein' seen;
Becose just across there comes Alderman Stott,
An' he get's th' warm greetin' th' poor bard should ha' got!
"Only a poet"—he's nowt he con spare;
If his feelin's *are* hurt a bit, what need yo care?

For a poet is noan a much use as a friend,
Since he's nowt he con give one, nor nowt he con lend.
" Only a poet," so let him alone,
Or, if yo think fit, yo may fling him a bone ;
He lives o' sich stuff—bones an' owd meawldy books,
At least one would think soa, to judge by his looks.
Yo keep eawt o' th' way on him, foalks, for he's sure
To speak abeawt summat yo'n ne'er yeard befoor ;
He's likely to tell yo yo'n brains i' yo'r yead,
An' a soul that'll live when yo'r body's gone dead ;
He'll talk about spirit friends hoverin' areawnd,
When yo know they're asleep, fast asleep, deawn i'th' greawnd.

He'll offer to lead yo through nature's sweet beawers,
An' bid yo admire her grand fruitage an' fleawers.
Very grand an' poetical ; nice food for kings,
Or bein's 'at flutter abeawt us wi' wings ;
But one couldn't weel offer to clothe a bare back,
Or feed hungry bellies wi' stuff o' that mak'.
" Only a poet," like Bloomfield or Burns,
'At may happen amuse yo an' vex yo i' turns ;
Neaw charmin' his readers wi' th' thowts fro' his pen,
Thus winnin' their heartiest plaudits, an' then,
It may be th' next minute yo'r filled wi disgust
At some sarcastic hit, or some pointed home-thrust !

" *Only* a poet " ! What moor do yo want ?
Some narrow-souled parson to rave an' to rant
Abeawt th' heat an' th' dimensions, an' th' people i' hell,
Till yo fancy 'at th' chap must ha' bin' theer hissel.
Yet there are foalk i' th' world 'at don't think it amiss
To pay hundreds a year for sich twaddle as this ;
While others, entitled to love an' respect,
Are treated too often wi' scorn an' neglect !
" *Only a Poet*," what moor do yo crave,
To sweeten life's journey fro' th' cradle to th' grave ?
Which is th' likeliest—think yo—to help us along,—
An owd musty creed, or a good hearty song ?

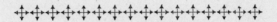

"WHAT IS HOME WITHOUT A MOTHER!"

Lines on receiving a card bearing the inscription, "What is Home Without a Mother?" the writer's wife being away at the time holiday making :—

THAT depends; if hoo's bad tempered,
　　Fond o' givin' th' bairns a "seawse,"
Puncin' th' cat for bein' hungry,
　　There's no peace when hoo's i' th' heawse.
If hoo's one 'at tak's to drinkin'—
　　Puttin' th' husband's clooos i' pop ;
One 'at never mends her stockin's,
　　Let her "tak' her hook," an' stop.

If hoo's one 'at's fond o' gossip,
　　Leavin' th' heawse i' th' childer's care ;
Puttin' th' weshin' off to Friday,
　　That's a mother we can spare.
Idle mothers, dirty slatterns,
　　Lost i' filth fro' morn to neet ;
Hair teed up wi' durty garters,
　　These are best when eawt o' th' seet.

But a mother nicely tempered ;
　　One 'at's wisdom mixed wi' mirth,
Wheer hoo dwells—yo may depend on 't—
　　Home's a little heaven on earth !
Would to God we'd moor o' this sort,—
　　Happy homes wheer concord dwells ;
Less domestic scenes o' discord,
　　Fewer heart-breaks, fewer hells !

Doctor Watts (aw think it's th' Doctor),
　　Tells us little birds agree ;
Well, if they can do beawt wranglin'
　　When together, cannot we ?
Homes are what we pleos to mak' 'em.
　　Never better, never worse ;
Some are breetened up wi' blessin's,
　　Others blighted wi' a curse.

What is home beawt prattlin' voices—
   Ringin' eawt fro' morn to neet ?
Still we never seem to miss 'em,
   Till they're dead an' eawt o' th' seet !
Home's not *walls*, but summat grander ;—
   Lovin' hearts, an' tender fleawers ;
Let's protect an' prize these jewels,
   While they're with us, while they're eawrs.

Wintry winds may come an' smite 'em,
   Smite 'em while i' youthful bloom ;
While we're feastin' on their beauties,
   Drinkin' in their sweet perfume.
What is home without a mother ?
   Lonely, cheerless, heartless, cowd ;
Wealth can never warm that homestead,
   Tho' its floors are paved wi' gowd.

Have we answered th' question fairly ?
   Come, neaw, dunno be to' hard :
Can yo hope to get owt better
   Fro' a poor an' wifeless bard ?
Birds can warble best when mated,
   Hutched together, so they sen ;
Well, aw hardly need to tell yo
   'At it's just that way wi' men.

Let th' owd brid 'at sits here mateless,
   Frettin' on a leafless tree,
Croonin' songs o' grief an' sadness,
   Once ogen his partner see ;
Then he'll tune anew his harp-strings,
   Warble once ogen i' th' grove ;
Pipe eawt notes o' hearty welcome,
   Sing to th' mate he's learned to love.

TO MY SON JOHN EDWARD ON HIS BIRTHDAY.

OHN Edward, it's thi birthday, lad: it's th' twenty-
ninth o' May:
Theaw should be gerrin' on a bit, tha'rt eight year
owd to day.
Aw recollect that Sunday morn when furst aw seed thee here;
Thi gronny had thee on her knee, sit deawn i'th' rockin' cheer.
A little tiny thing tha wur—a pratty babby too:
We wur some pleosed to see thee, mon; we did mak' some ado!
We lapped thee up i' flannel cooats, for fear tha'd get a cowd,
An' couldn't ha' cared moor for thee, choilt, iv tha'd bin made
o' gowd.

What change sin' then! thi gronny's deod, hoo'll ne'er come
here no moor,
To pick thi tops an' marbles up when t' let's 'em fo on th'
floor;
Thoose arms wheer oft tha'rn used to ceawer, han long bin
stiff an' cowd;
For when hoo deed tha'rn nobbut young—a year an' three
months owd.
Thi dear owd grondad's deod an' o, an's wi' thi gronny laid;
Not mony weeks afore he deed he bowt thee a wooden spade:
Aw recollect he coom i' th' heawse, an' hondin' it to me,
He said he'd just bin deawn to th' fair, and bowt it theer for
thee.

Soon after this bad toimes set in, when theawsands had to clem :
What made things wur for us, we'd twins, an' had to do for them ;
We'd two moor then t' rigg eawt wi' clooas, an' two moor meawths to feed ;
An' this went on for seven long months, when little Sarah deed.
We laid her in a stranger's grave ; this pains mi heart to tell ;
We thowt it hard to put her theer, an' leov her bi hersel'.
We're noan beawt troubles, then, mi lad, we'd summat t' bear tha sees :
Aw hope tha'll never ha' to feight wi pinchin toimes loike these.

Just six months after this event, another babby coom—
An' bless it ! tho' we'rn quite full up, we'rn loike to foind it room.
We co'd it Robert, doesto know ? a bonny little lad ;
An' when aw had him on mi knee aw used to feel so glad !
But summat used to tell me then 'at we should ha' to part,
An', oh ! the very thowt o' this would pierce me reet to th' heart.
Mi fears wur soon o realised—th' poor little thing geet cowd ;
He'd th' measles—an' they took him off when nobbut ten months owd.

Well, toime went draggin' on, until, one dull December morn,
We'd one moor little stranger coom, for th' " Bonny Brid " wur born.
An' bless it ! it wur welcome, too,—we'rn fain to see it come ;
Aw towd it t' try an' settle deawn, an' mak' itsel' awhoam.
Eh, lad, we wur some busy then ! we'rn welly fast, doest' see ;
We'rn short o' pobbies, clogs an' stuff, for little Joe an' thee ;
An', so to let th' choilt have a share, an' mak' things tee an' fit,
Thi mother, me, eawr Joe an' thee—we'rn forced to pinch a bit.

But, lad, aw've th' worst to tell thee yet, for th' truth mun neaw be towd,—
Thi mother ventured eawt to' soon, an' so hoo geet a cowd.
We laboured hard, an' prayed to God, that dear one's life to save ;
But o wur vain, hoo deed, an' neaw hoo's restin' in her grave.

An' Lizzie's gone! that bonny lass 'at went wi' thee to th'
     schoo';
Yo used to romp abeawt i' th' fields, an' play at bab-heawse
     too;
A lovin' little thing hoo wur, her feyther's hope an' pride;
His heart wur welly broken, lad, that mornin' when hoo died.

Aw've never held mi yead up reet sin' aw'd that heavy blow;
An' what aw've suffered i' mi moind there's very few 'at know;
Aw connot feel reet settled neaw, whatever aw may do,
But allus live i' fear an' dread lest aw should lose thee too.
It may be 'at aw shannot have this bitter draught to drink;
God may see fit to bless me moor nor aw con hope or think.
At onyrate, aw feel resolved to trust Him as 'i th' past,
These trials may prove blessin's yet, an' turn eawt reet at last.

Let's hope for th' best. Well, come, mi lad, aw think we'rn
     beawn to bake,
An', as tha loikes 'em, tha shall have a noice oon-bottom
     cake;
An' here's a penny for thee, too, tha'rt fond o' summat sweet,
So ware a haupney on it neaw,—save t' other whoile to-neet.
Neaw, then, look sharp, be off to th' schoo', aw've towd thee
     o aw want:
Tha'll foind thi bag an' slate i' th' nook, an' here's thi top an'
     bant;
Be sure tha comes streight whoam at noon, we're havin' pie
     to-day;
We allis get thee summat noice for th' twenty-ninth o' May.

TO MY FRIEND, SAMUEL ASHTON.

HOWD thi noise, Sam Ashton, wilta—
    What's this bother—o this fuss;
    Ax me t' write ogen if t' dar do,
        Tha'll be in for 't iv tha does.
Does ta think awve nowt else t' do mon—
    Only write for foalk loike thee?
Iv tha does, tha'rt off it rarely;
    Come on here, an' then tha'll see.

Tell thi friends i' Hyde an' Newton,
    Those 'at's wantin' summat new,
Aw'll noan write till awm i' th' humour,
    Now, awm beggared iv aw do!
Are o th' owd uns read aw wonder,
    Those to Wed an' Single Men?
Ax 'em—iv they sey'n they'n read 'em,
    Tell 'em t' read 'em o'er ogen.

Here I am at th' soide o' th' ocean—
　(Eh, mon, it's a whoppin' dam!)
Iv tha's never been to see it,
　Hie thee, come an' see it, Sam.
Talk abeawt that dam at th' printworks,
　On theer past th' Commercial Broo!
Why, mon, when compared wi' th' ocean,
　That owd stinkin' hole's a foo'!

Howd thi noise abeawt th' broad wayter;
　Never mention th' Brushes Clough;
Aw could sup what those contain mon,
　Iv aw're nobbut dry enough!
Mon, yo' foalk 'at live at Newton
　Ne'er see nowt worth namin' theer;
Blackpool's th' place for sights worth seein',
　Lots o' wayter sturrin' here.

Heaw art gerrin' on neaw, Sam, lad?
　Lookin' cuts aw recon yet?
Tha'll ha' thy cuts looked o'er some day,
　Tha'll be in for 't then aw'll bet.
Well, ne'er moind; heaw's th' wife an' childer—
　Mitch as usual? Well, that's reet.
We're all weel at present, thank thee;
　Compliments, owd chum—good neet.

LOINES

ONE loikes to see childer i' frolicksome glee ;
Youths an' maidens, as happy as happy can be ;
But we think a moor touchin', a nobler seet,
Is presented i' th' picture afore us to-neet.
Here are totterin' sires, wi' their silvery hairs,
An' wrinkles 'at tell us they're noan witheawt cares ;
Their owd dames—bless 'em—arno so honsome an' strong,
Nor quite as bewitchin', as when they wur young.

Toime plays weary pranks wi' these bodies o' eawrs ;
We may hang 'em wi' jewels, or deck 'em wi fleawers ;
But we're never noa better for th' trouble we'n made,
For th' jewels ull tarnish, an' th' fleawers ull o fade.
Here's owd Betty Smith—what there's left—skin an booan—
Wheer's thoose plump rosy cheeks hoo once had ?
        Ole gooan !
It's fifty long year' sin' hoorn decked as a broide,
An' trudgin' to th' church, wi' young Tim at her soide.

But tho' it's so long sin' this happen'd, aw'll bet
Th' owd dame can distinctly remember it yet ;
Just look heaw hoo's sittin' theer smilin' !   Bi th' mass !—
It's a bit ov a leetenin' up for th' owd lass.
But we'll leov her, or else ho'll be settin' her cap,
An' runnin' away wi' some other young chap ;
We munno speak eawt abeawt some foalk so leawd,
Or they'll very soon get to' conceited an' preawd.

Well, there's two dear owd foalk aw've bin ax'd just to name,
Aw meon owd Dick Brierley, an' Ailse his good dame :
No deawt they're weel known to yo all abeawt here,
As their manners are thowt rayther oddish an' queer.
We're towd 'at whenever they sit deawn to ate,
They allis contriven to do wi' one plate ;
Well, this looks rayther childish, bo' let 'em a-be,
They'n nobbut one pot to wesh-up, do yo see.

Th' owd chap drives a cart, an' says, " Aw, gee, come up,"
An' when he s bin tastin' o' summat to sup,
Th' owd brid's gradely merry, an' sings loike a lark ;—
Bless yo'r loife, it's a treat to see him at his wark!
He's eawt i' o weathers, but, still, for o that,
It's bo' seldom yo'll see him abeawt in his hat ;
An' it isn't 'at he has noan, as some foalks have said,
But becose he loikes th' air blowin' cool on his yead.

Still, tho' he's no need for his hat at his wurtch,
He dons it when goin' to Stubbins Vale Church ;
For owd Dick goes to th' church neaw an' then, do yo know ;
An' tho' he's noa idols he worships below —
Sich as wealthy employers, an' lordlin's o' th' sod,
He isn't witheawt reverence an' love for his God ;
An' he's quite as sincere i' what little he does,
As some ov his nayburs 'at mak' so mich fuss.

Well, we'll leov owd Dick Brierley, an' turn to his woife,
Who, it seems, never wore a foine geawn in her loife ;
But allis at parties hoo's seen to appear
In a plain printed bed-geawn, loike that hoo has here.
Neaw, owd Ailse is a good hond at talkin', aw'm towd ;
Hoo met wi' a parson one day i' their fowd,
'At had gone wi' th' idea 'at he'd mend her a bit,
But he soon larned 'at preitchin' to her wouldn't fit.

" Whoa art theaw, doesta recon ? theaw'rt donned very foine ;
Art a parson or summat ? Theaw looks i' that loine ;
Iv theaw art, let me tell thee theaw's no need to come,
For aw've just said mi prayers, an' eawr Dick's noan
    awhoam."
" My good woman," he said, as before her he stood,
" I have called here desiring to do you some good."
" Theaw con ne'er convart me," said owd Ailse, " go thi
    ways,
Or aw'll throw this burn-canful o' suds i' thi face !"

Well, we'll leov this strange couple, an' do th' thing 'at's
    reet:
That is—thank these good foalk 'at han gan us this treat.
There's Porritt, an' Ratcliffe, an' Maden we'll name;
An' other kind friends, who can equally claim
Eawr warm plaudits, for havin' done o' they wur able
Tort bringin' th' good things 'at we'n seen upo' th' table.
It's bo' seldom one looks at a bonnier seet
Nor these dear aged people afoor us to-neet!

God bless yo, owd foalk! thoose deep furrows declare,
'At yo'n had some hard crosses an' trials to bear;
Yo'll know what it is to ha' stood at th' bed-side
O' some favourite fleawers ere they'n wither'd an' died.
Yo'll remember that drawer wheer yo keep th' little shoon
At wur worn bi th' dear angels 'at's gone up aboon!
Well, come, dunno fret or repine o'er 'em here,
But get yorsel's ready to meet 'em up theer.

Dear owd friends, we respect, an' we honour yo, too;
After o, it's but little th' best on us can do.
Yo'r journey deawn here's gettin' close to an end,
But there's One up aboon 'at ull stond as yo'r friend.
Yo may go to Him neaw, tho' it's th' evenin' o' th' day;
Just yo try Him, owd friends—He'll noan send yo away;
An' when thoose frail bodies get knocked eawt o' tune,
Yo'r souls ull be baskin' i' bliss up aboon.

Well, neaw, mi dear friends, aw'm as set up as owt,
'At aw've getten to come to this party for nowt;
Aw live deawn at Blackpool, as some on yo know,
Wheer storm-music greets one, an' hurricanes blow;
An' often these een have beheld a grand seet,
But noa grander nor that 'at aw've witnessed to-neet;
An' o' one thing aw'm sure—aw shall never need rue,
'At aw've bin to this party at Stubbins Vale Schoo'.

MI GRONFEYTHER.

A W'VE just had a ramble to th' owd farmheawse,
  Wheer mi gronfeyther lived at so long ;
So aw'll draw eawt a bit ov a sketch, which aw hope
  Will noather be tedious nor long.
I' th' furst place, aw feel very sorry to find
  'At th' place isn't same as it wur,
For th' di'mond-shaped windows have o been pood eawt,
  An' they've ta'en th' wooden latch off th' dur.

They've shifted that seot wheer mi gronfeyther sat,
  When at neets he read th' Owd Book :
An' aw couldn't find th' nail wheer he hung up his hat,
  An' th' pot-shelf wur gone eawt o' th' nook.
There's th' dog-kennel yonder, and th' hen-cote aw see,
  An' th' cloos-prop just stonds as it did ;
There's a brid-cage hung up wheer mi gronfeyther's wur,
  But aw couldn't see owt ov a brid.

A rare fine owd fellow mi grondfeyther wur,
  Wi' a regular big Roman nose ;
An' tho' nearly eighty, he're lusty an' hale,
  An' his cheeks wur as red as a rose.
There wur nowt abeawt him 'at wur shabby or mean ;
  As to sense, well, his brain-pon wur full.
He wur allis straightforward i' o 'at he did—
  An owd-fashioned Yorkshur John Bull.

He'd a farm 'at he leased, an' a nice little pond,
  Wheer we used to go fishin' for treawt ;
An' aw haven't forgetten when th' hay-time coom reawnd,
  For we childer had mony a blow eawt.
An' when th' " heawsin' " wur done, eh, we had some rare fun,
  Wi' tipplin' an rowlin' on th' stack ;
An' then mi owd gronfeyther 'd come wi' his pipe,
  An' carry us abeawt on his back,

ASHTON BINN (*Residence of the Author's Grandfather*).
(See Poem, "MI GROSFEYTHER," on opposite Page).

Charles Auty, 99.

When aw wur a lad abeawt thirteen year' owd,
  Aw used to have mony a good ride;
For mi gronfeyther kept a young horse or two then,
  An' a donkey, but th' poor thing died.
He'd a bit ov a garden, at th' backside o' th' heawse,
  Wheer eawr Bobby an' me used to ceawer,
Eatin' goosebris, an' curran's, an' rhubard, an' crabs;
  In fact, owt wur reet 'at wur seawer.

Neaw, mi gronfeyther, bless him! reet doated o' me;
  An' he'd tell me aw geet a fine lad;
An' he'd mony a time say—as aw've sat on his knee,—
  "Eh, bless thee! tha favours thi dad!"
Then he'd say to mi gronny, "Gie th' lad here some spice,"
  An', whenever hoo happened to bake,
He'd tell her to reach deawn a pot o' presarves,
  An' mak' me a nice presarve cake.

Well, he's long been gone; but a kinder owd mon
  Ne'er existed than Abram wur!
Th' last time aw wur o'er theer, an' saw him alive,
  He wur sittin' eawtside his dur.
He geet howd o' mi hond when we parted that day,
  An' aw think aw shall never forget
Heaw he looked i' mi face when aw're goin' away:
  It wur th' last time 'at ever we met!

A week or two after th' owd fellow 'd a stroke;
  An' fell off his cheer on to th' floor;
They lifted him up, an' they took him to bed,
  But he never wur gradely no moor.
Good-bye, dear owd gronfeyther! nob'dy i' th' world
  Could be fonder than aw wur o' thee;
An', if in th' future dear bonds are renewed,
  Tha'rt one 'at aw'm hopin' to see!

READ ON THE OCCASION OF A PRESENTATION
TO EDWIN WAUGH, APRIL 11TH, 1887.

WELL, aw'm fain thi good friends here have gan thee
    this stick,
    To help thee a bit on th' way here while wick.
    It connot i' thy case be truthfully said,
'At th' honour's kept back till th' poor author's gone dead.
Mon, these Lancashire foalk are a warm-hearted lot;
They only want ticklin' a bit i' th' reet spot,
An' tha's managed to do this job grandly, owd brid,—
Soa as noa other songster i' th' grove ever did.

So tha'rt seventy year' owd, friend, thi toppin's turned grey ;
It's wi' thee as wi' me—gettin' latish i' th' day.
These cuts 'at we're weavin' will soon be wove eawt ;
An', Edwin, they aren't quite faultless, aw deawt.
But whoa is there perfect, beawt blemish or spot ?
One weaver i' th' world, Ned ?   Aw rayther think not.
There'll be flaws feawnd i' th' pattern, an' faults among th'
    fleawers,
If their work's nobbut held up to th' leet same as eawrs.

Well, for mitch 'at aw've done, Waugh, aw have to thank thee ;
When aw furst saw " Come Whoam to thi Childer an' Me,"
It worked on mi mind like a charm or a spell ;
Th' result wur—aw started o' scribblin' misel' !
It's to thee 'at aw owe mi *furst* Lancashire lay ;
It's for thee 'at aw'm croonin' this *last* one to-day ;
But we're noan here to listen to owt abeawt *me*,
But to mak' thee a present, an' talk abeawt *thee*.

Tha'rt seventy year' owd, an' for th' hawve o' that time,
We've fairly been charmed wi' thi Lancashire rhyme.
Tha started wi' mendin' up th' fire wi' a cob,
An' puttin' some nice bacon collops on th' hob ;
An' tha's kept goin' on till we'n roared at thi wit,
Or been melted to tears at some tenderish bit.
If we'n sixpence to spare, an' dull axes to grind,
Tha's gan us a hint wheer we're likely to find—

A soft-lookin' lad—very mitch like a foo'—
'At would rayther turn hondles nor go to a schoo'.
Still, aw think tha macks Enoch a trifle to' bad,
I' keepin' that sixpence he promised to th' lad ;
An' it doesn't mend th' matter—at least to my mind—
Enoch givin' th' young urchin " a lifter behind."
After o, it's a sample o' th' world's cruel tricks ;
Even poets must get fewer haupneys nor kicks.

Well, worthy owd songster, it's pleasin' to see
Heaw thi grateful admirers are honourin' thee.
Tha'rt sure ov a pension as long as tha'rt wick ;
Th' other week tha'd a banquet ; to-day tha's a stick;
But what are grand banquets, or purses o' gowd,
To a Lancashire poet 'at's seventy year' owd !
Mon, tha'd rayther walk eawt i' th' breet sunshine, an' sing,
Than be petted an' placed on a throne as a king !

We're honourin' thee *neaw*, while tha'rt livin', tha sees ;
An' not keepin' back these good things till tha dees.
'At we love an' respect thee we want thee to *know* ;
But heaw con we tell thee when sleepin' below !
Costly urns raised to worth may be ole reet enuff,
But to thoose 'at have left us it's useless puff.
An' it's seldom these matters get into one's yead,
Till th' scribbler's been hurried fro' th' warkheawse—dead !

But we're rayther moor fair to these wielders o' th' pen ;
While we prize th' gowden eggs we tak' care o' th' hen.
We're preawd o' eawr bards here, an' th' bit 'at we give,—
While it softens their death pangs, it helps 'em to live.
There's no jealousy here among th' bards ; oh, no ;
An' there's no need there should be ; there's reawm for us o.
On one point at least aw feel perfectly clear,
Tha'll play on th' furst fiddle so long as tha'rt here !

Aw'm content wi' a meaner place, somewheer at th' back ;
Turnin' th' leovs o'er for th' players, or owt o' that mack.
Mon, aw shouldn't consider aw're stoopin' to' low
If aw pieced thee thi strings up, an' rosin'd thi bow.
It's respect for th' owd bard 'at's induced me to come
Fro' th' comforts an' joys o' mi sea-side whoam ;
But aw'll risk gettin' cowd—ah, aw'll risk a damp bed,
To tak' part in a meetin' to honour thee, Ned !

Tha'rt seventy year' owd ; may thi last days be th' best ;
May th' owd brid long be spared in his snug, cosy nest !
Tha'd warbled thi notes, an' tha'd addled thi wage,—
Ere some o' us brids had been hatched i' th' cage ;
An' we're feelin' to-day 'at it's time to begin
To do what we owt to have done long sin !
Heawever, we're glad 'at tha'rt lookin' so wick,
An' hope tha'll be spared to mak' use o' that stick.

When tha's that i' thi hond—as tha'rt trudgin' on th' way,
Tha'll think o' thi friends, an' this meetin' to-day ;
An', noa deawt, tha'll have larned—fro' present we've browt,—
'At tha hasn't been livin' an' thinkin' for nowt ;—
But 'at th' country 'at's th' honour o' givin' thee birth
Has decided, tho' late, to acknowledge thi worth.
Perhaps we may venture to hope an' expect
'At tha'll kindly forgive us for past neglect.

Aw'm obliged to mi friends here for bein' so kind
As to gie me this chance to unburden mi mind ;
As aw've hinted before, worthy friend, I for one,
Feel indebted to thee for a deol 'at aw've done.
Tha's lit up life's journey wi' mony a breet ray,
For which let me publickly thank thee to-day !
An' i' th' last words aw'll say ole will join me, aw'm sure,—
May God's blessin' rest on thi *own* silver yure !

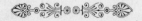

A LANCASHIRE CANDIDATE FOR THE LAUREATESHIP.

READ AT THE CHRISTMAS DINNER OF THE MANCHESTER LITERARY
CLUB, DECEMBER 20TH, 1892.

IT'S but seldom one gets to these dooments;
   But aw find—when aw do get a chance—
    Tho' so little, retirin' an' modest,
      Aw seem to be "spotted" at once.
To me yo'll be th' mooast on yo strangers,
   So aw might ha' slipp'd in unseen,
But there's one or two keen-seeted stagers
   Keep a sharpish look-eawt wi' their een.

There's eawr worthy owd President Milner—
   Beg pardon, sir, hope aw'm forgiven;
But aw really believe 'at he'd know me,
   If he happen'd to meet me i' heaven!
Of course he'd be struck wi' amazement,
   An' think aw wur eawt o' mi sphere,
But aw should be just as asteawnded
   An' stagger'd at seein' him theer.

Well, this is a joke, an' a bad un,
   An' aw'm freetened yo'll tak' it amiss,
To be drawn here fro' o' parts o' th' country,
   To hearken sich stuff as this.
An' gentlemen, to', men o' letters,
   White-choker'd men, trained for th' "tub,"
Cracked poets, an' college professors,
   An' ole members o' th' Literary Club.

Why, it's awful! an' comin' fro' Blackpool
   Yo'd hardly expect sich thrash,
Sich thowtless an' meanin'less twaddle,
   Sich a senseless an' tasteless hash.
So aw'll put a fresh cop i' mi shuttle,
   That is, if it's reet to yo ;
An' aw'll tell yo a bit ov a secret,
   'At aw think yo owt to know.

As Alf. Tennyson's post is still vacant,
   An' aw'm weary o' ceawrin' bi' th' hob,
An' findin' mi brains gettin' reawsty,
   Aw'm determined to try for th' job.
So stond o' one side yo young rhymsters,
   " Nunquam," " Walt. Whitman, jun.," an' " Boggs ;"
Clear away eawt o' th' field' an' be handy
   Or aw'll help yo a bit wi' mi clogs.

Not fit to be th' Laureate !   Who says so ?
   Aw con fancy aw hear somb'dy yell,
" There's another chap slipp'd em' at Prestwich,
   An' a poet, 'at connot e'en spell."
What care I for their jeers an' fine larnin' :
   Their A.S.S. or D.D.'s ?
Is it likely 'at Tennyson's mantle
   Will fall on sich " cads " as these ?

Not it ; an' aw think Mr. Gladstone
   Will noan ha' mitch trouble to see,
'At there's only one chap in creation
   'At th' mantle 'll fit, an' that's me !
What's that ? have aw had ony practice ?
   Well, well, aw should think aw have that !
Have'nt aw penn'd " Mi Experience i' th' Warkheawse,"
   An' a lyric on th' " Death of a Cat ?"

An' this isn't ole 'at aw con do ;
　　Aw've lots o' ideas i' mi knob,
Grand thowts 'at are ready for hatchin',
　　Just suited for th' rhyme-makin' job.
Neaw, aw should'nt need mitch of a pension,
　　Aw could manage to think a good think,
An' put my ideas on to papper,
　　Witheawt oather 'bacco or drink.

Aw could write what aw knew to be wanted,
　　Mak' mi rhymes oather merry or sad ;
An' as to political matters,
　　Aw could oather be Tory or Rad.
Neaw, aw'm noan very strong on religion—
　　A failin' mi friends must ha' seen ;
Aw'm deficient i' reverence for parsons,
　　An' turnin' up th' white o' mi een.

Still, this should'nt go mitch against me,
　　For dunnot aw every day see
Foalk 'at do sich like tricks to perfection,
　　'At couldn't howd a candle to me !
If thoose i' high places were guilty
　　O' panderin' to filth an' vice,
Aw could mak' 'em appear as pure angels,
　　An' turn 'em eawt clean an' nice.

Well, isn't ole this i' mi favour ?
　　Need Gladstone to bother his brains—
As to who pipes th' best an' th' sweetest,
　　An' turns eawt th' grandest strains ?
If he'll send me a ticket for Lunnon,
　　Aw'll go theer, an' get on th' scales,
An' he'll see 'ut aw'm weight for a Morris,
　　Or owt they can find i' Wales.

Aw should like an engagement o' some mak',
    For mi brains are fast runnin' to waste,
An' this shop 'at neaw waits for a tenant,
    Is exactly the one to my taste.
Aw should never succeed as a lawyer;
    Mi ideas are to' strange for a " tub,"
So as th' rhyme mill's i' th' market, aw'll run it
    For ten " Bob " a week an' mi grub.

Aw may tell yo, bi th' way o' conclusion,
    'At it's said 'at aw'm th' favoured pet ;—
'At th' other rhyme spinners are nowheer ;
    But, of course, its noan sattled yet.
Well, aw'm pleased to be with yo this evenin' ;
    As yo know, its but seldom aw come ;
But a chap 'at imagines he's poorly,
    Is best at his sea-side whoam.

Aw've oft felt ashamed o' mi absence,
    An' wish aw could mak' some amends
For what may appear as indifference,
    Or a slight upon you, dear friends.
As a club we have had eawr changes,
    We've experienced booath kisses an' kicks,
Sin' yo did me th' great honour aw'm preawd of,
    I' Eighteen Sixty-Six.

Death's robbed these Christmas parties ;
    For some we were wont to greet
Wi' brotherly love an' affection
    Are sadly missed to-neet !
Thank God, we have still Ben Brierley ;
    Like mysel', he's grey wi' age ;
We're waitin' for th' curtain fallin',
    An' th' order to come off th' stage.

A few more brotherly greetin's,
    An' a few more peeps at th' sun,
Then life's excitin' battles
    Will oather be lost or won !

READ AT A MEETING HELD AT MOSSLEY, TO CELEBRATE MR. WILLIAM HEAP'S 60TH BIRTHDAY.

A'M reet glad to be wi' yo this evenin' ;
    For nothin' soa peawerfully tends
    To leeten an' sweeten life's journey
      As these meetin's o' dear owd friends.
For th' crosses an' th' cares ov a lifetime
    Soa harras an' worry a mon,
'At aw hardly need say it behoves him
    T' get from 'em as mitch as he con ;—

Not bi wilfully shirkin' one's duties
    Or eawr lawful engagements to shun,—
But wi' mixin' one's pains up wi' pleasure,
    An' sweetenin' th' physic wi' fun.
Soa lay yo'rsel's eawt for enjoyment ;
    Let noa sign o' sorrow be seen ;
Noa mournin' man's many misfortunes,
    Or turnin' up th' white o' yo'r een.

True, there may be a time for reflection,
    For sadly bewailin' one's lot ;
For balancin' gains against losses,—
    But certainly this isn't th' spot.
Soa, Frank, bring thi favourite fiddle,
    An' scrape eawt a bit ov a tune ;
An', tho' th' wintry wind whistles wildly,
    We'll mack things look lively, an' soon !

Come, Burgess, thee square eawt thi pappers,
    An' prepare for a slashin' report,
For we're fairly on th' job, aw con tell thee ;
    We're in for a neet o' good sport.
Mon, there'll be a rare sale for th' *Reporter* ;
    Soa mind 'at tha lays in enoo ;
Foalks 'll want to scan o'er these proceedin's,
    To see who's been th' bigg'st foo !

We've come fro' ole parts o' th' creation;—
　　Well,—aw mean that creation reawnd here;
Aw've come trailin' to Mossley fro' Blackpool,
　　To read this stuff, an' drink smo'-beer!
Eawr worthy friend Bardsley's fro' Owdham,
　　Wheer it's said they float Hencoats an' things;
Wheer they eat cheese an' "tommy" i' th' neet time,
　　For th' poor, paltry "divi." it brings.

Well, then, we've eawr friend William Heap here;—
　　Th' dear guest we've to honour to-neet.
As aw said th' other week on at Blackpool,—
　　We're intendin' to do this job reet.
We've talent enuff i' this meetin'
　　'At—when it gets fairly drawn eawt,
An' th' listeners are leawdly applaudin',
　　They'll hear us i' Yorkshire, noa deawt.

Well, this is friend William Heap's birthday;—
　　At onyrate—that's what aw'm towd;
An', tho' he may noan like to hear it,—
　　He's neaw getten sixty year' owd.
'At he'll live to see mony moor birthdays,
　　Is what we're ole hopin', aw'm sure.
A brid 'at can warble like he con,
　　Should live to a hundred or moor.

Well, aw've been rayther selfish wi' th' footbo;
　　'An it's time someb'dy else had a kick;
But aw'm gettin' to th' end o' mi tether,
　　An' shapin' for cuttin' mi stick.
Aw'm freetened aw've wearied the spectators,
　　Wi' th' very poor play aw've supplied;
For—tho' aw've noan given mony "corners,"
　　Aw've often been playin' "off-side."

But this 'll do noan, friends, aw'm ramblin' ;
  An' must have a slate off mi thatch ;
Aw'd getten th' idea aw're at Blackpool,
  Tackin' part in a footbo' match !
An', aw'm here, at a Literary gatherin',
  'Mong poets, an' writers for th' press ;
An' th' Mayor o' Mossley here near me !
  Well, aw've getten misel' in a mess.

Shades o' Byron, Burns, Shelly, an' Wordsworth ;
  Ah, an' th' muse o' th' reneawned " Poet Close,"
Come, lend a poor chap yo'r assistance
  An' pity his follies an' woes.
Lead me eawt into climes moor congenial,—
  Wheer th' surreawndin's moor pleasure can yield ;
An' th' ideas are mitch purer an' grander
  Than we get in a footbo' field.

Ave bards, an' professors o' music,
  To be fed wi' sich fodder as this !
Are these to be th' heights they're to climb to,
  To reach intellectual bliss !
Well, friends, aw'm reet glad to be wi' yo,
  To join i' yo'r music an' song ;
For, to my mind, i' meetin's o' this sort,
  We connot get very far wrong.

We shall ole be good lads here this evenin',
  As His Worship the Mayor will see ;
That is, iv yo'll tak' my example,
  An' drink yarb beer, like me.
Well, thank yo for th' kind invitation
  Yo Mossley foalk thowt fit to send ;
For aw'm sure it affords me great pleasure
  To join yo i' honourin' eawr friend.

READ AT A BAND OF HOPE MEETING AT
SOUTH SHORE.

HEN axed bi eawr friend, Mr. Newsholme, to come
here an' help yo a bit,
    Instead ov a deawnright refusal, an' shewin' some
wisdom an' wit,
I alleawed him to tak' an advantage—attack th' weakest part
ov a mon ;
So must neaw 'at aw've got i' this hobble, get eawt on't as weel
as aw con.
But what con aw do for yo, bless yo! or heaw con aw help
yo' along ?
Yo'n surely no need for reciters, when yo'n get so mitch music
and song.
If aw gave " Bowton's Yard," or th' " Owd Bellman," yo met
tell me yo'd yeard it before ;
An' it certainly wouldn't be pleasant to come an' be snubbed
as a " bore."

Aw've travelled life's journey soa long, friends, that aw feel aw
could do wi' a rest ;
An' aw think it would sometimes be better iv yo left th' owd
brid in his nest.
Aw've been toilin' i' my simple way, sir, for close upo' fifty
long years ;
Th' seed's sometimes been sown wi' rejoicin', at other times
waytered wi' tears.
A writer stands mitch like a farmer ; th' seed sown may be
perfectly seawnd,
But to get a good crop we've to see to boath' th' state an' th'
position o' th' greawnd.
Th' surreawndin's will have to be genial, on th' surface as weel
as at th' root,
If th' sower's t' be paid for his labour, an' his heart to be
gladdened wi' th' fruit.

We're here, at this Band of Hope meetin', wheer we're tryin'
   to sow *good* seed ;

Is it likely to grow to perfection, or will it be choked wi' weed ?

Will th' enemy come here i' th' neet time, an' secretly sow his
   tares ?

Must these childer' be blasted an' blighted wi' legalised traps
   an' snares ?

We shall never succeed i' eawr efforts while feightin' wi'
   Nature's laws ;

We can never get rid ov *effect* till we set to an' stamp eawt th'
   cause !

Can we hope to keep th' little uns sober, while their parents
   are dabblin' i' th' cup ?

If th' example they set brings their deawnfall, what's th' use o'
   us poikin' 'em up ?

Here these childer are gethered areawnd us—are their lives to
   be blest or curst ?

Are these plants 'at we value so dearly—at we've carefully
   trained an' nurst—

Are these to be left uncared for, or heartlessly flung i' th'
   ditch ?

Is it needful 'at these should be *beggared* to gie others a chance
   to get *rich ?*

It's a terrible battle we're wagin'—a wearisome uphill feight !

A conflict 'tween Good an' Evil—a struggle 'tween Wrong an'
   Reight !

It's sad, an' one connot help feelin' a certain degree o' disgust,

When th' heartless an' Godless are chosen for places o' honour
   an' trust !

Need we wonder at moral reformers—seein' matters so mitch
   eawt o' square—

Should be tempted to strip off their armour, an' throw th' job
   up i' despair ?

Havin' given up ease an' home-comforts, to labour for justice
   an' reet,

They're looked on as fools an' fanatics, an' shunned when
   they're met i' th' street.

Aw dar say yo'll some on yo wonder why aw've chosen soa
   mournful a theme,

An' perhaps yo'll be tempted to call it a purely poetical dream ;

A dream ! when one's brothers and sisters are fallin' on every
   hond !

An' slayers an' th' slain eawr own nayburs, browt up in a
   Christian lond.

A dream ! when we know 'at eawr loved ones, 'at we're doin'
  eawr best to save,
May be heartlessly drawn into th' whirlpool—dragged deawn
  to a drunkard's grave !
Aw should like to pen summat moor cheerful, at a season when
  all should be glad,
But th' surreawndin's at present are gloomy, an' one connot
  help feelin' sad.
" There's a time," soa Solomon tells us, " for everything under
  the sun,"
A time for serious reflection, as weel as a time for fun ;
While Rachael mourns loss of her childer, shall we be unfeelin'
  as stone,
An' foldin' our arms unconcernedly, leave her to suffer alone ?

Yes, we'd like to hear summat moor hopeful, an' iv we could
  have eawr own wills
We should all select joy before sorrow—tak' puddin's i'
  preference to *pills*.
Would a doctor, when called in to tackle some dangerous an'
  deadly disease,
Gi'e th' patient a paper o' toffy, 'cause he knows ut that toffy
  may *please* ?
Would treatment o' this kind be honest, or e'en his *own*
  interests advance ?
Wouldn't he show more discretion an' wisdom by skilfully
  using his lance ?
Can *I*, as a teacher o' morals, successfully tackle a wrong,
Or rouse up mi audience to duty wi' a humorous Lancashire
  song ?

It's pleasant to come to these meetin's, wheer all seems so
  hopeful an' breet,
But what o' eawr brothers an' sisters, 'at are creawdin' reawnd
  th' vaults to-neet ?
Must th' Spoiler go on desolatin', still wantonly crush these
  fleawers ?
An' shall we stand by unconcerned, an' say it's noa business o'
  eawrs ?
That poor tattered thing 'at's i' th' gutter, 'at they'n flung eawt
  o' th' " Piebald Ceaw,"
Wur once as pure an' as happy as these dear little childer are
  neaw !
What changes these angels to demons—fro' which thoose 'at
  love 'em must shrink ?
It's th' curse 'at's induced me to scribble, an' scribble so
  savagely—*drink* !

Let th' childer go in for enjoyment, that only seems nat'ral an'
    reight ;
But *men* should tak' lessons fro' th' "Redskins," an' show
    they're determined to feight ;
Not wi' foes in imagination, conceived in a poet's brain,—
Mere fleshless phantoms o' fancy, 'at yo'r shots may strike i'
    vain,
But a foe ever lurkin' i' ambush, an' secretly tryin' to steal
Whatever is noblest an' fairest, or adds to this country's weal ;
Yo'r minister here—Mr. Newsholme—invited me here to *recite*,
But yo see 'at aw've felt it mi duty to tak up mi pen an' *write*.

Noa deawt, when yo looked at yo'r programmes, yo'd think
    yo wur in for some fun,
But, instead o' mi frolicsome fiddle, yo'll see 'at aw've browt
    mi gun ;
Still, aw haven't mitch taste for feightin', aw'd a theawsand times
    sooner play,
But there's sich a thing known as a conscience, 'at we're
    sometimes beawnd to obey.
When dram-shops are turned into churches, an' breweries made
    into schools ;
When swords are converted to ploughshares, or harmless an'
    useful tools ;
When toilers reap th' fruit o' their labours, an' plenty an' peace
    shall abeawnd ;—
If these glorious reforms should be won, before aw'm put
    deawn i' th' greawnd ;—

Aw *may* look up summat moor tasty fro' eawt o' mi curious
    store,
Attempt once ogen to amuse yo, as aw've oftentimes done
    before ;
But time an' tide wait for no man, an' age creeps on, as yo
    know ;
While reforms an' praiseworthy movements, are nat'rally tardy
    an' slow.
But, puttin' eawr shoulders to th' wheels, friends, we may help
    th' car o' progress along ;
An' tho' not permitted to join in that grand, triumphant song ;
These childer, neaw gathered areawnd us, whose cause we are
    pleadin' to night,
May join in this song o' thanksgivin', an' *we may look deawn
    on th' sight !*

Q

Aw wish yo success at South Shore here; an' tho' neaw in a humble way,

Yo'r doin' good wark wi' these childer, 'at may cheer yo'r hearts some day;

These plants 'at yo'r carefully trainin', are certain to thrive an' bloom,

An' repay yo for ole yo'r labours, wi' grateful an' lastin' perfume;

These soldiers yo'r trainin' for th' army, 'at we look on wi' hope an' pride,

Will carry on th' battle for Temperance, when we shall be laid aside;

So aw wish yo success, Mr. Newsholme, an' thank yo for havin' seen fit,

To ax an owd Temperance worker to come here an' help yo a bit.

LIFE.

IFE'S a wearisome journey to travel;
    A battle wi' sun an' wi' dust;
A terrible feight for existence,—
    A shelter, a drink, an' a crust!
It's a voyage across a wild ocean,
    Wheer treacherous winds oft blow;
An' wheer we may get to' at th' finish,—
    Its certain we none of us know.

Its a *race* for a goal 'at we see not;
    A conflict wi' th' world an' sin;
An' th' greawnd bein' so hard t' get over,
    A deol ov us have to give in;—
A *game* we may ole tak' a part in;—
    Some failin' while others may score:—
A *play*, an' we're everyone actors,
    Till th' curtain falls deawn, an' ole's o'er.

JOHN BULL.

Tune: "John Brown."

W'VE noa guinea aw con spend,
Aw've a woife, but hoo's noa friend—
Bringin' hungry little childer
Into th' world, John Bull.
Aw've a cottage—not mi own—
It belongs to Smith, i' th' lone,
An' mi garden fleawers are droopin'
Same as me, John Bull.
Here aw'm sittin' at mi door,
Bearin' ills aw connot cure,
Keepin' th' " bumbs " fro' tackin' th' stuff
To pay mi "tithes," John Bull.
So if theaw mi cot should pass,
Tha'll get neither poipe nor glass,
But aw'll tell thee what aw love
An' what aw hate, John Bull.

Aw love thoose songs o' th' birds,
An' mi childer's winnin' words,
An' a woman, when hoo's talkin'
Common sense, John Bull.
But aw hate to yer their tongues
Allis pratin' o'er their wrongs,
When they owt to shut their meawths
An' fall asleep, John Bull !
Aw'm fond o' pratty fleawers,
Lover's walks an' shady beawers,
An' aw love a honest heart
'At's free fro' guile, John Bull.
But aw hate those cunnin' knaves
'At would mack their nayburs slaves ;
Drones should never live o' th' honey
Th' bees have made, John Bull.

Neaw, aw love a good owd song,
One 'at raps at vice an' wrong,
An' raises hope i' th' breasts
O' th' good an' pure, John Bull;
But aw hate thoose tricks o' thine,
Steppin' o'er thi nayburs line,
Robbin' other people's gardens—
Oh, forshame! John Bull.
If there's one thing 'at aw hate,
It's thy cunnin' an' decate,—
Th' way tha'rt shufflin' wi' th' nayburs
Ole reawnd, John Bull.
Sich loike conduct pains mi mind,
An' mi heart may seem unkind,
But aw never can excuse
Sich faults as these, John Bull.

But, if tha'll mend thi ways,
Tha may yet see better days,
An' thi nayburs may respect thee
As i' th' past, John Bull.
Let ole envious feelin's sink;
Th' world's noan thine tha need'nt think;
Spend thi brass o' stuff 'at's useful
If tha'rt wise, John Bull.
An' don't be over nice,
Tack this bit o' good advice,—
Plain an' whoamly an' unpolish'd
Tho' it be, John Bull.
Aw shall keep mi conscience clear,
Tho' I live a theawsand year'.
An' get nowt to eat but porritch
Ole mi loife, John Bull!

JOHN PARKINSON,
A Member of the Blackpool Lifeboat Crew.

OOD-BYE a bit, John ; we shall meet ogen soon ;
    Aw shall noan be long after, tha'll see ;
  So aw want thee—when settled i' th' mansions aboon,
    To look eawt for a place for me.
Tha'll know what'll suit me—a bit ov a spot
  Aw con ceawer in, an' feel 'at it's mine ;
Just a few simple fleawers reawnd a plain-lookin' cot,
  An' let it be nearish to thine.

As a naybur an' friend, John, aw feawnd tha wur true ;
  When tha piped aw wur tempted to dance ;
An' aw think we could manage Eternity throo'—
  That is—iv we'd nobbut th' chance.
Aw went to thi berrin' ! an', dear-a-me, John,
  Sich a seet aw've but seldom seen !
There wur theawsands o' foalks stood watchin' it, mon,
  An' they'd th' mooast on 'em tears i' their een !

It's not merely th' public 'at's mournin' their loss,
  But it's thoose 'at's lost husband an' dad ;
Th' poor mother wur fairly weighed deawn wi' her cross,
  An' th' childer wur just as bad.
Th' tall, wasted form 'at tha left behind,
  We reverently put into th' greawnd ;
Feelin' certain at dear Mother Earth 'll be kind,
  An' thi sleep undisturbed an' seawnd.

This isn't to th' dead husk, but to th' livin' grain ;
  Aw'm speakin' to John hissel !
To th' spirit, an' not to th' lifeless brain ;
  To th' kernel, an' not to th' shell !
Aw'm aware these 'll strike some as strangish views ;
  An' one's lots o' times yeard it said
'At nobody but idiots an' crazy foo's
  Would pretend to converse wi' th' dead.

Well, they may be reet, an' th' writer wrong;
　　We're none of us feawnd o'er breet;
But these are mi thowts, an' they're put i' mi song,
　　Becose aw believe 'em reet.
Shall aw get a response?　Well, it's hard to say;
　　But supposin' aw don't get a word,—
Must silence be ta'en as a proof 'at mi lay
　　Has noather been read or heard?

Well, good-bye a bit, John; we shall meet ogen soon,
　　Wheer th' sun never hides his rays;
Wheer there's never a veil o'er th' face o' th' moon,
　　Nor gloomy November days.
Wheer tha's cast anchor on th' gowden strand,
　　There'll be no storms to brave;
No oars to grasp, no boats to be man'd,
　　Nor shipwrecked foalk to save!

TO A CRICKET.

ING on, there's nobbut thee an' me;
　　We'll mack th' heawse ring, or else we'll see.
　　Thee sing thoose little songs o' thine,
　　As weel as t' con, an' aw'll sing mine.
We'll have a concert here to-neet,
Soa pipe thi notes eawt clear an' sweet:
Thee sing a stave or two for me,
An' then aw'll sing a bit for thee.
That's reet, goa on, mi little guest,
Theaw tries to do thi very best,
An' aw'll do th' same, then thee an' me
May get eawr names up yet tha'll see.
Why, th' childer's listenin' neaw at th' door;
There's creawds abeawt! there is, forshure.
Heaw pleosed they seem—dear little things!
Aw'd sooner sing for them than kings.

ON RECEIVING A LETTER FROM A FRIEND WHO HAD PREVIOUSLY WRITTEN ANOTHER ONE, BUT HAD NEGLECTED TO POST IT.

EAR D., thy epistle has just come to hand ;
An', lookin' it o'er, aw con weel understand
Heaw mi worthy owd friend would be taken a-back,
When he feawnd 'at his letter wur still i' th' rack.
But his version—'at "spirits" to Owdham might tramp,
To collar his letter' an' tak' off th' stamp,—
Or prevent this same missive fro' comin' to me,—
Well, this explanation aw connot just see.

My experience o' "spirits" would leod me to think
'At they'd ne'er visit Owdham—unless they're "i' drink."
Noa respectable ghost would go sully it' wings,
Or seek penny stamps among chimneys an' things.
No, mi worthy friend D., gie th' spirits fair play,
An' clear this mishap up i' some other way.
Mon, aw think yo' good Owdham foalk rayther to' cute,
To throw blame on a *tune* 'at belongs to th' *flute*.

Aw'm obliged for thoose kindly remarks 'at tha's made ;
An', comin' fro' one like thee 'at's "i' th' trade,"
Aw'm sure tha's noa interest or wish to deceive ;
Nor would tha pen deawn what tha doesn't believe.
An', mon, aw feel preawdish o' th' wark 'at aw've done,
Neaw aw know it's admired booath bi thee an' thi son.
As tha says—aw've long tried, i' mi own simple style,—
To help an' encourage th' poor childer o' toil.

An'—to use an owd Lancashire word—aw'm " fain"
To know 'at aw haven't been toilin' i' vain ;
But 'at th' seed 'at aw've sown in a humble way —
Is springin' to life 'neath a friendly ray ;
For opinions like thine—fro' ole prejudice freed—
Aw prize an' esteem very highly indeed ;
An' must try—for a short time at least—not to " meawt,"
But push these owd quills o' mine still further eawt.

In a postscript to th' letter tha'rt pleased to state,
'At, iv aw'll observe, aw shall see fro' th' date,
'At thi letter wur written on March twenty-nine ;
An' then tha assures mi i' th' very next line,—
After swearin' on schoo books' or owt i' thi way—
'At tha posted ole th' lot on th' 30th o' May.
Well, it certainly looks like a trick o' some ghost,—
'At aw've this some three weeks ere it's put into th' post !

But Owdham foalks do some queer things, we must own ;
Still, this one is th' queerest 'at ever aw've known.
An' yet, after ole's said, aw've not the least deawt,
But mi friend D. will wriggle an' worm hissel' eawt.
If a " brave Owdham roughyead " should ever get fast,
Wi' owt 'at belongs oather th' present or th' past,—
Th' great Ruler o' ole things may fling off his robe,
An' say it's quite time he should wind up th' globe !

Aw'll send thee thi letter back, then tha may see
What it is 'at's so seriously botherin' me.
After ole, friend D., it could never be meant
'At aw should read letters before they're sent.
But, really, aw musn't be wastin' thi time,
Or expose mi own folly wi' foolish rhyme ;
But dunno neglect puttin' letters i' th' post,
An' then throw th' blame on some wanderin' ghost.

TO MY BROTHER JOHN, ON HIS SIXTY-FIRST
BIRTHDAY.

MY compliments, dear brother John;
　　Tha'rt sixty-one to-day, owd mon;
　　Tha'rt nobbut wantin' nineteen moor
　　To mak' thee ten past up—fourscoor.
An' aw keep followin' close behind;
An', same as thee—gone grey, aw find.
Sixty-one! what hopes an' fears!
What joys an' sorrows, smiles an' tears!

But aw've no wish at ole, mi lad,
To mak' a brother's birthday sad;
So here aw feel inclined to stop,
An' let this painful subject drop;
For life to us—like other foalks—
Has been mixed up wi' groans an' jokes;
An', while we've had eawr gloomy heawers,
We've had th' breet sun, an' th' bonny fleawers.

An' neaw we're gettin' on i' life,
An's past thro' mooast o' th' toil an' strife
'At meets us on eawr pathway here,—
Aw think there's nowt one needs to fear.
Why should we fret becose we soon
May have to meet eawr friends aboon?
It surely connot give us pain,
To meet these loved one's once again.

Well, thowts come slowly; an' tha'll see
Mi rhymes are rayther lawm—like me;
But then—tha's gan me little time,
To put a birthday wish i' rhyme.
Aw'll only say " Aw wish thee health;
A moderate share o' this world's wealth
Well,—not a lot o' useless stuff,—
Tha'll never need, but just enuff."

WHAT AW LOIKE TO SEE.

TTENTION, please, an' look at me,
An' aw'll tell yo what aw loike to see;
Neaw aw loike to see foalk doin' weel—
Heaw glad it allis makes one feel!
For tho' aw'm gettin' grey an owd
Mi heart is noather hard nor cowd;
Aw feel as free an' strong on th' wing
As when aw furst began to sing.

Aw loike to ceawer mi deawn i' th' nook
An' read a bit fro' some noice book.
Good books are th' thowtful student's gowd—
They'll pleos an' bless booath young an' owd.
Aw loike to join i' th' evenin' song
When th' days are short an' th' neets are long;
Aw loike to mix wi' th' good an' true
To spend a pleasant heawr or two.

Aw loike to tak' a walk at neet,
When th' moon an' stars are shoinin' breet;
When th' fleawers have shut their een' an' said
" Good neet " to th' dew' an' gone to bed;
When youths are walkin' eawt i' th' grove
Wi' th' maidens 'at they fondly love,
An' many an artless lover's tale
Is borne along on th' evenin' gale.

Aw loike to yer a good owd song,
Uphowdin' th' right, deneawncin' wrong;—
A song 'at cheers one on his way
An' points him to a breeter day; —
A song o' gratitude to Heaven
For th' sheawers o' mercies freely given;—
A song o' thankfulness an' love
Fro' man below to God above.

Aw loike to see an aged pair
Ceawered side bi side wi' silvery hair,
Waitin' wi' anxious tearful eyes
A call to "mansions in the skies."
Aw loike to read o' noble deeds,
Wheer rich men see to poor men's needs,
An' love to stretch their hands to bless
An' comfort thoose i' deep distress.

Aw loike mi friends, mi country too,
An' everythin' 'at's good an' true ;
Aw'm fond o' rhymes, an' neaw an' then
Aw loike to tak' mi humble pen
An' paint some thowt 'at pleoses me
For other curious minds to see ;
An' tho' mi pictur's fail to please
Aw'm satisfied an' feel at ease.

Aw'm fond o' trees, aw'm fond o' fleawers,
Aw like to stroll thro' leafy beawers
Wheer th' merry song-birds meet to sing,
An' th' woods wi' th' echoes fairly ring ;
When earth an' air unite to raise
One grand triumphant song o' praise,
While angel bands are hoverin' reawnd
As if entranced wi' th' joyful seawnd.

Aw loike to worship, not to scoff ;
Aw loike mi foes —a long way off ;
Mi cat an' dog aw loike to see ;
Mi childer clamberin' reawnd mi knee ;
Aw loike a bit o' good advice ;
To kiss a pratty woman twice ;
Aw've one loike moor, but shame to tell—
Well, this is it—aw loike misel' !

TOMMY O' DAN'S.

chap up i' Yorkshur, a little bit soft,
At had never bin eawt o' their heawse very oft,
Bethowt him one day he should loike a nice eawt ;
For he said he wur weary o' idlin' abeawt.
Well, one Seturday mornin' he donn'd hissel' up,
Put some meat in his pocket, an' summat to sup,
Then shook honds wi' his mother, an' bid her good day,
An' said he wur goin' tort Manchester way.

When he geet eawt o' th' dur, an' wur goin' deawn th' fowd,
He met Robin Shay—a chap eighty year owd ;
" Neah then, lad," said Robin, " an wheer art tha bean ?
Tha looks as if somb'dy been strooakin' thee dean ;
Well, well, arta bean up to Lunnon, or wheer ?
Heigh ! Ailse, my owd lass, does ta yer ? Sithee, here !
There's Tommy o' Dan's, he's for off, doesta see."
" Hello ! Tommy, lad," said owd Ailse, " Is that thee !

" Wheer arto for off this fawn mornin' soa suin ?
Well, tha art some an' smart i' thi halliday shuin !
" Ah, middlin'," said Tommy, " aw lawk to be fawn,
They're nawcer are these nor yond wooden uns o' mawn ;
They'll be leeter to wolk in nor clogs, a fawn seet !
Besawds bein' a great deol yezzier to th' feet.
Aw'd noa bobbins to waund for mi uncle to-day,
Soa aw thowt aw should lawk to goa Manchester way."

" Nowt but right, noather, Tom ; nowt but right," said th'
        owd lass,
" But, lad, do thee mawnd an' ta care o' thi brass."
" Eh, aw ha nobbut fourpince," said Tom, " un it's here ;
Aw shall ware it o' dinner, Ailse, when aw get theer."
" Reight ogain, lad," said Ailse, couldn't do better iv t' trawd ;
They'll sure-ly noan steyl what tha has i' th' insawde.
But maw breod ull be burnin' o' th' bakstone, aw fear,
Soa guid day to thee. lad ; aw wish thee safe theer."

Well, Tommy seet off i' good matter again—
As he passed Slawwit church th' clock wur just strikin' ten ;
He seed lots o' owd whistlin' shops upo' th' road,
But noather bein' hungry nor dry he ne'er co'd.
He geet into Manchester just abeawt dark,
When foalk wur o' hurryin' whoam fro' their wark ;
They elbow'd an' push'd an' shoved Tommy abeawt,
An' trod on his toes, till he fairly roared eawt.

At length he turned off, an' slipp'd deawn a back street,
Wheer he poo'd off his shoon, an' he looked at his feet :
" By George," he exclaimed " but aw'm hurt, aw am sooa !
Plague on 'em ! they'n varry near split maw gret tooa !"
But he'rn hungry, wur Tom, till he couldn't abide,
An' wrinkles began to appear in his hide ;
An', altho' th' foalk had been rather rough wi' th' owd lad,
Aw believe 'at his stomach just pained him as bad.

Well, he went treawnsin' on at a very slow rate,
Lookin' eawt for a shop wheer they sowd summat t' ate ;
At length, to his joy, he spied eawt across th' way
A sign, wi' these words on, " Fresh stew every day."
" Come," he said to hissel', " this is th' reet place for me ;
An' aw'll have a blow yeat i' this hoyle, or aw'll see.
He went in, as he thowt, but soa bothered he wur
That he made a mistake an' went into th' next dur.

Neaw th' next dur there'n a barber sat mendin' a harp ;
" Fourpenorth o' stew," Tommy bawled, " an' be sharp."
Th' barber, bein' a bit deof, didn't yer Tommy sheawt,
Soa he geet a white cloth 'at wur lyin' abeawt,
An' went tort Tommy, an' put it him on,
An' wur fotchin' some lather he had in a pon,
When Tommy said, " Measter, neah, neah, are yo wauld ?
Tay this back, an' bring th' stew, awst noan slatter me,
        chawld !"

ON THE DEATH OF JAMES WHITTAKER, THE POPULAR AND WELL-KNOWN VOCALIST.

WHEN one's friends are cast deawn wi' bereavements
    an' cares,
    An their hearts are nigh brocken wi' grief,
It's a difficult matter to know what to do,—
  To console 'em, or give 'em relief;
An' this is th' position aw'm in just neaw;
  For aw've friends 'at are mournin' their loss;
An' aw'm anxious to help 'em as mitch as aw con,
  While they're bearin' their heavy cross.

But when troubles o'er tak' us heaw helpless we feel,
  An' con do nowt but murmer an' groan,
If we try to help others, we stagger becose
  We're o'erburdened wi' cares o' eawr own.
Well, it's strange 'at a songster soa charmin' an' sweet
  Should be ta'en away from us so soon!
But, it may be, it's ole for th' best, an' let's hope
  'At he's singin' i' th' mansions aboon!

Yo'n been favoured at Failsworth wi' two men at least—
  'At have made life moor joyous an' breet:
Aw refer to th' esteemed an' reneawned "Ab o' th' Yate,"
  An' th' dear friend 'at's just gone eawt o' th' seet.
An', tho' yo sit wringin' yo'r honds i' dispair,
  Yo'n surely some cause to rejoice
At what Brierley's so cleverly done wi' his pen,
  An' James Whittaker's done wi' his voice.

No deawt yo'll feel preawd o' yo'r notable " Pow,"
  An' yo'r handicraft's oft been praised ;
But there's one thing yo owt to feel preawder on still,—
  An' that is—th' grand men 'at yo'n raised !
It's likely enuff 'at yo'll murmur an' fret,
  For one on 'em's knocked eawt o' tune,
An' th' other one's toddlin slowly abeawt,
  An' must finish his journey soon !

Yo'll excuse me, aw hope, for intrudin' neaw,
  For aw couldn't help pennin' a line
To tell yo if sympathy meets yo'r case,
  Yo'r heartily welcome to mine.
An' it's ole aw con give, an' ole 'at yo need ;
  For riches can never console
Wheer Death's been an' hurried some loved one away,
  Nor mack a poor brocken heart whole.

IRELAND'S VICEROYALTY UNDERPAID.

WELL, it's shameful to ha sich a salary as that!
It isn't enuff to provide for a cat.
Of course this affair is noa business o' mine,
If it wur aw should throw th' job up an' resign.
To' mitch, did yo say?   Why, surely, yo joke;
Twenty theawsand for mindin' five million o' foalk!
Just think o' th' big meetin's he has to disperse;
An' then look at th' numbers he has to coerce!

Don't yo see 'at o' *this* wage he'll never get rich?
True, some foalk may grumble, an' say it's to' mitch.
Neaw, aw once did some wark at a guinea a week,
But aw'd nowt mitch to do but to carry up breek.
Why, aw'd sooner wheel turnips six days for a " bob,"
Than tackle that Irish Viceroyalty job.
Aw'm noan seekin' Government offices yet,
Nawe, aw'll stick to mi rhymin', iv *that's* o' they get.

Aw'm here, an' the devil won't get me to stur,
For that poor, paltry wage,—twenty theawsand a year!
Come whoam, for tha'rt th' worst abused mon upon earth,
An' we'll get thee moor pay, an' a easier berth.
Con t' carry a hod, or mix mortar an' stuff?
What! freeten'd tha hasn't had practice enuff!
Well, come on to Blackpool towards th' middle o' June,
An' we'll find thee a job here at polishin' shoon.

If tha'rt freeten'd that business may durty thi honds,
Tha con drive thi relations abeawt on th' sonds.
Con t' work in a soof?   Wheel a barrow o' muck?
Howd a pig while it's killed? or scrape it when stuck?
Oh,—heaw would ta like leetin' th' lamps up at neets?
Or bein' a policeman, an' guardin' th' streets?
There's lots o' nice jobs 'at would suit thee, noa deawt;—
Howd! aw've dropp'd on it neaw,—art a good " chucker eawt?'

Arta strongish i' th' arm, an' weakish i' th' yead?
Arta willin' to sacrifice manhood for bread?
Can ta freawn upo' honesty, smile upo' cant?
If tha con, come at once, for tha'rt th' chap 'at we want.
Th' best berth here i' winter, mon;—drink an' a " bob;"
An', when argument fails, tha'll be sure ov a job.
What's that 'at tha'rt botherin' abeawt—who's to pay?
Well, tha'll soon find that eawt iv tha comes this way.

POEMS & SONGS
Not in the Lancashire Dialect.

~~~

MARSDEN: THE AUTHOR'S BIRTHPLACE.

IT was upon thy lovely hills,
Thy running brooks, and murmuring rills
These eyes first learned to gaze;
And often in thy meadows green,
In youthful sport might I be seen
The butterfly to chase.

Oh, those were happy hours to me;
Oft have I roamed in childish glee,
My bosom free from care,
Where the young lambkins joined in play,
And neighbouring children loved to stray,
Each other's sports to share.

Alas! we ne'er shall meet again;
Some of those children now are men;
Yes, men with silvery hair.
The old oak tree I loved to climb
Seems altered by the hand of Time,
Since last I saw it there.

Charlie Auty, 99.

INTAKE HEAD, MARSDEN (*Birthplace of Samuel Laycock*).

The mountain heights and shady wood
Where, when a child I often stood,
  Come fresh before my mind ;
Though forty years have passed away,
Still, I remember well that day
  I left them all behind.

Alas, alas, why should I leave
The things to which I fondly cleave,—
  The heath, the mountain wild ;—
Those scenes on which I loved to look,—
The trees, the flowers, the babbling brook
  I bathed in when a child.

Good-bye ! good-bye, my native hills;
Those running brooks and murmuring rills
  No longer yield me joy.
This heart is not so free from care,
As when I first breathed thy pure air,
  A happy little boy.

A SEA-SIDE INCIDENT.

GOOD people attend, while I briefly relate,
    An incident witnessed at Blackpool of late;
    'Tis a picture one's fancy may easily trace,
    If he lives, like myself, at some watering place.
'Twas winter, the wind whistled loud through the panes,
Nearly freezing the blood as it coursed through our veins;
The Sun, full of glory, had gone down to rest,
Behind the great ocean, far, far in the west;
The Moon, taking hold of the reins of the night,
Drove steadily on in her chariot of light;
The Stars, her attendants, were twinkling on high,
As if proud of their posts in that wintry sky.
'Twas a bitter cold night for the shelterless poor,
When a rather loud tapping was heard at my door,
Which I hastened to open, when lo! and behold,
A poor ragged urchin stood there in the cold.
He was tattered and shoeless, his poor little feet
I could see were exposed to the cold of the street.
With feelings of sadness I gazed on the lad,
As he stood on my doorstep so scantily clad;
And I thought of my own, with their bright curly heads,
So nicely, so snugly asleep in their beds;
And my feelings, which I could no longer disguise,
Were expressed in the tear-drops that stood in mine eyes.

The Moon, which awhile had been hid from our sight
Behind a dark cloud, now poured down her light,
And her silvery beams, falling full on the face
Of that child as he stood there, methought I could trace
Some resemblance to one lately ta'en from us here
To bask in a fairer and happier sphere.
With pity and sadness pourtrayed on my brow,
I addressed him, and said, my dear lad, who art thou
That cometh to us in this pitiable plight,
Exposed to the cold of this bleak winter night?
I fear thou art some wild, untractable youth,
Disobeying thy parents; come tell me the truth.
His eyes, which were hitherto hid from my gaze,
Now anxiously, pleadingly, looked in my face,
And his half-covered bosom seemed throbbing with grief;
So I said, " Speak out, child, it may give thee relief."
He spoke, and these words pierced me right to the heart,
" Dun yo want ony mussels, threeaupence a quart ?"

MY GARDEN.

MY home is my Garden, and thousand of hours,
  Have I tended and watched o'er my plants and
    flowers,
   And this heart often throbs in my bosom for fear,
Less the Spoiler should rob me of what I hold dear.
'Tis but a few weeks ago, deeming all right,
I retired from my watching to rest for the night,
When the Angel of Death, in the dark midnight hour,
Bore away from my garden a favourite flower.
O what anguish I felt, as I stooped o'er the bed,
And knew that the soul of that dear one had fled !
Let us cherish, and love, these dear flowers while we may,
Since we know not how soon death may take them away.
Let us train the young plants which our Father hath given,
Till His own loving hand shall transplant them to heaven.

JOHN BRIGHT.

WRITTEN ON THE EVENING OF HIS DEATH.)

AD news to-night!
    The call has been made,
    And promptly obeyed,
And we miss John Bright!

His race is run!
    We who stood around,
    Saw him clear the ground,
Exclaimed, "Well done!"

The Master calls!
    And the hoary sage
    Steps off the stage,
And the curtain falls!

Escaped from prison—
    The sorrows of earth—
    To a nobler birth
The soul hath risen.

The "Great Tribune"—
    Tho' he struggled long
    In the busy throng—
Has gone too soon.

His sun has set !
   While we stand and gaze
   On the lingering rays
Our eyes are wet !

Our hearts are sore,
   And our tears we blend
   O'er the dear dead friend
We shall see no more !

The sturdy oak
   That defied the blast
   Has fallen at last,
'Neath Death's sure stroke.

And standing there,
   Amidst piles of lore,
   From ceiling to floor,
Is a vacant chair !

Thus ends the fight--
   The battle of life—
   The wearisome strife—
In the cause of Right.

The voyage is o'er,
   The danger is past,
   And the anchor cast
On a deathless shore.

BLACKPOOL: LIGHT AND SHADE.

NEAR the ancient town of Poulton,—
　　Poulton, where the people often
　　Live to eighty or a hundred—
　　Is the famous borough, Blackpool.
Would you know what makes it famous?
Why the people go in millions?
Ask the pale-faced factory workers;
Ask the toilers in the coal-mines;
These will tell you—gladly tell you—
How the breezes from the ocean
Seem to put new life within them:
How the lame throw down their crutches,
Pallid cheeks turn plump and rosy,
When old Neptune blows upon them.
Say you prejudice may blind me,—
That my interests are at stake here?
Be it so; but ask the thousands
Crowding Blackpool every season,—
Why they leave the towns and hamlets
When the engine ceases working,
And a holiday is given them.

Still, my tongue shall not be silent,
Lest the very stones reprove me.
Shattered nerves and sad bereavements
Forced me from my friends and kindred;
From the graveyards of my fathers;—
Where my children's forms lie mouldering;—
Where I penned my first effusion,
Earned some little fame as author.
Silent! 'midst these grand surroundings!
Silent! not till memory fails me!
Or the brain has ceased its thinking,
Or the hand has lost its cunning!

Would to God my song was ended!
That no shadow crossed my vision;—
That the picture was completed!
But 'tis not so; justice bids me
Tell the truth, however painful.
There's a sadder, darker picture,
That I'm loth to bring before you,
But a sense of public duty,
Mingled with a love of justice,—
Bids me—as a faithful painter,
Bring to view both lights and shadows;
And, God helping me, I'll do this!
Would a just and wise physician
Trifle with his ailing patients,
When a word from him might save them?
Shall the bard,—however humble,—
Feeling he has got a mission—
Falter in the path of duty,
Fearful of the consequences;—
Fearful of the fame of Blackpool?
No! let all the truth be spoken,
Whether for us, or against us,
Hiding faults can never cure them:
Like some unseen, fatal cancer,
Errors hid may prove disasterous.

True it is we've much to boast of,
With our theatres and gardens,
With our Mayor and Corporation,
And our stirring motto, "Progress."
Yes, and we have got our failings :
Vice succeeds where virtue suffers ;
Dram-shops thrive while churches languish :
Money is the god we worship ;
Brains are at a serious discount ;
Wealth, not worth, is what we honour ;
Musty creeds are held in reverence ;
Facts ignored because they're modern.
Temperance men are christened "Weaklings ;"—
Wearing "bits of blue," or badges ;
Marching through the streets with banners,
Singing "Glory! Hallelujah!"

Bring us here the scales of Justice ;
Weigh these poor men's actions fairly ;
Let us test results and motives ;
What's the verdict of the jury ?
Are these fools, or vain fanatics,
Preaching what they think the gospel,
Heedless of the storm or sunshine ;—
Headless of men's blame or praises ?
Mr. Foreman, come, what say you,—
Is their teaching good, or harmful ?
Do you find the people better
When the bottle is forsaken,
And the temperance pledge is taken ?
Have I drawn this picture truly ;—
Put in all the lights and shadows ?
Let the public give the verdict !

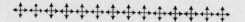

AN EVENING PRAYER.

NE night, when all was hushed and still,
    I paced the meadows lightly ;
Below me ran the murmuring rill,
    Above, the stars shone brightly.

The moon shed forth her silvery light
    O'er mountain, dale, and ocean :
And all I saw and heard that night
    Inspired me with devotion.

Old Farmer Jones, across the way,
    To rest was just retiring ;
And as he bent his knees to pray,
    I could not help admiring :—

His brawny arms were raised on high ;
    A smile sat on his features :
His manly voice was heard to cry,—
    "Almighty ! hear Thy creatures :—

We thank Thee for Thy tender care,
    Bestowed on these before Thee ;
That we are kept from every snare,
    Lord help us to adore Thee.

We thank Thee for the hour of rest ;
    How sweet it is to gather
With those we love below the best,
    And pray to Thee our Father.

O help us all to share Thy love,
    Till death these bonds shall sever ;
Then grant that we may meet above,
    To worship Thee for ever."

The prayer being done, the old man rose ;
    His head with age was hoary ;
"Amen !" said I ; and here I close
    This brief and simple story.

TO A SON ON HIS THIRTIETH BIRTHDAY.

YOU are thirty years old to-day, dear son;
 You are thirty years old to-day;
 But we cannot enrich you with presents or gold,
  Still we humbly and fervently pray
That God may preserve you in health and in strength,
 For many a long year to come;
That the vine and young branches may circle you round
 In a happy and prosperous home!

Thirty years have passed o'er, and the arms where you lay
 Are neither so nimble or strong
As they were when we first tossed you up in the air,
 And sung you the first little song.
Time hath whitened our hairs; youthful vigour has fled,
 And these foreheads—once handsome and fair
Betoken the strife, the great battle of life,
 And are terribly wrinkled with care.

Still, 'tis pleasing to know, that the efforts put forth
 In your interests have not been in vain;
For the filial affection you've shown to us both,
 Has repaid us again and again.
The lessons instilled in your mind as a child,
 (Though you oft from this punishment ran)
Have been a great help through your childhood and youth,
 And are blessing you now as a man.

And now that we travel the downhill of life,
   It is some consolation to know,
That the seed we have sown has already sprung up,
   And the fruits are beginning to grow.
Yes, the flowers of a good and a virtuous life,
   The flowers of good acts and deeds;
And these are more manly; more God-like too,
   Than blind faiths, professions, and creeds.

'Tis goodness, not greatness, that makes the true man,
   Let this be impressed on your mind.
We pray not for great worldly wealth for our son,
   But a heart that is gentle and kind.
For riches are fleeting, they soon pass away,
   And our efforts to keep them are vain,
While filial affection lives on in the soul,
   And praiseworthy actions remain.

Heaven guard you through all the temptations and snares
   You may meet in your journey through life;
May your pathway be smooth, and the rest of your days
   Be passed without jarring and strife.
And when Death's icy hand shall have severed the hearts
   That were lovingly blended of yore,
May a blessed and lasting re-union take place
   Where the Spoiler can part us no more.

O GIVE ME A HOME IN SOME QUIET GLEN.

 give me a home in some quiet glen,
 With my wife and my children, my books, and my pen;
 There surrounded by Nature and all that is fair,
 I can roam at my leisure, and breathe the pure air.
I long to be free, both in body and mind,
To worship my Maker, and love all mankind ;
And would flee from the scenes I detest and abhor,
Impurity, drunkenness, slavery, and war.

I am weary of all the low pleasures of earth,
Of the wrangling and discord, and boisterous mirth ;
And this soul of mine struggles and yearns to be free,
To rise from this thraldom, O Maker ! to thee.
I would leave this vile world that can yield me no joy,
Where the heartless and thoughtless delight to annoy ;
Where poor men are often the slaves of the great,
And ignorance generates envy and hate ;
Where the seeds of disorder are thoughtlessly sown,
And love and good feeling are almost unknown.

Let me once more enjoy some of childhood's bright hours,
And roam with the children to gather wild flowers.
Oh ! those are sweet seasons I long to review ;
I had then youthful friends, honest-hearted and true ;
And I basked in the sunshine, amused myself there,
A stranger to sorrow, annoyance, and care ;
My conscience as clear as the murmuring rills,
That glided along through my native hills.
But, alas ! many changes I've witnessed since then
Which 't were vain to attempt to describe with my pen ;
Suffice it to say, that I do not enjoy
My life half so well as I did when a boy.

LINES WRITTEN IN MRS. FISHER'S ALBUM.

RS. FISHER may fish in the river,
  And much "grist to the mill" she may bring;
  But when she goes "fishing" for poems,
    Why, that's quite a different thing.
Fish breed in the river untended,
  And may sometimes be caught without pains;
But "songs" are the product of thinking,
  And thoughts are the product of "brains."

But I've no wish to tease Mrs. "Fisher,"
  So while casting about with her hook,
I will try to oblige her with something,
  If that something is only a "fluke,"
I wish her success with her album;
  She is welcome to my little mite;
And so long as she "fishes" for poems
  I hope she will meet with a "bite."

JOHN CRITCHLEY PRINCE.

FAREWELL, thou gifted singer! thy sweet songs
    Have charmed the ears of thousands in our land:
    Now thou art gone, we feel that we have lost
      One of the greatest of the gifted band.
Tho' thou art dead, thy honoured name shall live
  For ages yet to come: and thy pure lays
Be read and prized by myriads yet unborn,
  And in their hearts thy songs shall find a place.
His like again. alas! we may not see:
  Few living Bards have sung so well as he!

LINES ON THE DEATH OF A YOUNG MOTHER.

IT was a cold and dull December day;
The sun's bright rays were hidden from the sight;
The clouds hung heavily above our heads,
When something darker, gloomier still than these
We saw. Ah! who can picture that sad scene :—
A youthful mother on her dying bed ;
Around her those she loved—her tender babes ;
Her sorrowing husband overwhelmed with grief ;
Her mother, brother—those with whom she spent
Her sunniest hours when yet a little child.
Down on his bended knees, the man of God
Poured out his soul, and prayed that heaven would spare
That suffering mother ; but it must not be ;
In less than one short hour she breathed her last ;
Th' immortal spirit winged its flight to God.
Oh, what a picture here of human life !
The day before, she rose as was her wont,
Performed her household duties until noon,
Nor dreamed that death would mark her for his prey.
Ah! who can tell what agony was felt
In those few hours ! How those who loved her wept ;
Yes, wept as if their very hearts would break.
Her little children, one by one, were brought,
And as we stood beside that mother's bed,
Watching to see her eyelids gently close,
She gazed upon us sadly, and she cried,—
" Ah, who will care for my poor children now ?
I feel that I must leave them—I must die !
O God ! O God ! have mercy on my soul."

Large sweat drops stood upon those pallid cheeks ;
Her quivering lips were turned a deadly pale ;
We saw her eyes grow motionless and dim,
She gave a few deep sobs and then she died.
Oh, God ! it is a sad and touching sight,—
A mother dying, and with gasping breath
Bidding farewell to husband, children, friends ;
The husband with whose fate she linked her own
So short a time before : and those dear babes—
Her own beloved offspring who were wont
To gather round her, and her blessings share,
And on whose bosom they so oft had lain.
The funeral day arrived : the silent train
Of mourners followed, full of inward grief.
The sorrowing neighbours stood there, one and all,
Wiping the tear-drops from their streaming eyes,
And wondering how it was that one so young
And so beloved should thus be called away.
They thought of days gone by, when, strong and hale,
She moved amongst them ; how her winning ways
And cheerful temper made her loved of all ;
And now that she was gone they mourned and grieved,
As a fond mother for an only child.
The place of graves was reached, the burial rites
Performed in mournful and in tremulous tones ;
" Ashes to ashes, dust to dust " was said,
And then the meek and pious man of God,
With hands and eyes uplifted to the heavens,
Pronounced " The grace of God be with you all."
Closely we gathered round that open grave,
And, stooping over, took a last sad look,
Ere the old sexton shovelled in the clay,
Hallowed and moistened with the tears we shed.
We stayed awhile and gazed upon the scene,
Our hearts o'erwhelmed with sorrow at our loss ;
Loth to depart and leave the one we loved
So tenderly in the cold, silent grave.

WHITSUNTIDE HYMNS.

No. I.

SING aloud, ye British children;
    Sweetly sing the joyful lays;
Join in one harmonious concert,
    Rend the air with songs of praise;
        British children,
You can boast of happy days.

Sunday schools, and faithful teachers,
    Noble hearted Christian men,
Anxious for your future welfare,
    Working hard with tongue and pen;
        Sunday scholars,
Shall they labour on in vain?

Will not some young hopeful saplings,
    Nourish'd 'neath their tender care,
Rise to fill important stations?
    Shine with Christian graces there?
        Christian teachers,
This should be your earnest prayer.

Slacken not; your cause is glorious;
    Sunday schools are England's pride;
Teachers, persevere in earnest,
    Spread your influence far and wide;
        Tell the children,
Of the Christ who lived and died.

Gird afresh the Gospel armour—
　Helmet, shield, and two-edged sword,
Sin in youthful hearts to battle ;
　God will strength to you afford ;
　　　You shall conquer—
　Win great battles for your Lord.

Yes ; and when life's work is over,
　Shall they not to honour rise ?
Heavenly, lasting and eternal,
　Sure and firm, beyond the skies ?
　　　There, for ever,
　Feast, in bliss, their wond'ring eyes ?

———————

No. II.

THOUGH home is so endearing,
　　Its joys so soft and sweet,
　　Where friends and dear relations
　　In closest friendship meet,
We love the school as truly,
　Where, on the Sabbath day,
Thousands of children gather,
　To read, and praise, and pray.
No place on earth more lovely,
　Though heaven will far excel
In happiness and pleasure,
　The school we love so well.

How happy British children !
　Like lambs safe in the fold,
With faithful shepherds o'er them ;
　How changed from days of old !
'Neath our own vine and fig tree,
　In the clear open day,
Not fearing persecution,
　We all can read and pray.
Then come ! with songs of praises,
　Let every voice resound ;
Praise God that he has placed us
　Where Sunday schools abound.

No. III.

THE birds their songs are singing,
The woods and forests ringing,
And oh ! how sweet the sound,
How joyful all around.
Come, children, raise your voices,
Since Nature thus rejoices ;
Nor be ungrateful found,
But let your songs abound ;
Oh ! would you sing
The songs of heaven,
Come learn to sing them now.

The lark her song is raising,
And, on the mountain grazing,
The lambkins skip and play :
O, what more blithe than they ?
And shall not children render,
Now, while their hearts are tender,
To heaven some grateful lay ?
Why not begin to-day ?
Oh ! would you sing
The songs of heaven,
Come learn to sing them now.

Each Sabbath morn rise early,
E'en while the dew drops pearly,
Are hanging on the trees ;
Fall down upon your knees,
Send up your adoration,
And fervent supplication,
To Him who ever sees
A child upon its knees.
Oh ! would you sing
The songs of heaven,
Come learn to sing them now.

Go search the graveyard yonder,
And o'er its lessons ponder;
  You read of tender flowers,
  Blooming a few short hours—
Then borne aloft to glory,
To sing the Saviour's story,
  And bloom in fairer bowers,
  Bedewed with heavenly showers.
    Oh! would you sing
    The songs of heaven,
  Come learn to sing them now.

We learn from God's blest pages,
Angels have sung for ages;
  How perfect, then, that song,
  Chanted in heaven so long!
O, would you join in chorus
With those long gone before us,
  Your harps should now be strung,
  And played while you are young.
    Oh! would you sing
    The songs of heaven,
  Come learn to sing them now.

No. IV.

RIGHTLY the morning sun
      Gilds hill and dale;
      Warblers (their songs begun)
      Flood all the vale.
Green fields and verdant bowers,
O'erspread with lovely flowers,
  All these conspire to raise
  Their meed of praise.

Down where the willows grow,
  Shady and cool,
Children are seen to go
  Early to school.
Come, join this happy band,
Bound for a better land,—
  Pure and unfading joys
  Beyond the skies.

Prize not the joys of earth,
　　Brief is their stay ;
Seek gems of priceless worth
　　While yet you may.
Youth is the season fair
While free from worldly care ;
　　Now, ere the night shall come,
　　Seek out a home.

No. V.

OW that every heart rejoices,
　　Old and young, weak and strong,
　　Raise aloud your voices ;
　　　Let us banish care and sadness,
And to-day, while we may,
Tune our hearts to gladness.

'Tis in vain we sit repining
O'er our woe here below ;
See the sun is shining :
Round our feet the flowers are springing,
In the air, free from care,
Birds are sweetly singing.

True, this world is full of sorrow,
Grief and tears, pain and fears,
Care about to-morrow ;
Still we need not be despairing ;
" God is love,' and above
He is for us caring.

If in wisdom he should chide us,
Still we must, in Him trust,
He will keep and guide us.
Gloomy clouds around may gather,—
All appear dark and drear ;
God is still our Father.

Though our earthly friends forsake us—
Pass away, day by day,
Christ our Lord will take us
Where fond hearts no more shall sever.
O may all, great and small,
Dwell with him for ever.

No. VI.

OME to the Sunday school,
    And join the youthful throng;
Come to the Sunday school
    And swell the children's song.
Hark how the merry bells
    Peal forth from yonder tower;
And every scholar tells,
    'Tis now the opening hour,
      Come, come, come.

Come, tune your lips to praise;
    Come, bend your knees in prayer;
Ask God to guide your ways,
    And save from every snare.
In youth pursue the way,
    The sainted father's trod;
It leads to endless day,
    To happiness and God,
      Come, come, come.

Come while the pulse of life
    Beats high within your veins;
While love and joy are rife,
    And conscience knows no stains.
Now, while the morning sun
    Shines in the eastern sky,
Be love to God begun,
    Love which shall never die.
      Come, come, come.

Come, ere the hand of Time
    Carves furrows on the brow;
While full of youthful prime,
    The Saviour calls you now.
Life is but short at best,
    Then come without delay;
We long to see you blest,
    And from our hearts would say,
      Come, come, come.

No. VII.

NOTHER year has passed away,—
  A year of joy and sadness ;
Once more we hail this festive day
  With mingled grief and gladness.

But, oh ! we're bound for fairer ground,
  Where naught these hearts can sever ;
For we shall stand on Canaan's land,
  Where pleasures last for ever.

Disease and death disturb our joys,
  And fill our hearts with sorrow ;
To-day we grasp our cherished toys,
  Death calls them home to-morrow.

  But, oh ! we're bound, &c.,

In vain for friends we look around,
  Imperfect is our chorus ;
They've reached the goal to which we're bound,
  And crossed the stream before us.

  But, oh ! we're bound, &c.,

Their well-known voices join no more
  As hills and dales are ringing ;
Now, landed on heaven's blissful shore,
  In nobler strains they're singing.

  But, oh ! we're bound for fairer ground,
    Where naught these hearts can sever ;
  For we shall stand on Canaan's land,
    Where pleasures last for ever.

ON THE DEATH OF ERNEST JONES.

H ! cruel Death ! could'st thou not lay thine hand,
On some one less beloved in the land ?
Was there not one in this vast, teeming world,
Into whose breasts thy arrows could be hurled !

Why in such dreadful haste ?   Had'st thou looked round,
But for one moment, Death, thou would'st have found
Those for whom none would breathe, nor sighs, nor groans,
Then why strike down our much-loved Ernest Jones !

Could'st thou not enter at some other door ?
Hast thou not heard of what we had in store
For the departed one whose loss we mourn ?
Hast thou not heard of bitter hardships borne !

O, why not warn us of thy mission here
Ere thou did'st hurl thy darts at one so dear.
Can'st thou not see our hands uplifted now,
To place the laurels on his honoured brow !

But why thus blame thee, Death, or thus repine,
Since faith assures us that this act of thine
Hath snapped the chain, and freed the patriot bard ;
His trials o'er, he's gone to his reward.

Heaven,—grown impatient at our long delays,
Of tendering our homage, help, and praise,—
Called him away, from hearts so hard and cold,
To dwell with martyrs, and the brave of old.

BRIGHT DAYS.

BRIGHT days; how soon they seemed to pass,
    How swift the moments flew;
When, arm in arm with her I loved,
    We sat beneath yon yew,
And spoke in accents soft and sweet,
    As lovers always do.

Hope buoyed our youthful spirits then;
    Our prospects oh, how bright!
The future seemed a long, long day,
    We dreamed not of the night;
Nor did we think that Death's cold hand
    Such tender plants could blight.

My darling, she was young and fair,
    And gentle as the dove;
She never learned to scorn or hate,
    But early learned to love;
And often she would speak to me
    Of fairer worlds above.

With the bright stars above our heads,
    The grass beneath our feet,
And all around us hushed and still,
    We thought it right and meet
To leave awhile the busy world,
    And hold communion sweet.

When the sad hour for parting came,—
    I need not mention why,—
But neither of us liked to speak
    That parting word good-bye.
Whene'er I grasped my darling's hand,
    This breast would heave a sigh.

I loved that girl with all my heart,
    And she loved me, I know;
For when I asked if she'd be mine,
    She spoke in accents low—
These loving, charming, welcome words,—
    "Yes, if you wish it so."

TO A LITERARY FRIEND.

Y dear old friend, you kindly state,—
And this you've done at various times,
That most of my unpublished rhymes,
Are worthy of a better fate.

You may be right, you may be wrong;
While *you* admire poetic wares,
The man whose eyes are fixed on " shares,"
Would look with coldness on a song.

The race for wealth makes millions blind;
The frantic rush for fame and gold;
The views of life that most men hold,
Must starve the soul, and cramp the mind.

But what a blunder! what a loss!
They pass their time in Nature's bowers;
They choose the thorns, but leave the flowers;
Reject the gold, and choose the dross!

My pen must soon be laid aside;
The lessons I have tried to teach,
The sermons I have tried to preach,
Must either perish or abide.

I cannot hope to win the praise,
So needful to the bard and seer,
Or win the sympathetic cheer
Of those whose friends are in the race.

I toe the mark, and do my best ;
Strain all the powers of heart and soul
To gain the prize, and win the goal ;
To time and fate I leave the rest.

But, laid aside from human gaze,
No songs from either man or bird
Can vex or please the ear unheard,
Or call forth either blame or praise.

But shall the bard, or bird on wing,
Because, perchance, the unasked for strain
May fall upon the ear in vain,—
Be silent, or refuse to sing ?

A SONG FOR SUMMER.

Tune: " Tramp, tramp, tramp, the Boys are Marching."

IT is glorious summer time,
　　Pretty flowers are in their prime,
　　Bounteous Nature is rejoicing all around;
　　While the hawthorn, now in bloom,
　　Spreads around a sweet perfume,
Hills and valleys are with lovely verdure crowned.

CHORUS:

Shout, shout, shout, my boys for gladness,
Shout till the balmy air shall ring;
　　Oh, let us ne'er forget
　　There are pleasures for us yet,
Free to all men, from the peasant to the king.

Oh, come, let us haste away,
　　It is now the time for play,
Nature for us spreads around an ample feast!
　　There are daisies on the grass,
　　We can pluck them as we pass,
Fruits in clusters, too, refreshing to the taste.

　　Chorus: Shout, shout, shout, &c.

It is sweet to roam about,
　　When the sun is peeping out
From his hiding place behind the lofty hills;
　　Sweet to watch his shadows play,
　　On some calm sequestered bay,
See his antics from the gently flowing rills.

　　Chorus: Shout, shout, shout, &c.

Let us seek the pebbly shore,
   Hear the grand old ocean roar ;
Oh, how deep are all the notes, and how sublime !
   Never changing in their sound,
   Just the same the seasons round,
Heard by men of every nation—every clime.

   Chorus : Shout, shout, shout, &c.

Haste away to yonder wood,
   With its lovely solitude ;
Like a sturdy race of giants stand the trees.
   How refreshing to recline
   'Neath the branches of the pine,
While the wearied frame is fanned by the breeze.

   Chorus : Shout, shout, shout, &c.

Oh, how sweet to watch the sun,
   When his daily work is done,
Like a toiler sinking quietly to rest !
   Oh, 'tis glorious to behold
   How he " tips the hills with gold,"
When retiring to his chamber in the west.

   Chorus : Shout, shout, shout, &c.

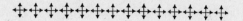

TO MY FRIEND, S. WOLSTENHOLME.

O my old fellow-traveller, and excellent friend,
This rhyming epistle I cheerfully send,
With the hope that yourself, your daughter and wife,
Are enjoying yourselves with the good things of life.

I trust you have found things to suit your best wish;
That the rivers abound with most excellent fish;
That the flowers are as pretty, the skies quite as clear,
As they were when we paid them a visit last year.

If you feel in the mood, when the daylight shall fade,
Go and look at the spot where poor *Wilson is laid;
How my heart aches to think that a star of such worth,
Should so soon be extinguished, and dashed to the earth.

But away with sad thoughts! lift your eyes to the hills;
And your ears—let them list to the murmuring rills,
Till your minds are enlarged, and o'erjoyed with the sight,
And your souls are up-borne with a sense of delight.

Need we wonder that grand noble thoughts had their birth
In Lakeland,—the loveliest spot upon earth!
Why, the poet of Nature would fall on his knees,
And almost go frantic 'mid scenes such as these.

If you find you have got a few minutes to spare,
Let us know how you're getting along over there;
You might say if the fish kindly take to the bait,
Or if they seem calm, and resigned to their fate.

But I must not thus " chaff" you, I must not indeed,
I have written as much as you'll find time to read;
Give my kindest regards to your host, Mr. Wright,
And believe me, as ever, S. Laycock,—good night.

* WM. WILSON, Poet.

GOD HELP US.

OD help us amid all the changes of life,
When pleasures surround us, when dangers are rife
O grant that the former may not prove a snare,
Nor the latter the means of producing despair.

O help us in childhood—those bright, sunny hours,
When our pathway before us seems planted with flowers ;
May our lives then be pleasant, our young hearts be glad,
Let no evil befall us to make us feel sad.

O guard our young footsteps from treading those ways,
Which, sooner or later, must lead to disgrace ;
And, O may we learn in the days of our youth,
To love what is noble, and reverence the truth.

Be with us, O God, in that critical state,
When impulse is strong, and temptation is great ;
When the world and its pleasures conspire to allure,
May we shun what is sinful, profane, and impure.

God help us when we unto manhood attain ;
O keep us from being conceited and vain ;
Make us humble, and childlike, and help us to see
That for all we possess we're indebted to Thee.

God help us, when we shall engage in the strife
Which awaiteth us all in the battle of life ;
May we boldly and bravely go forth to the fight,
And, O give us strength to do that which is right.

Give us patience to bear all our crosses and cares ;
And wisdom to guard 'gainst temptations and snares ;
Let not earth's gaudy toys, which around us we see,
Draw our souls from integrity, virtue, and Thee.

God help us in sickness ; God help us in health ;
May we smile through our troubles, be humble 'midst wealth ;
O give us Thy spirit to comfort our hearts,
When afflictions press heavy, and vigour departs.

Be with us when age comes upon us, good Lord ;
Be near us, and sweet consolation afford ;
Smooth the pathway we tread, may the last of our days
Be employed in Thy service, in worship and praise.

Be with us in death—in that sad, solemn hour,
When the stern "King of Terrors" comes vested with power ;
Kind Parent watch o'er us, and in Thy great love,
Prepare us a place in Thy Kingdom above.

AN AFFECTIONATE TRIBUTE TO THE MEMORY
OF MY MOTHER,

Who Died August 8th, 1860.   Aged 69 Years.

H ! cruel Death ! why thus my peace destroy ?
　　Thy victim is my Mother—on whose knee
I sat so often when a little boy ;
　　Deal gently with her, she is all to me.

Those loving eyes watched o'er me, while as yet
　　A child, unconscious of a Mother's care ;
Alas ! since then those eyes have oft been wet,
　　Those lips for me breathed many a fervent prayer.

Oh, Death ! awhile hold back that fatal dart,
　　Methinks I love her more than ever now ;
Oh ! let me smooth her pillow ere we part,
　　And wipe the death-damp from her wrinkled brow ;—

Speak some kind word, support her dropping head ;
　　What, though these filial actions prove in vain,
We must perform them at her dying bed,
　　She will not need them at our hands again !

The blow is struck which sets her spirit free,
　　And now she soars aloft on angel's wings ;
Soon those glad eyes her future home will see,
　　Rich with the splendour of eternal things.

Farewell, farewell to every anxious care,
    Sorrow and pain shall rack that breast no more ;
To mar her peace no foe can enter there ;
    O blessed spirits on that blessed shore !

Here, we are toiling up life's rugged steep,
    Many our sorrows, few alas ! our joys ;
These eyes of ours have often cause to weep,
    Our sweetest songs are often mixed with sighs.

Fond social ties are round these hearts entwined
    Claiming our love, as though they meant to stay ;
Vain earthly hopes ! how often do we find
    The loveliest flowers are first to die away.

Ah, me ! ah, me ! her frail unworthy son,
    Plodding life's path with all its lurking snares ;
How shall these youthful feet securely run,
    Without her bright example, and her prayers !

My darling boy ! 'tis well that thou art young ;
    O how unconscious of the loss sustained !
Thy heart, like ours, is not with anguish wrung,
    Though she is dead, thy bosom is not pained.

Come, nestle closer to thy parents, love ;
    To us, her dying lips breathed forth a prayer—
That we should train thee for the realms above,
    And treat thee, for her sake, with special care.

But how can we, who are but sinful dust,
    Direct thy footsteps to that blissful land ?
Father Divine ! in thee we put our trust ;
    O guide us all by thine unerring hand.

Support and cheer my Sire—whose hoary head
    And furrowed cheeks bespeak a host of cares ;
Since one by one his earthly joys have fled,
    And sorrows mark his last declining years.

By you, her dear old friends the stroke is felt ;
  Her company to you has long been dear ;
Oft at the throne of grace with her you knelt ;
  Now she is gone, well may you shed a tear.

Her seat is vacant in the House of Prayer ;
  That old familiar face we see no more ;
Our mutual joys no longer now we share,
  Nor hold sweet loving converse as of yore.

But shall we mourn that she is now at rest ?
  No, God forbid ! but rather we rejoice
That she has gained the regions of the blest,
  For this she strove, and early made her choice.

Long years ago, ere time had blanched her hairs,
  Or life's rude storms swept o'er her youthful head,
She sought the Lord—he heard her humble prayers,
  And on her future path rich blessings shed.

Most of her life (near threescore years and ten),
  Her willing feet the path of duty trod ;
Then left the Church below, without a stain,
  At peace with all men, and at peace with God.

Ah ! blessed Mother ! may thy sorrowing friends
  Tread in thy footsteps towards that blissful shore ;
That when our journey through this desert ends,
  We all may meet in heaven to part no more.

REST TO-MORROW.

CHRISTIAN life is one great warfare,—
    One fierce fight with hell and sin,
    Foes without and foes within.
    Christian! buckle on thine armour,
Let not aught thy heart dismay;
Quell rebellious thoughts to-day,
           Rest to-morrow.

Hark! the bugle calls to battle;
Onward, then, thy foes to meet,
Lay them bleeding at thy feet.
Rouse, shake off thy sluggish nature,
Now's the time to act for God,
Rest thyself beneath the sod,
           Rest to-morrow.

Forward! Forward! Christian soldier;
Draw thy sword, make bare thine arm;
Force the battle, brave the storm.
Nerve, oh nerve thyself to action;
Bravely, nobly do thy part;
Labour on with hand and heart—
           Rest to-morrow.

Indolence hath slain its thousands;
Be not thou to this a slave;
Rise! be vigilant and brave.
Labour while the sun is shining,
Soon will come the shades of night;
Work to-day with all thy might,
           Rest to-morrow.

Up, and battle hard with error,
Truth the weapon thou must wield ;
Go at once and take the field.
Would'st thou win the conquerer's laurels,
Wear the victor's honoured crown ;
Lay not yet thy weapons down,
                    Rest to-morrow.

Onward, brother, on to victory !
Dread no foe, however strong ;
Right must triumph over wrong.
Angel bands are watching o'er thee,
Faint not till the race is run,
Stay not till the goal is won,
                    Rest to-morrow.

Go, and like thy Lord and Master,
When this lower world He trod,
Point some wandering soul to God.
Lo, the fields are white to harvest,
Go, and work with heart and mind ;
Grow not weary, thou shalt find
                    Rest to-morrow.

Rest is sweetest to the weary,
Those who toil and struggle hard ;
Work, and gain this rich reward.
Scorn to rest while others labour ;
Use the powers thy God hath given ;
Toil on earth and rest in heaven,
                    Rest to-morrow.

Rest when all thy toils are ended ;
Rest when all thy work is done ;
Rest when life's short race is run.
Christian soldier, be thou ever
First and foremost in the fray ;
Labour, suffer, die to-day,
                    Rest to-morrow.

SUNSHINE AND SHADE.

WHILE we tread this world below,
Many changes we must know;
Now life greets us bright and fair,
Now we pine with grief and care.
Friends whose presence cheers the heart,
Soon slip from us, soon depart;
Lovely flowers must droop and fade,—
Sometimes sunshine, sometimes shade.

Full of hope are life's first hours;
Childhood's path is strewn with flowers;
Day by day time glides along,—
Hope and sunshine, mirth and song.
Youthful pleasures do not last,
Life's fair morning soon is past;
Hope deserts us, pleasures fade;
Sometimes sunshine, sometimes shade.

Manhood's vigour comes and goes;
Side by side grow thorn and rose;
Pain and pleasure, weal and woe,
Come to all while here below.
Summer, Winter, Autumn, Spring,
These their various changes bring.
Here God's wisdom is displayed,—
Days of sunshine, days of shade.

Oft we see the morning sun
Clouded ere the day is done;
So with man, his little day
Opens bright, his heart is gay.
Soon the Spoiler's hand appears ;
Eyes once bright are dimm'd with tears ;
Useless all the plans he's laid ;
Treacherous sunshine ! blighting shade !

Still, take heart, immortal soul ;
Upwards ! this is not thy goal ;
Yonder—in thy native skies,
Tears no more shall dim thine eyes.
Keep that goodly land in view,
All thy earthly journey through ;
There the flowers shall never fade ;—
Welcome sunshine ! farewell shade !

TO A FRIEND ON HIS BIRTHDAY.

EAR friend, on this thy natal day,
        When those who know and love thee most,
Send in their greetings through the post,
        Accept from me this humble lay.

My Muse is rather lame, I fear ;
    And younger men with clearer brains
May pen their thoughts in loftier strains,
    Though not more heart-felt, more sincere.

God bless thee, valued friend ! and may
    The clouds now hovering o'er thy head,—
Filling thy soul with fear and dread,
    Soon break, and, harmless, pass away !

May genial sunbeams ever shine,
    And cool, refreshing dews descend
On thee, my best, my dearest friend,—
    Is the fervent prayer of me and mine !

A THORN GROWS NEAR THE ROSE.

HE sweets of life are mingled up
With cares and bitter woes;
Joy, mixed with sorrow fills our cup;
A thorn growns near the rose.

Give man whate'er his eye can please,
Some adverse wind soon blows
To blast his prospects, mar his peace;
A thorn grows near the rose.

In vain we build on earthly good,
And think to find repose;
Our hopes are nipp'd while in the bud,
A thorn grows near the rose.

Few are the friends that we can boast,
While many are our foes;
The good is in the evil lost,
A thorn grows near the rose.

The Tempter comes, deceives our friends,—
Some seed of discord sows;
And soon, alas! he gains his ends;
A thorn grows near the rose.

Grim Death will come! the cold green sod
O'er these frail limbs must close;
To wean us all from earth to God,
A thorn grows near the rose.

In heaven there is a glorious rest:
" Peace like a river flows;"
No foe can enter to molest,—
No thorn grows near the rose.

SEASIDE PICTURES.

ASHING and splashing upon the sea shore,
Hear the wild billows, how grandly they roar
Here we find Nature untrammelled and free,
In the restless, excited, majestical sea.
Out in the west is the setting sun,
Looking back on the race he has run ;
Silently, cheerfully, doing the will
Of One who is brighter and greater still.

Now he is vanishing out of our sight ;
Oh, let us thank him, and bid him good night.
Has he not smiled on this landscape of ours ?
Ripened the fruit for us, painted the flowers ?
Has he not been to dispel the thick gloom,
And throw a bright ray in the sick man's room !
Oh, what great blessings he hath to impart,
Cheering the sad and the sorrowing heart ; —

Leading the downcast to lift up his eyes
To fairer climates, and sunnier skies.
God! thou art kind to Thy children here ;
Why should we doubt Thee, or why should we fear !
All things created around and above,
Speak of a Father of goodness and love.
Shall we such mercies ungratefully spurn,
Shall we not thank such a Friend in return ?

Twilight sets in, and the stars are in sight,
And are flinging their rays of silvery light
On the heaving breast of the troubled sea,
As it roars like a giant in agony.
And now let us gaze on another spot :
The lamps are lit in the fisherman's cot,
And there are the fisherman's children, see,
Lisping their prayers at their mother's knee.

An old man sits in the chimney nook,
With his tearful eyes on that good old book
That points man's soul to a brighter day,
When the things of earth shall have passed away.
He closes the book, and his tearful eyes
And his brawny hands are raised to the skies ;
What mind can conceive of a grander sight !
Thou art very near home, aged Christian—good night !

Out on the ocean a light burns clear,
Warning the sailor that land is near ;
In a lonely cot on the distant sands,
A fisherman's widow sits wringing her hands,
Her poor heart bleeding with sorrow and woe,
For the husband she lost but a week ago.
Out on the ocean are stout hearts and brave,
Battling right nobly with wind and with wave.

So with our lives ; the big waves often roll,
O'erwhelming the spirit, disturbing the soul ;
And thus we go onward from day unto day,
Laughing and weeping the moments away.
Now we are joyous, and now we're dismayed ;
Now in the sunshine, and now in the shade.
Thus it must ever be, while on this earth,—
Seasons of sadness, and seasons of mirth.

ROGER BELL.

F all my good and faithful friends,
　　But few I loved as well,
　　As the subject of my humble song,
　　The good old Roger Bell.

Oft have we, at the close of day,
　When all our work was done,
Together climbed some lofty hill,
　To watch the setting sun.

Old Roger was a thoughtful man,
　Of cultivated mind ;
And in the meanest things of earth,
　Some lesson he could find.

He loved whatever God hath made,
　In earth, in air, and sky ;
Nothing appeared too mean for him,
　And nothing seemed too high.

The modest daisy at his feet ;
　The dew-drop on the grass ;
The tiny insect on the leaf,
　He did not idly pass.

To him each dull and passing cloud
　Was something to admire ;
When musing on the works of God,
　He never seemed to tire.

And oh! to me it was a treat
This good old man to see
When seated at his cottage door,
With the Bible on his knee!

At early dawn, with stick in hand,
　This veteran might be seen,
Pacing with feeble steps and slow,
　Around the village green.

And, oh ! to me it was a treat,
　This good old man to see,
When seated at his cottage door,
　With the Bible on his knee.

The thin, grey locks upon that head,—
　That broad and thoughtful brow,—
The gentle look and well-known voice,
　I well remember now.

I saw him on the day he died,
　And o'er his corpse did bend ;
My heart was full ; my tears came fast ;
　For I had lost a friend.

We saw that pale and wasted form
　Enveloped in the shroud : —
Beheld his children o'er him stoop,
　And weep, and sob aloud.

We bore him to the silent grave ;
　Few cheeks that day were dry ;
And, tho' the village mourned his loss,
　None felt it more than I.

Now lone and sad, I move along,
　Among the haunts of men ;
And wonder when my friend and I
　May hope to meet again.

I've lost a many valued friends,
　Relations, too, as well ;
But none for whom I sorrow more
　Than good, old Roger Bell !

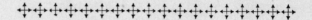

TO HUGH MASON, Esq., M.P.

MY Dear Sir,—
　　　May I ask you to kindly excuse
A few simple thoughts from a homely muse.
And as I now write to a Parliament man,
I will make this epistle as brief as I can.
Allow me to say I am gladdened to see,
That the people of Ashton have made you M.P.
'Tis an honour well-earned, and most richly deserved ;—
An acknowledgment, too, from the party you've served.

That grand scene near Jerusalem comes fresh to one's mind—
Where Christ rides in triumph ; the people behind
Waving branches of palm trees along the highways,
And rending the air with hosannas of praise !
But, alas ! for our frail human nature !—next day
The very same people cried " Take him away !"
But at Ashton it seems the whole thing was reversed,
They gave you the thorns and the crucifix first.

We remember the time, and now pen it with shame,
When the spirit of hate sought to tarnish your name ;
But your foes were frustrated in all they could do,
And were hung on the gallows intended for you.
But the eyes of the people were opened, and now,
Instead of the thorns there's a crown on your brow !
And those who were harsh and unkind in those days,
Now load you with honours, extol you with praise.

The cross came first, while the crown was delayed ;
The bright glowing sunshine came after the shade ;
And we hope these dark shadows will haunt you no more,
But that brighter and happier days are in store.
May your life long be spared, and the powers of your mind
Employed in the cause of your God and mankind.
Gird your armour afresh, Sir, and manfully fight,
For freedom to all men, for justice and right.

We call ourselves Christians, and wet up the sword,
To murder and rob in the name of the Lord.
O Christ ! it is men of thy pattern we want,
To expose this barefaced, hypocritical cant !
Where are all the grand saints !—we need Cromwell again,
With his high-souled adherents, his broad-shouldered men.
We need brave John Milton, that Master of Song,
To denounce this impurity, bloodshed, and wrong !

The priests and the Levites still grasp after wealth,
And the gods that they worship are Mammon and self.
We may boast and feel proud of these dear British Isles,
On which it is said a kind Providence smiles ;
But what will yond poor despised savages think
Of the freedom of those who are slaves to drink !
I have long been considered an " ill-natured thing,"
For fiddling and scraping so much on one string.

Still, I've faith to believe that the seeds we have sown,
Will firmly take root ;—that our Father will own
These earnest endeavours the people to bless,
And crown them at length with a glorious success.
And I venture to hope I shall yet live to see
The drink traffic crushed, and poor drunkards set free.
I have long been devoting my own humble powers,
To pluck up the weeds, and replace them with flowers.

And I know that the weariness, heart-aches, and pain,
Have not been endured altogether in vain.
Oh, no ! for behold ! on the far distant hills
The morning is breaking ! The sparkling rills,
As they stream down the mountains are silvered with light,
And these streamlets strike out to the left and the right,
Gaining swiftness and strength as they rush on their way,
Till at length they arrive in the great open bay !

So with our noble cause ; we have toiled through the night,
And already the mountains are flooded with light ;
The day-star of Temperance is now shining clear,
And silently telling us victory is near.
Come, thou with pale face and impoverish'd blood—
Who hast worn out thy life for thy country's good—
Step out to the breeze, bare thy brow to the sun !
And join in the shout, " The great battle is won !"

Excuse me for tiring your patience so long ;
I've been tempted to ramble a bit in my song,
But I wanted to state in a plain humble way,
What has been in my cranium for many a long day—
Namely—congratulate you, at this distant hour,
On your upward advance to distinction and power.
And tho' this small trifle may seem out of date,
Perhaps you will pardon me sending it late.

By way of excuse, just allow me to say,
That I've purposely caused this protracted delay ;
For I did not desire to appear as a pest,
At a time when I knew you must wish for some rest.
But, now that you've leave to absent from the House
To make speeches, read letters, write books, or shoot grouse—
I thought one might venture to scribble a song,
And say what has been in reserve for so long.

I remember last Spring, when the telegram came,
To say that M.P. had been placed to your name—
You will think I was greatly excited, of course—
But I actually shouted until I was hoarse !
When I got to my home, our dear girl—ten years old—
Said " Dada ! you seem to have got a bad cold."
" Bless thee, child," I replied, " I've been shouting for fun,
Because of the victories the Liberals have won !"

Well, I see they have christened you " Member for Hurst ;"
Now, I do not profess to be very well versed
In matters like these ; still, I venture to say
That the Banker would jump at your shop any day !
Never mind their bad temper, their venom and spite,
Still hoist up the standard of justice and right ;
And when in the future the goal shall be won,
May you hear the glad sound of the Master's " Well done !"

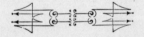

TO AN UNKNOWN FRIEND, ON RECEIVING FROM
HIM SOME VERSES ENTITLED
" WORDS OF CHEER."

I know not who thou art, my friend,
　　But thou art well-disposed, 'tis clear ;
How very kind of thee to send
　　Such soothing words, such words of cheer.

Art thou acquainted with my grief ;
　　Ah, me ! I've lost a faithful wife ;
And I have none with me to share
　　The sorrows and the sweets of life.

Bereft of one to me so dear,
　　No wonder I am lone and sad.
Alas ! alas ! she is not here
　　To cheer my soul, or make me glad.

I do not wish to pine or fret,
　　Or doubt the goodness of my God ;
I try to check my grief ; and yet,
　　'Tis sometimes hard to kiss the rod.

'Tis hard to see our friends depart,
　　To see them from our presence borne ;
And O ! what sorrows fill the heart
　　To think that they shall ne'er return.

Dost thou admire me ? then I feel
　　I have not wrote or sung in vain ;
And, if these wounds of mine should heal,
　　I'll try to pen some nobler strain.

I'll try to tune my harp once more,
　　My silent harp, now laid aside,—
And wake its music as of yore,
　　Ere my beloved partner died.

And since I know not who thou art,
　　These lines may never reach thine ear ;
But, oh, I thank thee from my heart ;
　　God bless thee for those " Words of cheer."

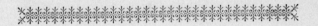

BEWARE! FOR THE CLOUDS ARE GATHERING.

BEWARE! for the clouds are gathering,
   And the rumbling noise that we hear
Is the murmer of suffering people,
   That tells us a storm is near.
Shall we dare to despise this warning,—
   Pressed upon us again and again?
Beware of the sullen storm-clouds,
   On the brows of desperate men!

We may boast of our vast dominions;—
   Of our national wealth and might;
But be sure that God and the People
   Will be found on the side of Right.
When the storm-clouds burst in the heavens,
   And the fiery bolts descend,
The proudest hearts will be shaken,
   And the reign of oppression end.

Why all this magnificent splendour
   Adorning the halls of the rich,—
While the toilers who made them their fortunes
   Are pining away in the ditch?
Must the masses be beggared, in order
   To bolster up kingdoms and thrones?
Are the bees to be forced into silence,
   While the honey is eaten by drones?

Who amongst us are found most deserving?
   The labourers delving the soil?
Or the inhuman, land-grabbing tyrants,
   Who fatten and feast on the spoil?
Are these to have British protection,—
   Their halls and their lands made secure,—
While bludgeons, and cowardly insults,
   Break the heads and the hearts of the poor!

Who gave these proud lordlings their mansions,—
   The riches with which they are blest ?
Who bribed them to use their great influence,
   In crushing the weak and opprest ?
Were these business transactions done fairly ?
   Do they add to our honour and fame ?
Ah, no ;—but quite the contrary,—
   To our lasting dishonour and shame !

Shall England still swagger and bluster ?
   Is the world given up to our care ?
If so, why not bottle the sunshine,
   And peddle it out with the air !
Look out, for the clouds are gathering !
   Yes, gathering on poor men's brows ;
Beware of the pent-up feelings
   Which your heartless acts may arouse !

Feast on, ye proud Belshazzars !
   Let joy fill the banqueting hall ;
But be sure of this—that God's finger
   Is writing upon the wall !
Go on with the feast, but remember
   That while you are feeding your pride,
The storm-clouds are ready for bursting,
   And Lazarus is starving outside.

What is it we hear from Old Ireland ?
   The children's innocent songs ?
Oh, no ! 'tis the down-trodden, groaning ;
   Yes, groaning beneath their wrongs.
Her patriots and priests are in prison ;
   Her sons and her daughters in tears ;
And yet we have men so degraded
   As to mock them with jibes and jeers !

How long shall this conflict continue ;—
   This war between Wrong and Right !
And when shall the weak be successful
   In their struggle 'gainst Wealth and Might !
Take heed to the gathering storm-clouds,
   And the writing upon the wall ;
For pride goes before destruction,
   And the haughty in spirit must fall !

A FATHER'S LAMENT FOR HIS ABSENT SON.

THANK you the same, but while that chair is vacant,
    Your kindly wishes must be all in vain;
For while the wandering one is absent from us,
    I cannot join you in the merry strain.
Here we are met, 'midst scenes of peace and comfort;
    The lamps are lit, the fire is burning bright;
But such a festive scene must needs remind us
    That *one* is absent.   Where is *he* to-night?

Cold hearts still ask " Am I my brother's keeper? "
    Their laugh is merry as they sip the wine;
But how can I, a sickly, sorrowing father,
    In such gay sport,—in such amusement join!
My mother, with her latest breath, besought me
    To make this first-born son my special care,
His mother, too, in her last painful moments
    Made him the subject of her dying prayer.

And yet, a father's heart needs no reminders
    From dying lips, long, long ago at rest.
How can a bird forget its absent fledgling,
    Or gaze unmoved on the forsaken nest!
Say you my boy's unsteady,—fond of roving?
    Leaving his lawful duties here undone?
It may be so; but I am still his father,
    And he, the prodigal, is still my son!

Is *he* the only one who introduces
    A note of discord into this our song?
Are all the others innocent and blameless?
    Is he the weak one? all the others strong?
If so, I point you to the gentle Jesus;—
    Who were the characters to whom He clave?
The Pharisee,—the wealthy, vain, self-righteous?
    Or was it sinners that He came to save!

Gather your robes about you, O ye virtuous !
    Spurn the poor brother crawling in the dust ;
Boast of your piety, but please remember,
    That He who holds the balances is just !
And who are *we*, that we should sit in judgment !
    Are *we* all perfect ?—all our actions pure !
Have we no faults to hide ?—no secret failings ?
    Does all the filth lie at our neighbour's door ?

On with the dance, all ye whose hearts are merry !
    Bring to your banquet beauty, wealth, and wine :—
All who can drown their sorrows in their pleasures ;—
    But, for the present, don't ask *me* to join.
Deem it a weakness, if it so should please you ;
    All my good feelings ridicule and spurn ;
Still, I must wait with saddened heart, and joyless,—
    Wait for the absent prodigal's return !

I like the ring of hearty, merry laughter,—
    The harmless frolic and the sober jest ;
But cannot take a part in the enjoyments,
    This festive season brings, with proper zest.
This being so, perhaps you'll please excuse me,
    If my cold manners seem to cast a blight
On what, to you, are lawful, healthy pleasures ;
    And more so now, on this glad New Year's night.

My thoughts are wandering o'er the great Atlantic,
    Where one we love may now be sat alone ;
And, while we rest our weary frames in comfort,
    His only bed to-night may be a stone !
Excuse me, then, if I may seem unsocial,
    Or sit in silence when the cup goes round ;
I cannot form a link in this dear union,
    Until the chain's complete,—the lost one found !

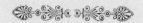

AN APPEAL ON BEHALF OF SUNDAY SCHOOLS.

READ AT A BAZAAR AT OSWALDTWHISTLE.

AT the outset, I think I can truthfully say,
That it gives me much pleasure to meet you to day,
And take—though it may be a very small part,—
In promoting the object we all have at heart.
Sunday Schools are our nurseries,—Eden-like bowers,
Where we keep our most cherished,—most beautiful flowers ;—
The training-ground, where our young saplings must grow,—
Have their minds stored with truths it is well they should know.

We see from the programme that one of your wants
Is more room for the health and the growth of these plants ;—
Where the sunshine must enter, and strike at the root,
Ere the saplings can thrive or put forth their fruit.
For though not skilled farmers, we all of us know
That seed must have room or it never can grow.
Let us hope that those present their duty won't shirk,
But see that our friends are not cramped in their work.

For I hardly need say—neither wise men nor fools
Can build, if they have not materials and tools.
But I must not thus needlessly take up your time,
And I need not appeal to your reason in rhyme.
As a stranger, perhaps you'll allow me to say,
That for what little help I may give you to-day—
I must thank my dear parents, who made it a rule,
That their children should go to the Sunday School.

An appeal on behalf of Sunday Schools.

The good lessons there learned I shall never forget,
And the hymns have a place in my memory yet ;
I name this to shew that the seed you may sow
In the minds of the young will assuredly grow,
And gladden the hearts of the reapers, we trust,
When the hands of the sowers have crumbled to dust ;
We labour in faith, and our eyes may not see
The struggling blade as it strives to be free ;—

But obstructions will vanish ; and, bursting to bloom,—
The sweet flowers will repay you with grateful perfume.
We are reaping to-day what was sown in the past,
And the fruit so long looked-for has ripened at last.
Yes, the men who are served, and the women who wait ;—
The great minds that now guide the affairs of the state,—
These are all the results of the care and the toil
That our fathers bestowed on the virgin soil.

It is *our* turn now, and the world looks on,—
Not only to thank the grand souls that are gone,—
But to see if *we* quit ourselves well in the fight,—
For God, for humanity, justice, and right.
Then let us so build, that in years to come,
Our children may meet in a beautiful home,
And sing once again the old hymns that were sung
With such pleasure and profit when *we* were young.

OH! THIS RAIN!

H! this rain, rain, rain;
　　It has rained all afternoon;
　I have tried, but tried in vain,
　　To strike up a merry tune.
I have sought relief in books,
　Culled thoughts from the brightest, best;
But my jaded and restless looks
　Proclaim the mind's unrest.

I long for the sun's bright beams,
　To come and dispel the gloom
That gathers around my dreams,
　As alone I sit in my room,
And think of the days gone by
　When my pen had the power to charm,
When I basked 'neath a cloudless sky,
　And the hearts of my friends were warm.

And wherefore now are they cold?
　And why do my warblings tire?
Has my Muse, like myself, grown old?
　Is there nothing left to admire?—
No flashes of humour or wit,
　Such as tickled my readers of yore?
Is the striker now powerless to hit?
　Is the lion unable to roar?

Who dares to approach my den!
   Who dares to enslave my mind!
Can ye silence the angry waves?
   Have ye power to control the wind?
Do men look out at night
   Expecting the sun to shine?
Or have I complete control
   Over these poor thoughts of mine?

Oh! this rain, rain, rain!
   Will it never, never cease!
Must I seek relief in vain,
   For a mind so ill at ease!
Must all my efforts fail?
   Is there no bright cheering ray,—
No kind and friendly gale,
   To chase the clouds away!

AN ESSAY ON A COW.

IT is said that a girl living out in the West,
   On her knowledge of cows being put to the test,
   Wrote the following essay, which surely will serve
   To show that the girl had begun to observe:—
"A cow is an animal (that's not denied),
And has got four legs on the under side.
The cow, too, has got a long tail, you know;
But the cow doesn't stand on it—oh dear, no.
Now the animal under review is wise,
For it uses its tail for the killing of flies.
A cow has big ears, which she flaps like a sail,
And they wriggle about much and so does the tail.
The cow, too, is bigger a deal than the calf;
But a full-grown elephant's bigger by half.
The cow is so small (as they make them at Rooking)
That they get in the barn when there's nobody looking."

A WINTER'S NIGHT AT BLACKPOOL.

'TIS a wintry Sunday evening, I am here in the house alone;
    Outside, a storm is raging; the sea-god is on his throne,
And hark to the wind, how it whistles through keyholes and under doors;
While here,—confined in the chimney—the storm-fiend rages and roars!
Here I am surrounded with comforts; the lamps and the fire burn bright;
But what of my storm-bound neighbours who are out on the sea to-night!
And what of the wives and children with features sad and pale,
Whose hearts are struck with terror, as they list to the fearful gale!

The churches are open for worship; there the young and the old repair,
To listen to words of comfort, and join in praise and prayer.
From the pipes of the grand old organ are heard the sweetest notes;
While through every part of the building the sacred music floats.
Ah! listen again to the storm-fiend! how restless and reckless to-night!
Now drowning the voice of the preacher, now filling the hearers with fright;
For they know from sad experience that many a tearful eye
Must have seen the last of their loved ones, and uttered the last good-bye!

The gale increases in fury: huge billows are dashed on the
    shore;
And the angry elements clashing make a terrible, deafening
    roar.
The foam from the madden'd ocean is driven about on the
    Strand,
And the scene, as beheld from the shore, is exciting, and
    awfully grand.
The moon is now up in the heavens, and appears to look down
    on the sight;
But the clouds sailing o'er full of mischief, hide from us her
    silvery light.
The stars—with but few exceptions—are hiding behind the
    clouds,
And,—like poor frighten'd children—are huddled together in
    crowds.

In the fishermen's cots, on the sand hills, where the turf-fires
    brightly burn,
Warm suppers are waiting for loved ones who may never again
    return !
Oh ! ye who are blest with riches, who can sit in your homes
    at ease,—
Do pity these seaside dwellers in trying times like these ;
For many a loving father, and many a bright-eyed boy,
Have gone down with the ships that were bringing the
    comforts you enjoy !
And pity the widows and orphans who this evening are sitting
    alone,
And fancy that well-known voices are heard in the wind's sad
    mourn.

God help and protect the poor sailors, who,—out on this
    winterly night,
May be struggling for very existence, and getting the worst of
    the fight.
And ye who profess to be Christians, when down on your
    bended knees,—
Know you cannot petition High Heaven for braver men than
    these !
We read of the fields of battle, and the heroes in the strife ;
But these go out as destroyers, and not as the savers of life.
The noblest deeds of daring, the deeds that all else eclipse—
Are performed by the large-souled sailors who " go down to
    the sea in ships !"

AT THE GRAVE OF JOSEPH COOPER.
[" THE DERBYSHIRE BARD."]

O-DAY, 'neath the clods of the green graveyard,
We lay the remains of an aged bard ;
A bard we have known and have honoured long,
For the lessons he taught by his life and song ;—

For the pleasures experienced by those who might roam,
To see the old man in his " flower-fringed home."
But those days are past, we shall meet no more,
Till we join the glad throng on a happier shore.

His well-known cot on the brow of the hill ;
The garden and posies are all there still ;
But he has departed who graced those bowers,
And others must watch o'er the plants and flowers.

The pen he long handled is now laid aside ;
The pictures and books that he looked on with pride
Will be squandered and pass into other hands,
And admired by the dwellers in far-off lands.

His neighbours will miss his well-known face,
And the children who lisped his simple lays
Will go with sad hearts and with tearful eyes,
To look on the grave where the old man lies !

Though death hath silenced the throbbing brain,
The thoughts that were born there still remain,
And take—though it may be—a humble part,—
In cheering many a sorrowing heart.

What joys and sorrows, what hopes and fears
Must have crowded a life-time of fourscore years !
And he oft must have stood with uncovered brow,
And mourned o'er some lost one, as we do now.

What a spot is this for the grave of a bard !
For the hills all around us seem placed as a guard,
To assure the thousands of sleepers here
That their beds are protected, so need not fear.

Good-bye, brother-bard ! we shall meet again,
When the world shall have listened to my last strain ;
When—as Waugh says—" Death has ta'en his tow,"
And my lips silenced, as thine are now !

ON THE DEATH OF THE LATE RICHARD OASTLER.

THE SUCCESSFUL CHAMPION OF THE TEN HOURS BILL.

WEEP on! weep on! a People's tears are due;
We've lost a friend, right noble, brave, and true.
No traitor he, to flatter, then deceive;
No, 'tis for honest worth that now we grieve.
'Tis meet and right that we our sorrows blend,
For Richard Oastler was the Poor Man's Friend.
Time, wealth, and influence—all he freely gave,
To snap the fetters of the Factory Slave.
O ye, who like myself were doomed to toil
In pent-up rooms, 'mid stench of gas and oil—
Bone, blood, and muscle, time and talent given—
Shut from the pure, the blessed air of heaven—
Think of the boon his pen and tongue secured,
The insults, jeers, and hardships he endured.
Think of the time when children, young in years,
Paced the dark streets, their eyes bedewed with tears;
Dragged from their beds, their labour had begun,
Long ere those eyes beheld the morning sun.
Their feeble limbs were clammy still with sweat,
When that bright orb had run his course and set.
No time for needful rest or healthful play,
On, on they toiled from weary day to day.
Their cheeks, once ruddy, now were sunk and pale,
And crowded graveyards told a mournful tale;
For, ere brave Oastler raised his arm to save,
Poor worn-out childhood found an early grave.
But, oh! a brighter day has dawned, and now
The youthful toiler wipes his sweaty brow,
And leaves his workshop at an early hour,
Ere the cold dew hath shut his favourite flower.
The workman now, his daily labour o'er,
Can trim the garden at his cottage door;
Draw up his chair beside the chimney nook,
And spend an hour in poring o'er some book;
Or with the poet soar on fancy's wing,
And learn from him how sweet it is to sing.

Read how the man with patriotic zeal,
Gives time and talent for his country's weal;
How the philanthropist leaves home and friends,
And, like his Lord, o'er human frailty bends.
At close of day the labourer can repair
O'er hill and dale, midst prospects bright and fair.
Far in the west the gorgeous setting sun
Sinks to his rest like one whose work is done;
While from the eastern hills, the moon's pale light
Heralds her advent as the Queen of Night.
Above the head, the gold-tinged clouds are seen;
Beneath the feet, a carpet fair and green.
He hears the milkmaid chant her simple air,
The good old farmer offer up his prayer;
And he recalls to mind that happy day
When first his mother taught her child to pray;
And though she's dead, he thinks he sees her now,
With silvery hair smoothed o'er her wrinkled brow,
And hears that well-known voice say tenderly—
" Prepare, my son, prepare to follow me."
He hastens home, a tear is in his eye;
But, though he weeps, his soul is filled with joy.
Dark brooding care that preyed upon his mind
Is now dispelled, and wisely left behind;
Gone is the downcast look and manner strange;
His evening's walk has wrought this happy change.
All honour to the men whose tongue and pen
Secured this precious boon to toiling men—
The leisure hour, the season doubly fair,
To roam the fields and breathe the balmy air.
Brave men were these—they toiled and laboured hard,
Until at length success was their reward.
A thousand blessings on thy hoary head,
Thou veteran " King ! "   What, though thy spirit's fled,
Thy name shall live amongst the good and brave,
And thousands yet unborn will seek thy grave
With grateful hearts, to drop a tear or two
On the green sod that hides thee from their view.
Crowd round his tomb, ye youths and maidens fair,
For, oh ! a noble-minded man lies there !
When such an one as Oastler was departs,
His greatest monument is *grateful hearts.*

MR. SOPKIN'S MISADVENTURES AT BLACKPOOL.

(After Ingoldsby's "Misadventures at Margate."

WHEN down at Blackpool last July, and walking on the
        pier,
    I met a pretty maiden, so I said, "How do, my dear?
    What do you here, love, by yourself? How is it
    you're alone?
Come, tell me all about it now, and where your sweetheart's
    gone."

She smiled, as maidens always do, and turn'd her head aside;
Then walked along in front of me with some degree of pride;
And yet some outward signs of grief methought I did espy,
Her grateful bosom heav'd, and then she gave a deep-drawn
    sigh.

"Come, what's the matter with you now? Do tell me all," I
    said;
"Has some one been deceiving you, or is your sweetheart
    dead?
Come, now, and don't be backward, dear, for I'm a single man,
And shall be very glad, indeed, to help you all I can."

The teardrops in her bright blue eyes I saw began to spring;
Again her bosom heaved, and, oh! she cried like anything.
At length her tongue found utterance. Her tale was brief, but
    sad:
"I haven't got a sweetheart, sir—I only wish I had.

"My father's very cross to-day, and told me I must go,
And, ere I show'd my face again, be sure to get a beau;
I've walked along this very pier full twenty times or more,
Besides the many hours I've spent in walking on the shore;

" I'm quite as nice as Alice Jones, Miss Brown, or Lucy Young,
They're all as proud as peacocks, these, (she had a rattling
    tongue!)—
If they're selected out for wives in preference to me,
I've made my mind up what to do—I'll jump into the sea ! "

" Cheer up ! cheer up ! don't fret this way ! cheer up ! " I
    kindly said ;
" You should not get such silly thoughts as these into your
    head :
If you should jump into the sea you'd certainly be drown'd,
And months might pass away before your body could be found.

" Come, take a walk along the shore—-yes, come along with me—
I lodge a little way from here, they call it ' Number Three ;'
My landlady will be within, her name is Mrs. Coe,
A very nice old lady, too—you'll like her well, I know."

She went with me to " Number Three," 'tis inland from the
    shore,
And as we entered in the house the clock was striking four ;
I briefly introduced the maid, and then politely said,
" Two cups of tea, ma'am, if you please, and a little ham and
    bread."

But Mrs. Coe seemed rather cross, and made a little stir ;
She said she'd gladly wait on me, but wouldn't wait on her ;
She said I'd found her lying by, upon some dusty shelf,
And if I brought such hussies there, I must wait on them
    myself.

I did not speak, but took my hat, and called on Mr. Price,
And said, " A pound or two of ham, and please to cut it nice ;
A half-a-dozen eggs as well, and let them be new-laid ; "
I did not want them for myself as much as for that maid.

When I came back I gazed about, looked round on every chair,
But could not see my female friend—'twas plain she was not
    there ;
I looked behind the parlour door, beneath the sofa too ;
I said, " Oh, dear, my darling maid, why what's become of
    you ? "

I could not see my best cloth coat, I could not see my hat;
My silver-mounted cane was gone, yes, even more than that;
My gold repeater, too, I missed, I left it on the wall,
But this was gone, and what was worse, my albert chain and all.

I could not see my potted shrimps, my nice black currant jam—
Both these were in the cupboard safe, when I went out for ham;
I missed my bran-new dressing case, 'twas on the sideboard
     laid;
My scent and hair-oil—all were gone, and so was that dear
     maid.

What could I do?   I rang the bell, when in comes Mrs. Coe—
"Oh dear! oh dear! what do you think? ain't this a pretty go!
That modest-looking little maid, whom I brought here to-night,
She's stolen my things and run away!" Says she, "And serve
     you right."

Next morning I was up betimes, and when I reached the town
I told the people whom I met that I would give a crown
If I could only find that maid who'd gone and served me so;
I was so vexed to hear a boy exclaim, " Poor simple Joe!"

I went along the promenade, a half-a-mile or more,
And looked at every girl I met or saw upon the shore;
I went into a coffee house, my doleful tale did tell,
And many persons seemed to think I'd not been treated well.

An oyster woman said she'd seen, that morning on the shore,
A—something funny—'twas a term I'd never heard before,
" A little forrud-looking puss," (dear me, what could she mean?)
" Wi' a set o' movable teeth in her yead, an' a pair o' roguish
     een."

She spoke about her being " spliced," and having seen her
     " sheer "—
It's very odd these oyster girls should talk so very queer—
And then she drew her brawny hand across her ruddy nose,
It's very odd that oyster girls should have such tricks as those.

I did not understand her well, but think she meant to say
She'd seen the maid I wanted catching snugly sail away
In Captain Slipham's Friendly Gale, about an hour before,
And they were now, as she supposed, some miles away from
　　　shore.

A donkey boy came up and said, " I know the duck you seeks,
The bobbies call her ' Hook-'em-od,'—she's been in gaol six
　　　weeks."
He said he thought she " hooked me od, and nicely twigged my
　　　clo'es,"
But I could scarce tell what he said, he talked so through his
　　　nose.

I went and asked the man in blue my property to track ;
He said, " Now don't you wish that you may get it back ? "
I answered, " To be sure I do, it's what I've come about."
He only smiled and said, " Sir, does your mother know you're
　　　out."

Not knowing what to do, I thought I'd go to Mr. King's,
And ask him if he'd catch the girl who'd gone and stole my
　　　things ;
He very kindly said to me he'd try and find her out,
But hardly thought he should succeed—there were many such
　　　girls about.

He called Detective Twig'em in, and I sat down and wrote
A list of what I'd lost—my cane, my hat, and best cloth coat;
He said my wishes one and all should promptly be obey'd,
But never to this hour have I beheld that faithless maid.

MORAL :

Remember, then, what, when a boy, I heard my grandma say,
" Beware of strangers you may chance to meet with on the
　　　way."
Avoid loose girls who've got no home, but hang about the Pier,
Or they may rob you of your things, and, like this maiden,
　　　" sheer."

Well, now, don't mention this affair, or spread it through the
　　　town,
I do not want it to be known that I've been done so brown ;
And when you go to Blackpool next, just stop and ring the
　　　bell,
Give my respects to Mrs. Coe, and say I'm pretty well.

TO UNCLE MATTHEW.

DEAR Uncle, we hope you arrived safe at home,
  And feel none the worse for your " out."
You ought to be very much better, I think,
  For a fortnight's good knocking about.
Oh ! how sad and how sorry we all of us felt,
  When this morning we bade you good-bye !
The tear-drops came silently out of our eyes,
  And we fancy your own were not dry.
This is one of the shadows that darken our path,
  As we wearily travel along ;
We meet with the bramble as well as the flower,
  And sadness is blended with song.
But away with reflection, for spring-time is near,
  And the hedgerows will soon be in bloom ;
Dame Nature will put on her holiday dress,
  Spreading round her a grateful perfume.
Your springtime, your summer, and autumn are past,
  And wintry winds blow on you now ;
Your travel-stained limbs are beginning to tire,
  While care-marks are seen on your brow.
Life's journey with you must soon come to an end ;
  We shall see you no more as a guest;
The heart that has throbb'd on for seventy-nine years,
  Must soon be for ever at rest !
The garden at Hepworth you tend with such care,
  Will seem quite deserted and lone ;
The willows will weep, and the flowers will droop,
  When Old Matthew the gardener's gone !
But this must not be yet, dear old Uncle, oh, no !
  For you have not yet cracked your last joke ;
You have some of last summer's potatoes to eat,
  And an ounce of good 'bacco to smoke.
God bless you, dear Uncle, in this your old age ;
  May your last days on earth be the best ;
And when the last summons shall call you away,
  May you quietly sink to your rest !

THE REFORMER'S MONUMENT.

SUPPOSED TO BE DISCOVERED ON RE-VISITING THE EARTH.

WHAT! here a Monument, and this a graveyard!
    A curious casket for so rich a gem!
    There's nothing here but crumbling dust and ashes,
        And sculptured urns can be no use to them.
Their eyes are closed, who sleep in these dark chambers;
    These drooping flowers must rear their heads in vain;
Their ears are deaf to all the fulsome flat'ry,—
    Which—could they hear it,—would but give them pain.

The bells are chiming out the hour of midnight;
    A solemn, painful stillness reigns around;
I am the only one on this "God's Acre;"—
    Alone I hover o'er this hallowed ground.
But what is here,—in this secluded corner?
    Where careless footsteps have but seldom trod?
A faded wreath or two lie here untended;
    A willow, too, bends o'er the grassy sod.

Now, o'er my head, the queenly moon is shining;
    And, by her silvery light, I plainly see
A sculptured stone; and, by its brief description,
    Find that this stone is raised to flatter me.
Is this the boon for which I spent a lifetime?
    The goal I laboured for, and sought so long!—
The sole reward of all my best endeavours!—
    Alas! mistaken kindness, cruel wrong!

I fain had hoped for something far more human,
    Than this cold, lifeless monument of stone!—
Something more cheerful than these sad surroundings;
    And more akin to living flesh and bone;—
The merry ring that comes from human voices;—
    The sweet remembrance of a child's last kiss;—
A grateful heart for some kind word I've uttered,—
    Would be more welcome than a scene like this.

I waited long for what you never gave me,—
   A kindly word to help me on my way,
And give me courage in my poor endeavour,
   To bring about a brighter, better day.
This sculptured stone—raised here to do me honour,—
   Telling to passers-by my name and worth,—
Can ne'er wipe out, or blot from my remembrance,—
   The pangs of torture I endured on earth !

Oh, Queenly Moon, withdraw thy silvery brightness !
   Clouds ! roll along; shut out this painful sight !
And may this mocking scene be lost for ever,—
   Lost in the darkness of this winter's night.
How quiet round me lie these thousand sleepers !
   Forms that once trod this earth in health and life;
Some of them left the battle field uninjured ;
   Some, like myself, were worsted in the strife.

The very dust on which I tread is sacred ;
   These forms, though dead, are still to memory dear.
These clods shut out from view our great reformers ;—
   The men who fought our battles slumber here !
Here lie the shells that held the precious jewels—
   That simple Ignorance thought of little worth :—
Pushed from the stage to make more room for actors
   Of meaner talents, though of " nobler birth."

But why stay here ; the morn is slowly breaking ;
   Far in the east I see a gleam of light :
The King of Day will soon ascend the chariot
   Now driven by the stately Queen of Night !
Farewell, damp graveyard ! farewell, kindly Mother ;
   On thy dear breast thy children safely lie ;
The world can ne'er disturb their peaceful slumbers,
   Thy breast their bed, their coverlet the sky !

TO MY FRIEND COUNCILLOR W. H. BUCKLEY, J.P.

ON RECEIVING FROM HIM A NUMBER OF OLD MANCHESTER
"OBSERVERS," CONTAINING—AMONGST OTHER MATTER—AN
ACCOUNT OF THE TRIAL OF HENRY HUNT, AND OTHERS.

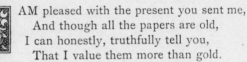 AM pleased with the present you sent me,
 And though all the papers are old,
I can honestly, truthfully tell you,
 That I value them more than gold.
These time-worn " Observers " remind us
 Of the struggles and desperate fights
The Reformers were called to encounter,
 While demanding their lawful Rights !

Ah ! little we know of the hardships
 Our forefathers had to endure,
When fighting the heartless oppressors,
 And pleading the cause of the poor !
They were hunted from village to hamlet,
 As foes to the King and Crown ;—
As firebrands bent on destruction,
 And turning things upside down.

But—thanks to the Lancashire heroes,
 Bad laws have been swept away ;
We can speak our thoughts out freely,
 And men *are* men to-day !
All honour to brave Sam Bamford,
 Who, while in the prime of life,—
Surrounded with dear home comforts,
 The smiles of his child and wife—

Led on his suffering neighbours,
　　With some cheering word or song,
To demand their Rights as a People,
　　And denounce all crime and wrong.
He has finished his work here, and left us,—
　　Gone to live in his home on high !
Has anyone caught his mantle,
　　And worn it ?　If not, then why ?

Have we got all reforms that are needed ?
　　Is the talked-of Millennium in sight ?
Have all bad laws been abolished ?
　　Have we got to the end of the fight?
Again let me heartily thank you,
　　And assure you of this one fact,—
That it gives me the greatest of pleasure,
　　To publish your generous act.

JUBILEE SONG.

GOD preserve and bless our Empress !
　　May His choicest, richest blessing
　　Fall in showers on Queen Victoria,
　　　On her Jubilee !
England's Queen, and India's Empress,
Widow of the Good Prince Albert,—
　　　Hail ! all hail to thee !

Join the chorus, swarthy Indians !
Waft the strains along, Columbia !
All can sing Victoria's praises
　　　On her Jubilee.
Prattling babes, and hoary vet'rans,
Stalwart youths, and lovely maidens,
Laud the name of Queen Victoria,
　　　Laud it o'er the sea !

TO MY SON ARTHUR, ON HIS TWENTY-FIRST BIRTHDAY.

TO-DAY you attain unto manhood, dear son;
Having served the three sevens, you are now
  twenty-one.
Like others before you, your journey through life,
Has had its full share of annoyance and strife.
But the seed has to struggle awhile in the soil,
Ere the labourer secures the results of his toil;
We have sickness and losses, the storms and the showers,
Mixed with health and successes, with sunshine and flowers.

You will find, son, as others before you have found,
That both good and evil come out of the ground.
We are ever surrounded by virtue and vice,
And can't be too careful in making our choice.
"This world is a stage"—so Will Shakespeare declares;
And you amongst others are one of the players.
It may be till now you've been much out of sight,—
Kept at work on the scenes, or arranging the light.

But to-day, my dear son, you've arrived at full age,
And you'll have to appear at the front of the stage;
Where your acts will be open to praise or to blame,
And the audience mete out to you honour or shame.
What an anxious position is this to be in,—
The applause of the public to lose or to win!
May you have many happy returns of the day,
And the people's "well-done" at the end of the play!

DEAR OLD ENGLAND, GOOD-BYE.

Tune—" The Mistletoe Bough."

EAR home of my childhood, I bid thee good-bye,
With a load at my heart, and a tear in mine eye;
Thou home of my forefathers, land of the free,
I sigh at the thought of departing from thee.
Dear Old England, good-bye.

Good-bye to thy mountains, thy moorland, and trees,
And the health-giving fragrance that floats on the breeze;
Other mountains and moors I expect soon to see,
But they cannot blot out my remembrance of thee.
Dear Old England, good-bye.

Good-bye to thy graveyards; I'm loath to depart
From the long-cherished objects that cling to my heart;
The graves of my fathers are sacred to me,
And now, my dear country, I leave them with thee.
Dear Old England, good-bye.

I go where more labour is found for the poor,
And the bread of industry is often more sure;
But in my new home, far away o'er the sea,
My thoughts will oft wander, dear England, to thee.
Dear Old England, good-bye.

I have basked in the sunbeams that play on thy rills;
I have trod thy fair valleys and roamed o'er thy hills;
And whate'er be my lot, wheresoever I be,
These fond recollections will cling unto me.
Dear Old England, good-bye.

There's a grandeur about thy old bulwarks and towers,
And lovliness seen in thy gardens and bowers;
Thy maidens are beautiful, lovely to see—
No wonder I sorrow at parting from thee.
                 Dear Old England, good-bye.

In the land I am bound to, whatever betide
Should fortune smile on me, or wealth be denied,
In sunshine or shadow, in sorrow or glee,
My true English heart will beat fondly towards thee.
                 Dear Old England, good-bye.

I am soon to be wafted away o'er the main,
And these eyes may not feast on thy beauties again;
But whatever the distance between us may be,
I shall never forego my attachment for thee.
                 Dear Old England, good-bye.

When surrounded by strangers in some far-off glen,
I will talk of thy greatness again and again;
How unworthy the land of my birth I must be,
If I fail to make known my affection for thee.
                 Dear Old England, good-bye.

When toss'd on the sea by the wave and the wind,
I will think of the dear ones I'm leaving behind;
And in my new home I will fall on my knee,
And offer a prayer, dear Old England, for thee.
                 Dear Old England, good-bye.

"BETHESDA,"

Read at the Meeting held to Celebrate the Re-opening of
Bethesda Chapel, Blackpool, February 16th, 1876.

R. Chairman and friends, it affords me delight
To respond to your kind invitation to-night,
And I venture to hope you will kindly excuse
A few rambling remarks of my wayward muse.
'Tis a pleasure to many now present, I know,
To meet where our fathers met long ago,
And tread in the very same steps they trod,
When they met in this building to worship their God.

There may be some here who remember the day
When God's people first met here to praise and pray;
And I'm sure it must please all good women and men
To meet with their Lord at " Bethesda " again.
And to some this old spot is especially dear,
For those they once loved are now slumbering here:
The father, who buried his pride and his joy,
Comes to drop a warm tear o'er the grave of his boy.

Others mourn over flowers faded early in life—
The wife mourns her husband, the husband his wife;
Many groans have been heard, many hearts have bled,
And open graves moistened by tears that were shed.
But we meet not to-night to lament or be sad—
Oh no! we are here to rejoice and be glad
That the " Pool of Bethesda " is open once more,
Where the sick their Physician may meet as of yore.

Where the sin-sick, the helpless, and impotent folk,
May again hear the Saviour say, " Rise up and walk "—
That this great healing power may be felt in our day,
Let us earnestly labour and fervently pray.
It was here the Dissenters their banner first raised,*
On this small hill of Zion.   And oh ! God be praised,
It has never been lowered, 'tis there to this day,
As a guide to the pilgrim through life's rough way.

To arms ! Christian soldiers !   The day draweth nigh
When the cries of God's people shall reach to the sky ;
When the curse of intemperance no longer shall mar
The fair face of this earth.   Truth's victorious car
Shall ride forth triumphant, and speed on its way,
And darkness shall flee at the dawning of day.
Then up, Christian soldier, and gird on thy sword,
And tread in the steps of thy Master and Lord.

Go up to the greatest, and down to the least,
And invite them to come to the gospel feast ;
Ask the envious to cease from his envy and strife,
And the drunkard to take of the " water of life."
Be kind to the erring—we all of us know
There is far greater power in a kiss than a blow ;
And a word spoken kindly, as everyone knows,
Is far more effectual than blame or blows.

But I must not detain you with words such as these,
So excuse the remarks I have made, if you please ;
There are those now before me more able to teach,
With attainments that I shall ne'er offer to reach ;
Who must always outstrip me, howe'er I may plod—
Whose heads have grown grey in the service of God.
With these I must leave you, but cannot do less
Than wish all our friends at " Bethesda" success.

Success to the preacher—may God's help be given ;
Success to the choir—may their songs rise to heaven ;
May the hearers—of whom I myself form a part—
Take the lessons and teachings of scripture to heart ;
And when we have ta'en our last look at the sun,
When the world disappears and the battle is won,
May we meet those we love in the realms of the blest
Where the flowers never fade, and the weary find rest !

*Bethesda Chapel was the first Dissenting place of worship erected in Blackpool.

CHRISTMAS SONG.

HOW Christmas-tide stirs our emotions,
   And we hail the return of the morn,
   When angels proclaimed the glad tidings,
   That Jesus the Saviour was born!
What a theme we have for the poet!
   What a subject is this for the pen!
But who can describe the sensations
   Of those who were witnesses then!

CHORUS:
   Still, we on this festive occasion,
      Our tribute of praises will bring;—
   Loud anthems to God in the highest,
      And to Jesus the new-born King!

The world had long groped in the darkness;
   God's people were sorely opprest;
His temples defiled by the stranger,—
   The noblest, the purest and best
Were objects of hatred and malice,—
   When the heralds of God came forth,
With tidings of joy to all nations—
   "Good-will to men! Peace upon earth!"
      CHORUS:—And we, &c.

And now, in the hall and the cottage,
   When this season of joy comes round:—
When hoar-frost is seen on our windows,
   And snow-flakes lie thick on the ground,
We meet in the family circle,
   And again sing the dear old song
We learnt at the knees of our mothers,
   So long ago; ah! so long!
      CHORUS:—And now, &c.

Then reach the old fiddle down, Robin;
   And, lads, get your voices in tune;
Wife, put by that knitting, and help us,
   And Peter shall play the bassoon;
And though our best efforts be feeble,
   And faults may be found in our strains,
Our songs shall at least be as hearty,
   As those heard on Bethlehem's plains!
      CHORUS.—Yes, we, &c.

VERSES READ AT A JUBILEE TEA MEETING

Held in the Congregational School, Stalybridge, on Saturday Evening,
April 23rd, 1887, on which occasion Messrs. John Laycock and
Joseph Hurst, the Superintendents, were each Presented with a
Purse of Gold and an Address in book form.

MR. Chairman and friends, it affords me delight
To be here and take part in this meeting to-night;
Tho' a platform, 'mongst parsons is hardly my sphere,
But your minister kindly invited me here;
And tho' you may some of you think me to blame
For accepting his kind invitation, I came;
If the general discovers he's picked the wrong men,
No doubt he will mind not to do it again.

This is Jubilee Year, and, to judge from this scene,
All the honours are not to be showered on the Queen—
For while city and hamlet and town are astir,
As to how they shall celebrate Jubilee Year
In a manner becoming, 'tis pleasing to find
That our Stalybridge friends are not lagging behind;
And for those they would honour they have not to roam
To London or Scotland, but find them at home.

You have learned to distinguish the wolves from the lambs,
And honour real heroes and not the mere shams—
The man who by labour increases our joy,
Not the warrior whose business it is to destroy.
I remember distinctly the year thirty-seven,
Altho' but a boy—not much more than eleven;
Fifty years have rolled o'er, but at this distant day
I can still see the school—the old school o'er the way.

Three lads sought admission—two brothers and self;—
The stones of this building were then in the delph;
I had not commenced spinning thoughts into rhyme;
Our old friend Mrs. Warhurst was then in her prime.
Fifty years since her wedding attire would be worn,
And two out of three of her children unborn!
We had then a dear brother—your guest here and I—
But for forty-nine years he has slept hard by.

Very few of the friends—I am sorry to say—
Who were here fifty years since, are with us to-day.
In fancy I see a whole host of them now :
The old pastor with silvery locks on his brow ;
The fine, manly bridegroom, and lovely young wife,
Setting out with great hopes in the morning of life ;
But the lurking disease with its withering blight,
Removed these dear loved ones away from our sight.

You will pardon these mournful reflections, I hope,
I have purposely given my feelings full scope,
Because it is well to reflect now and then,
And put these reflections in shape with the pen.
It is well to be merry, but if we are wise,
We must look for the storms that are sure to arise.
Let me speak to the young who are met in this place—
This life is a battle, a voyage, a race !

The honours of earth are not easily won ;
You must toil in the shade a deal more than the sun.
And you'll find this, my friends, while advancing in years,
The smiles will be few when compared with the tears.
The guests we have met here to honour to-night,
Whose locks, as you see, are both scanty and white—
Had entered the conflict, their armour had worn,
Before you young men and young women were born !

Fifty years in the fight, and not once known to yield !
Fifty years of hard service, and still in the field !
Have you thought of these hardships, denials, and strife,
Ye who think easy births the great objects of life ?
Their talents were used, the trees have borne fruit,
And the seeds they have sown here have taken deep root ;
And many brought up 'neath their nurturing care,
Are now women and men who are taking their share—

In the work of improving this country of ours,
And replacing the thistles with fruitage and flowers.
Please remember the lines I have published before—
I will venture to bring them before you once more :—
" Life's battles aren't fought upon couches of down ;
You've a cross you must bear before reaching the crown ;
The farmer for months has to labour and toil,
Before he can gather the fruits of the soil."

This is Jubilee Year, and these faces we see
Proclaim the great fact that their owners are free—
Yes, free from the many temptations that stand ;—
The traps set to ruin the youth of our land.
Our two worthy guests would ne'er dream of the day,
When their work would be noticed in this pleasing way ;
And I'm sure it must give them more pleasure than pain,
To find that they have not been labouring in vain :

That many from childhood were tenderly nurst
By my brother, John Laycock, and friend Joseph Hurst.
Ah ! worthy old neighbours, 'tis little we know,
What a deep debt of gratitude some of us owe
To the dear sainted parents now passed to the skies ;
No wonder the tear drops should start to our eyes,
As our minds wander back to the days of our youth,
When our minds were well stored with the lessons of truth.

There is just this one thought mars the meeting to-night,—
That our parents aren't present to look on this sight :
If the sons any praiseworthy actions have wrought,
These are due to the lessons the parents have taught.
Let me thank my old neighbours for being so kind
As to give me this chance to unburden my mind ;
For no doubt you have heard, and may think it seems strange,
That in some of my views I have ventured to change.

But to me it seems madness o'er dogmas to fight,
So long as the head and the heart are all right ;
I care not what censure you pass on my creeds,
So long as you cannot find fault with my deeds.
Let me say that the lessons I got at this place
Will influence my life to the end of my days.
As one suffering bad health—as a poor weaver's son—
I am not ashamed of the work I have done.

If what I've accomplished has brought any fame,
I am willing my friends here should join at the same ;
For allow me to say you have given me delight,
By the honour conferred on my brother to-night.
I am certain your gifts have been wisely disbursed,
Both on brother John Laycock, and friend Joseph Hurst ;
May their lives be long spared to enjoy what you've given,
Then receive a still grander reception in heaven.

A STALYBRIDGE SUPPER HOAX.

GOOD people, attend ; have you heard of the " hoax "
Which has lately been played upon some of our folks?
If you have not, pray read on awhile, if you please,
And I'll give you a few of the facts ;—they are these :—
Some " wags " in the town, who seem fond of a joke
At the expense of others, (od rot on such folk !)
Got some circulars printed and had them sent out
To our middle-class tradesmen, and " nobs " round about,—
Inviting them all to a supper, one night ;
And of course many went, thinking all would be right,
Well prepared, I've no doubt, for a " jolly good spree ; "
For some had been training all day, do you see,
In anticipation of what they might get ;
You could see by their looks they had stomachs " to let."
One man, whose employment is oft very high,
Between the green earth and the lovely blue sky,
Thinking this a nice offer, he left all his slates,
Determined for once he would clean them some plates.
So he dressed himself up in his white blouse and hat,
(He fills all his clothes very well, he's so fat,)
Went down in good time,—for this reason, no doubt,—
To loose a few buttons, and spread himself out ;
For his mind was made up long before he went in,
To take all the wrinkles clean out of his skin.

But, alas for the castles he built in the air,
Not a morsel of supper awaited him there.
Another man, very well known in the town,
As one very clever at knocking things down,
Was kindly invited along with the rest,
And a feeling of thankfulness rose in his breast.
Oh, he seemed quite delighted! it's likely he would :
I would draw you his portrait out now, if I could,
As he went to the " Angel," as clean as a pin,
(Though he never looks clean—he's a very dark skin.)
And, seeing the landlord, he nodded his head,
Threw the circular down on the table, and said—
" Aw'm goin' to a feed at th' Commercial to-neet ;
Th' lon'lord's givin' a supper,—an' nowt nobbut reet.
They sen there'll be sammon, plum puddin', an' lamb.
He's a jolly owd trump, mon—good-hearted—is Sam ! "
And away he went out, with a hearty good will,
Expecting, of course, very shortly to fill
His corpulent pouch, which had got rather flat,
With fasting so long,—but no matter for that,
For, along with the rest of the " nobs " of the town,
He very soon found he was " done " rather " brown."
A dealer in " fourpenny," living hard by,
(Now, I've nothing against this cheap beverage,—not I,)
Feeling troubled with wind,—having fasted since noon,
Some seven or eight hours,—went in rather soon ;
Of course, he'd no notion of how he was caught,
So he called for some ale, which the waiter soon brought,
To whom he just whispered, while handing his " brass,"
" Aw reckon this supper's noan quite ready, lass ? "
" Not quite," she replied, " you are rather too soon ;
You see we are plagued with a very slow oon."
" O reet, lass, o reet," said our friend, with a smile ;
Then he drank off his ale, and went home for awhile.
But he did not stay long there—he could not abide ;
For the wrinkles began to appear in his hide ;
And his boiler sung out in the key of " B flat ; "
Why, the fellow would almost have worried a rat.
He returned in this starving and famishing state,
To be told (oh, how dreadful !) he'd gone back too late ;
For some hungry scarecrow,—confound the old thief,
Had been in the house, and walked off with the beef.

Now one of the guests had been absent from home,
And his wife— not aware of the hour he would come,
Had not got any supper spread out on the board,
But she handed the circular o'er to her lord,
Which she said had been left for him during the day,
By a party residing just over the way.
He took it, and glanced it well o'er at the light,
Then said—with a smile on his features—" All right.
Aw'm invited to go to a supper, ha ! ha !
That's just what aw'm wantin',—aw'm off, lass,—ta ta."
And soon the Commercial he entered with glee,
For the thought of plum pudding, with brandy dip, free,
Had created most pleasing sensations, you know,
And made his saliva profusely to flow.
But, my eye ! he stood there as if shot from a gun,
When the company told him the stuff was all done.
Not a bit of a crust nor a bone could be seen ;—
A sickening look out when the appetite's keen.
He went home to his wife, and made known his sad fate,
When she said, " What a pity tha went deawn to' late !
But it's noan th' furst misfortin' tha's had sin we'rn wed,
So ne'er mind, get thi porritch, an' let's go to bed."
And now for a lesson such hoaxes may teach ;—
But don't be alarmed, I'm not going to preach.
Let nothing, my readers, induce you to roam,
In search of good suppers, but get them at home.
Should a neighbour invite you some night to a " stir,"
You can say " Please excuse, I'm obliged to you, sir."
Should it turn out a hoax, you can relish the fun,
And subscribe yourself thus :—

ONE WHO HAS NOT BEEN " DONE."

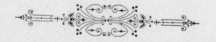

TO MY BROTHER BARD, THOMAS BARLOW.

(BORN ON THE SAME DAY AS MYSELF.)

EAR and worthy Mr. Barlow,
　　When I first began this letter,
　　I intended you should have it,
　　Through the medium of your pastor,
Who has lately been at Blackpool,
But I could not get it finished.

In the first place, let me tell you
That I felt extremely sorry,
When I heard from Mr. Lambley,
That your health had failed you lately.
Let us hope that splendid weather,
Grateful showers, and glorious sunshine,
And the warbling of the songsters,
May revive your drooping spirits,
To their wonted health and vigour.

As for me,—I'm much as usual ;—
Sometimes worse, and sometimes better ;—
One day full of joyous feelings,
And, perhaps, the very next day
Finds me fretful, sad and gloomy.
Such is life : we find our pathway
Strewn with thorns, as well as roses.
In the soil the seed must struggle,
Ere the flower gives forth its fragrance ;
And, to get a perfect picture,
We must have both lights and shadows.

But away with serious musings ;—
You are down, and need uplifting.
Would to God that I could help you,—
Write you out some safe prescription,—
Something that would raise your spirits,—
Help to put new life within you !
But you know, friend, I'm no doctor ;
But, like you, an ailing patient,—
Taking " Mother Seigel's Syrup,"
Boring others with my ailments ;
Preaching what I seldom practice,—
Namely, patience in our sufferings.

Well, we're all poor, weakly sinners,
Giving way to heavy dinners;
Grovelling, groping in the darkness,
When we ought to face the sunlight.
Come to Blackpool, dear friend Barlow,
Come, if possible, this week-end,
And inhale the healthy breezes,
Sweeping o'er the great Atlantic!
Overwork is always harmful;
Man must have some recreation.
You and I are getting older,
Work we once performed with pleasure,
Now we often find a burden,
And we long for rest and quiet.

Well, dear friend, we must not murmur;
We have had our youthful pleasures,
Now we stand aside for others;—
They're the actors, we're spectators!
Few can say what you and I can,
That we started life together;
You 'midst Derbyshire's attractions,
I amongst the hills of Yorkshire.
Both of us have had our trials;
Have we met those trials bravely?

Well, the fight is nearly over;
Now and then a shot may strike us,
But we let them pass unheeded.
Still a few more paces onward;
Slowly pass a few more milestones;
Then life's journey will be ended!
Here I close this long epistle—
Longer than at first intended.
Thoughts came fast as I proceeded,—
Thoughts I could not pass unheeded,
So I put them down in writing,
Very plain and very simple.
Well, good-bye, friend, for the present;
May God's blessing rest upon you,—
Is the earnest supplication
Of the writer,—Samuel Laycock.

HUGH MASON.

NOTHER great man fallen;
    A leader in the ranks;
    For whose kind benefactions,
    A Nation owes her thanks.

We mourn when the Spoiler snatches
    A brother from our side;
And this world of ours is poorer,
    Since good Hugh Mason died!

We read in history's pages,
    Of actions nobly wrought;—
Of difficulties conquer'd,
    And battles bravely fought.

We read of deeds of daring;—
    Of fearless men and bold,
Who fought for God and Country,
    In the warlike days of old.

All these we love and honour;
    And now we have one more name
To add to the band of heroes,
    Who grace the scroll of fame.

The people's friend, Hugh Mason,—
    So lately from us torn,—
Will live in the hearts and affections
    Of thousands yet unborn!

He fought, but with moral weapons;—
    The press, the voice, and pen;
And some of us well remember—
    Brave men were needed then!

As a large employer of labour,
    He was generous, just, and kind;
And, while seeking the good of the body,—
    He tried to improve the mind.

His generous, kindly actions
    Will live in our memories long;
And the honoured name of Mason
    Shall be handed down in song!

THE EXCURSIONISTS' SONG.

LL hail to the season when Nature is drest,
In her fine summer clothing, her gayest and best;
When the trees of the forest are laden with bloom,
And a thousand wild flowers breathe a fragrant
perfume.

Farewell, for a while, to the dull smoky town,
Where the seeds of diseases so often are sown;
Where the lingering consumption turns sickly and pale,
The cheeks of the girl once so blooming and hale!

We will leave these sad scenes, and away we will go,
Where the health-giving breezes unsparingly blow;
Where our ears may be charmed with the ocean's wild roar,
As we playfully gather the shells on the shore.

The clash of machinery is hushed for awhile,
And the care-burdened look is exchanged for a smile;
We leave the dull workshop, and haste to the bowers,
Where our hearts shall be gladden'd with music and flowers.

These foreheads of ours we will bare to the breeze,
Which gathers its fragrance from moorland and trees;
And for once in our lives we'll enjoy the rich treat,
Provided alike for the poor and the great.

We will gaze on the clouds tinged with purple and gold;
Feast our minds for a time upon beauties untold;
Thus refreshed with the journey, our voices we'll raise,
And join with the birds in a chorus of praise!

Then at night, as the sun gently sinks in the west,
We'll return to our homes, and the friends we love best;
Feeling thankful to Him whose all bountiful care,
Provides such enjoyment for mortals to share.

AN APPEAL ON BEHALF OF AN HOSPITAL
FOR BLACKPOOL.

WHEN asked to assist you this evening
　　With my poor, limping muse,
　　Though unwell, and unfitted for labour,
　　　I couldn't very well refuse.
Still, we all of us know what is needed—
　　From what we can hear and see,
Without any special exertions,
　　Or any appeal from me.

We do well to provide entertainments,
　　And places of public resort,
Where the care-worn may fling off trouble,
　　And join in pure, innocent sport.
We are proud of our beautiful buildings,
　　Such as this one in which we are met;
But there's something we haven't that is wanted—
　　We haven't a *hospital* yet!

We some of us claim to be Christians,
　　But religion is put on the shelf,
If it fails to promote our interests,
　　Or bring to us power and pelf.
Now, these raps at the people of Blackpool,
　　May appear to be very unkind,
But I'm sure you will please to excuse me,
　　If I venture to speak my mind.

That we've souls that require our attention,
　　Is a fact we admit as true;
But we must not forget—nay, we cannot,
　　That we've got our bodies, too;
And while men are exposed to danger,
　　Bruised limbs must be bound and set;
But we haven't provided for these things—
　　We haven't a Hospital yet.

I have long been a careful observer—
  An observer of men and things,
So am not without that knowledge
  That a long experience brings;
And I hardly need tell my hearers,
  It has pained my heart to think
How *vice* has been nursed and supported,
  And *virtue* left to sink!

Yes, and this in a land of Bibles,
  Where Queen Victoria rules;
Where we've colleges, churches, and chapels,
  And both day and Sunday schools!
How shall we account for this conduct—
  These strange, un-Christ-like deeds!
We are certainly wrong in our *practice*,
  Whatever may be our *creeds*.

We invest our money too often,
  In what tends to our National shame—
And we've naught but good wishes and pity
  To bestow on the sick and lame.
I am pleased with our grand motto—" Progress,"
  For it indicates breadth of mind,
And shows that the people of Blackpool
  Don't intend to be left behind.

We hail the new Tower they are building,
  And we hail the fine Pier down South;
These show we abhor stagnation,
  And favour intelligent growth.
We do well to provide all these things,
  But, neighbours, don't let us forget
That we live in a world of dangers,
  And haven't a hospital yet.

Have you never been called on to witness—
  What I've seen again and again—
The poor, mangled form of some brother
  Borne along through the streets by men!
And when we have known what followed,
  Haven't we felt a keen sense of shame,
And concluded that if we are Christians,
  We must only be so in name!

We know we're in danger of treading
    On some sensitive corns to-night ;
But that must not stop us from speaking,
    So long as we know we are right.
When some dangerous disease o'ertakes us,
    And our bodies get out of tune,
We cannot ignore the doctor,
    Or ask for his aid too soon.

Well, this is the *workpeople's* offering ;
    Who are going to come forward next ?
We hope the more wealthy amongst us
    Won't feel they have cause to be vexed
If we venture to throw a broad hint out
    That it seems to plain men like me
That the parson might spare a week's stipend,
    And the lawyer might give us a fee.

Then the various places of worship—
    What have these good folks yet done ?
Out of fifty collections per annum,
    Can't they spare poor humanity one ?
Can a Christian do anything better
    Towards making his " title clear,"
Than to reverence our Father in heaven,
    And take care of his children here ?

I wish I could speak to this audience
    In a pleasanter way than this ;
But one's bound to resort to a *blow*
    If he cannot succeed with a *kiss*.
If the iron shews signs of resistance,
    The workman must sharpen his drill ;
If *powders* don't answer our purpose,
    We must try the effects of a *pill*.

If we can't touch the hearts of the people
    With the fun in a humorous lay,
We must make a slight change in our weapons,
    And do it in some other way.
But surely it cannot be needful
    That one should put threats in his theme
To induce the good people of Blackpool
    To encourage this hospital scheme.

When asked to assist in this matter
　My spirits were greatly depressed ;
Fifty years of bad health had unhinged me,
　And I felt that I needed rest.
I mentioned the names of others
　That my visitors ought to see,
Such as aldermen, councillors, parsons—
　Much abler men than me.

But I found all this was useless,
　For when I dismissed them with " No ! "
And opened the door for their exit,
　They flatly refused to go.
Well, I found myself placed in a pickle,
　And, of course, I had to bow ;
And it's well that I did, I am thinking,
　Or they might have been there till now.

But don't run away with the notion
　That—because I refused my aid,
And only gave way to *pressure*,
　In short, did what I was *made* —
That I am not in sympathy with you ;
　For if ever I felt I was right,
It is *now*, as I stand on this platform,
　And make this appeal to night !

In conclusion, I feel rather sorry
　That the little I have to say
Is not done in a more inviting—
　In a more effectual way.
But, whatever the faults or failings,
　Be sure I have done my best,
And leave it to others more able
　To come forward and do the rest.

READ AT A TEMPERANCE MEETING, OF WHICH THE WRITER WAS CHAIRMAN.

Y dear friends, I must say I feel out of my sphere,
In taking this prominent part with you here;
There are other kind friends laid aside on the shelf,
More fit for a chairman than I am myself.
But our dear brother Carter so planted his bait,
Used his powers of persuasion—well known to be great,—
So praised my good points, that I'm bound to confess
I was "knocked down" at once, and I had to say "Yes."

Had you asked me to come here some two years ago,
I'm afraid my reply would have been a harsh "No!"
For then you had gained an unenvied renown
Not as sober "Queen's Park," but as drunken "Queen's
    Town."
Two years ago, some of the trees in this park
Were strangers to sunshine; they grew in the dark.
The young plants, if not bare, were but scantily clad,
And the fruit—well, I hardly need tell you—was bad.

But pioneers came from the left and the right,
Cleared away the obstructions, and let in the light;
Showers of sympathy fell, to refresh and illume,
Till the trees and young saplings burst forth into bloom.
And features long marred by the drink and its wiles,
Were becoming more human, and lit up with smiles;
And many were snatched from the drink traffic's jaws,
Who are now shining lights in the temperance cause.

Well. friends, I am pleased to be with you, I'm sure ;
Our warfare is God-like, our motives are pure ;
'Tis an honour to serve in this army of ours—
To cut down the thorns, and replace them with flowers.
We fight for the truth—not to curse, but to bless,
And—this being so—we may hope for success ;
We have brought to the sunshine those once in the dark,
Changed unlovely " Queen's Town " into lovely " Queen's
      Park ! "

In what nobler work can a mortal engage,
Be he statesman, or orator, poet, or sage,
Be he youthful or aged, be he poor, be he rich,
Than in helping his fellow-man out of the ditch ?
What mind can conceive a more soul-stirring sight,
Than the one we have here now before us to-night ?
Men made in God's image can reason and think ;
Once groping in darkness, and slaves to the drink !

I have lived in this neighbourhood twenty long years ;
I have joined in your hopes, shared your sorrows and fears ;
Done what little I could with pen, paper, and ink,
To put down this horrible traffic in drink.
Many years have I worn the Good Templar's badge ;
For I helped to establish the " Gleam of Hope " lodge.
My mind has experienced both pleasure and pain,
As our work might succeed, or our labour seem vain.

One has seen many efforts successfully made,
But the work at Queen's Park here throws *all* in the shade ;
The wonders achieved here no language can tell ;
For we now have a *heaven* where once was a *hell !*
The bright star of temperance has thrown down her light,
And homesteads once dark are now cheerful and bright ;
Men have knocked off their chains who were slaves to the
      dram,
  While the wolf and the lion lie down with the lamb.

Is not this a grand work, friends ?   Then tell us no more
Of the victories they won in the good days of yore !
Those victories were reeking with bloodshed and strife ;
While *ours* teem with hopefulness, happiness, life.
Their victories were won with the cannon and sword,
Ours are often achieved with a kind, loving word ;
We put on our armour, and march to the fray,
With a certain conviction of winning the day.

I am proud to belong to the temperance ranks ;
Tho' 'tis true we may meet with more *insults* than *thanks ;*
But a brave-hearted soldier who girds on his sword,
Must rise *above* these things when *duty's* the word !
Yes, the fight must be fought, and the race must be run,
Ere the battlements fall, or the goal can be won.
We get the pure gold by removing the dross ;
And the crown must be reached after passing the cross.

But you came to the *lecture*—I must not go on :
One word to the folks at Queen's Park, and I've done :
Stand firm to the pledge ;—more even than this —
Try to make all your homes into Edens of bliss.
A park should be blessed with a health-giving breeze,
With fountains and grottoes, with foliage and trees,
Where the robin may sing, and the lark build her nest,
And the sickly, and wearied-out toilers may rest.

Let *your influence*, like breezes, go sweeping along,
Flooding fountain and grotto with sunshine and song.
May the trees in this park have a permanent root,
And make known their existence by bearing good fruit.
May God's blessing fall on you, like soft April showers,
Unfolding the leaves, making fragrant the flowers ;
May light fall on spots that are still in the dark,
And the temperance cause flourish still more at Queen's
        Park !

GET IN HARNESS, YOUNG MEN!

HERE is something to our mind ennobling and grand,
In the efforts to train the young men of our land;
So the help and instruction we seek to impart,
Should aim to improve both the head and the heart.
Would to God we had wisdow to train them aright,
For the battle of life they are destined to fight!
Young men, be in earnest in all that you do,
For the future of England depends upon you.

'Tis to you we must look for the men of the day,
When the Gladstones and Salisburys have all passed away;
It is you who must fill posts of honour and trust,
When we who are older are laid in the dust.
Yes, a work lies before you important and great,—
Affecting the mighty affairs of the state.
Be true to your trust then; take care what you do,
For old England must one day be governed by you.

Yon sturdy oak trees that defy the rude blast—
Were but delicate plants in the days that are past;
But our forefathers nursed them and trained them with care,
And look at them now; how vigourous and fair!
How firm, how unmoved and majestic they stand,
In spite of the storms that sweep over the land!
Be firm like these oaks, and keep this fact in view,—
That the strength of this nation is centred in you.

One by one our great actors are leaving the stage;
They have written their names upon history's page:
And now they withdraw from the conflict and strife,
Leaving others to fight the great battle of life.
Give your names in, young men! there's a race to be run,—
A goal to be reached, and a fight to be won!
The old veterans are passing away from our view,
And the gaps in the ranks must be filled by *you*.

Young men! you've a lot of hard work to perform:
Do it *now*, while your hearts and affections are warm;
Do it *now*, —as life's morn opens out into day,
And the powers God has given you are all in full play.
Do it now, while your youthful ambition soars high.
And the sun seems unclouded and bright in your sky.
Oh! brothers and sons, you've a duty to do,
And much will be claimed and expected from you.

The great minds that now charm us with music and song,
Look to you to fill posts *they* have toiled in so long;
Yes, to you, the young men of our dear native land;
Oh, shall not your lives then be noble and grand!
Shall the talents with which Heaven hath blessed you be hid,
Or allowed to remain unemployed? God forbid!
Young men,—and this holds good to young women too,—
Your country is anxiously looking to you.

Would you rise to real nobleness, now is your chance,
If you've any bad habits, uproot them at once;
All that tends to degrade put away out of sight,
Have the courage to do what you know to be right.
Let the world ever find you to *be* what you *seem*,
And thus you will merit respect and esteem.
Young men, act with care,—conscientiously too;
Be honest and upright in all that you do.

In conclusion; I know it is not very nice,
To be acting as teacher, and giving advice;
Still, I'm free to say this—what I have to impart—
Is the fruit of much thought, and comes warm from my heart.
I have tried to amuse, and instruct in the past,
And hope to toil on in this groove to the last.
Like yourselves, I must try to be faithful and true,
And keep the great end of my mission in view.

TO MY BROTHER.

On Revisiting my Birthplace.

ONCE again (perhaps the last time,)
 I have been to see my birthplace;—
 Been to see the humble cottage,
 Where I first beheld the daylight,
Where I gained my first impressions,
Some of which have never left me.
These dear scenes I now revisit,—
This dear home of early childhood,
On the borders of the moorland.
Oh, how changed since first I saw it!
Then the garden near our cottage
Bloomed in summer-time with roses,
And in winter-time with snowdrops.
Now the house stands there deserted;
Not a trace is seen of garden,
Save one lone and rugged hawthorn,
Weeping o'er the desolation!
Where are now my childish playmates,—
Those who roamed the meadows with me,—
With me gathered honeysuckles,—
Chasing butterflies in summer,
Rolling snowballs in the winter?
Where are now my youthful schoolmates,—
William Schofield, Henry Dyson,
Sarah Hoyle, and Phillis Charlesworth?
Some are sleeping in the graveyard;
Others following, tired and weary,—
Count the milestones as they pass them,
Wishing they could end their journey!

Brother, you will still remember,
How one stormy winter's morning,
Every window in our cottage
By the drifted snow was darkened !
How we waited for the daylight,—
Waited hours, and yet it came not ;—
How we strained our ears to hearken
To the voices or the footsteps
Of the neighbours living near us,
Till at length our parents heard them,
Then arose and sought the doorway.
This the snow had blocked completely,
But the neighbours came to help us,
Moved the snow away with shovels,—
Told us it was nearly noonday,—
That the darkness had deceived us.
Yes, dear brother, you'll remember
How we had to make a pathway
Through the snow, right down the meadow,
So that we might hold communion
With the people in the village.
Yes, and winters then *were* winters !
Snow would lie for weeks together ;
Dams and ponds were frozen over,
While King Frost would show his skill-craft
In his sketches on our windows.
Then the spring-time—glorious spring-time !
How our youthful hearts were gladdened
When we saw the budding hedge-rows ;
Saw our favourite pinks and wallflowers,
Blooming in our little garden !
Saw the fields in all their glory,
Clothed with buttercups and daises.
We are old, now, and these pictures
Linger only in our memories,
Where they've lain for half a century.
Still, 'tis pleasant to revisit
Scenes we looked upon in childhood,
Where we formed our first impressions.
True, the homes once filled with gladness,—
With the sound of children's voices,—
Now are silent as the graveyard !

Prose in the Lancashire Dialect.

HEAW BILLY ARMATAGE MANAGED TO GET A NEET'S LODGIN'S.

THERE'S noan mony foalk abeawt here but what knew owd Billy Armatage, He kept toathry ceaws, an' a horse or two once, but he's swallowed 'em o long sin'; for he wur terribly fond ov his drink, wur Billy, an' mony a rare scrape it's getten him into. Aw've yeard it said 'at he once ate a peawnd o' candles for a pint ; but whether that's true or not aw conno' say ; but he did look loike a chap 'at wouldn't be very partickler abeawt what he ate, iv he could nobbut manage to sup what he'd a moind. He'rn summat loike th' chap i' Howmfurth—he loiked his drink—

> New an' owd,
> Warm an' cowd ;
> A sup in a possit aw lawk ;
> Saar an' sweet,
> Dark an' leet—
> Gie me ony o' these, an' aw'd empty a dawk.

Owd Billy 'ud ha' supped ony sooart, beawt oather smellin' or tastin' it aforehand. Iv it wur co'd drink it wur reet.

Well, one neet, him an' a lot mooar o' th' same stamp wur ceawered drinkin' at an owd aleheawse co'd th' "Plough Inn," an' it seems they didn't know heaw th' toime wur gettin' on, till th' lon'lord went an' towd 'em they'd better be goin' whoam. Well, owd Billy began o feelin' rayther uneasy, an' wonderin' what he must do, for he wur a long way off their heawse, an' he'd spent every hawpenny ov his brass. "Aw mun try iv aw conno' shape it to get lodgin's somewheer," he said to hissel ; "aw'll co' at th' furst aleheawse aw come at on th' road-side, an' aw'll pretend to be deof, an' iv they sen they conno' foind me reawm aw'll be same as iv aw didn't yer 'em." So he did as he said he would, an' co'd at th' "Waggon an' Horses," an owd licensed heawse upo' th' road-side. Th' lon'lord wur just gerrin' ready for shuttin' up, for it wur somewheer abeawt twelve o'clock.

"Han yo a bed at liberty here?" Billy inquired, "becose aw should loike to tarry here to-neet, if yo con do wi' me."

"I am sorry to have to say that I believe all our beds are occupied," said th' lan'lord.

"That's reet," said Billy, "aw thought aw shouldn't be denied. Aw wur towd aw should get a bed here—yo'd allis plenty o' reawm; so iv it winno be to' mich trouble for yo, aw'll have a hit o' supper afore aw goo."

"I told you we had no beds at liberty," said th' lan'lord, hardly knowin' what to mak' of his customer.

"Well, a bit o' cowd mate, or owt'll do; aw'm noan very partickler what aw have. Aw dunno' want to put yo to mich trouble, as it's gerrin' so late."

Th' lon'lady wur stood hearkenin', so thinkin' th' chap must he deof, went up to him, an' bawled in his earhole, "You cannot stay here; all our beds are taken up."

"Etten up, yo'r cowd mate, is it? Well, yo can let me have a bit o' cheese an' bread—owt'll do. Aw wouldn't trouble you at this toime o' th' neet, but aw'm feart mi back an' mi bally ull be foin' eawt afore mornin' iv aw dunno' get a morsel o' summat to keep 'em separated. This bit o' stomach o' moine's bin so used to havin' a feed abeawt supper toime 'at aw deawt aw shall ha' no quietness iv aw try to put it off beawt owt."

"Seein' 'at they could do no good wi' th' owd chap, they left him, an' went into another reawm to talk matters o'er.

"Come, aw'm gerrin' on very noicely," said Billy to hissel; "Iv all's weel aw shall nooan be long afore aw'm nestled among th' blankets. A chap may do as weel beawt brass as wi', iv he's nobbut his wits abeawt him. Aw'm goin' to work this dodge noicely to-neet, aw see aw am. Eh, aw wish owd Thatcher wur here neaw, an' could see this bit o' game aw'm carryin' on; wouldn't he shake that big corporation o' his! he would so. Aw shall tell him o abeawt it when aw leet on him—that is iv aw get through it middlin' weel."

"Well, James," said th' lon'lady to her husband, when they'rn getten bi theirsels, "what are we to do with yond man?"

"Nay, I don't know; he does not appear to take in any thing that we say. I suppose we shall have to do the best we can with him."

"Well, James, we have no room for him ; you know that as well as I do. Number one, over the parlour, is occupied by Mrs. Davies, and the one over the kitchen by that Scotchman. There is only the chamber over here, and that we shall want for ourselves."

Owd Billy had crept as near th' door as he could get, an' yeard so mich o' what they'd bin sayin' as gan him to understond wheer there wur a chamber to let ; so he made no moor ado, but he seet off upsteers as fast as he could leather away, went straight into th' chamber, an' fastened th' dur after him. Th' lon'lord thowt he yeard some soart ov a noise, an' went to see if th' chap wur wheer they'd left him ; an' as soon as he fun it eawt he wur gone. he off upsteers after him, an' th' lon'lady an' o, an' they tried to oppen th' dur, but couldn't. Of course, Billy yeard 'em, so he pretended to be talkin' to hissel. " They looken daycent foalk enuff here, for owt aw con see on 'em, but there's no tellin' who they may have lodgin' wi' 'em, so it's safest to ha' one's chamber dur fastened. Aw shouldn't loike to ha' th' bit o' brass at aw've getten for th' owd mare takken off me. Aw'd better ne'er ha' come. Aw've been at a deol o' places i' mi toime, but aw've never bin at one afoor wheer they tell'n th' lodgers to goa upsteers bi theirsel's ; but it matters nowt as aw know on. Aw'd rayther ha' had a bit o' leet after o."

Th' lon'lord an' his woife had bin hearkenin' at the dur, so when Billy gan o'er talkin', one on 'em gan it a regular good thump, an' th' lon'lord sheawted eawt " You cannot have this room, so you may as well come out at once. I don't know what business deaf people have away from home. Open this door, and come out."

Owd Billy pretended to yer nowt he said, but kept on talkin' to hissel. " This is a rare noice reawm ; aw'm fain 'at aw've let o' sich a shop. Aw dur say this bed belongs to th' lon'lord an' his woife. They'll very loikely mak' up a bed on th' floor, or else lie on th' sophy ; at ony rate, it stroikes me very powerfully at it's their bed, an' a rare good un it looks. Aw'll say mi prayers, an' then get in an' feel what mak' o' one it is. Th' best on it is, awst ha' nowt to pay; at least, Joe Winterbottom towd me soa, an' he's put up here mony a toime."

Thump went th' dur ogen, for th' lon'lady fot it a welt same as iv hoo wur beawn t' break it in. "Do you hear?" hoo said, "will you open this door? This room belongs to myself and husband, so be kind enough to leave it." It wur o' no earthly use hur sheawtin', for owd Billy pretended to yer nowt at hoo said, but kept talkin' to hissel. "It's a capital bed, this is; it feels as weel as it looks. Aw dar say its made o' fithers 'at they'n plucked eawt o' sich loike chaps as me; they'n had mony a hundred peawnd o' my brass among 'em, they han indeed. That's very loikely th' reason why they chargen nowt here. Aw wonder heaw my owd woman's gerrin' on awhoam; hoo'd expect me back afooar neaw, aw know hoo would. Good neet to thee, owd wench; aw nobbut wish tha'd as good a bed as aw have. But aw'm gerrin' sleepy, so aw'll have an eawr or two while aw've th' chance."

O wur as still as deoth for a minute or so, an' then owd Billy pretended t' begin a snoorin'. When th' lon'lord yeard that, he poo'd a great long face—abeawt as long an' as sweet as owd Nancy Platt's toffy sticks—an' said to his woife, "Sarah, it's of no use making any more bother; the fellow is fast asleep, and there is no possibility of arousing a deaf man; we may as well leave him, for any good we can do now." So they went deawn th' steers, an' left owd Billy to hissel, an' he wur no' long afoor he wur fast asleep, an' dreamin' abeawt sleepin' on fither beds, walkin' on carpets, an' eatin' cheese an' bread at other foalks' expense.

Well, after sleepin' very seawndly for a toathry heawrs th' owd chap wackened sometoime abeawt hawve-past seven i' th' mornin', dressed hissel, an' went creepin' deawn th' steers. He went an' ceawered on a couch cheer i' th' kitchen, an' th' lon'lord wur no' long afoor he wur at him, an' talkin' to him.

"I say, my good fellow, do you know you have been sleeping in my chamber?"

"O, aw loiked sleepin' i' yond chamber very weel; aw've had a middlin' good neet's rest. Couldn't ha' had a better, 'at a know on."

Th' lon'lord, seein' 'at owd Billy didn't appear t' understond what he said, went a bit nearer, an' bawled eawt in his earhole, "What I say is this, you have been occupying the bed belonging to myself and missis."

" Well, th' bed's reet enuff, aw've no deawt ; aw've noather seen nor felt owt o' th' sort. Aw should think 'at i' country places loike this yo'r noan mich troubled wi' bugs."

" I did not say anything about bugs."

" Ah, aw see ; they wouldn't boite me iv yo' had ony. They met boite somb'dy loike yo' 'at's so fat."

Th' lon'lord geet gradely vex'd at Billy for talkin' i' that road, an', fixin' his een on him, said, " What's the reason you talk in the way you do ? Are you deaf ? "

" Whor ? "

" Cannot you hear ? "

" Tarryin' here ? Now ; at leost no longer nor whoile aw've had a bit o' brekfast ; aw shouldn't exactly loike to set off beawt."

Th' lon'lady coom in while they were talkin', so Billy bid her good mornin' ; but didn't hoo look rare an' feaw at him ! Hoo looked abeawt th' same as a friend o' mine once did, when a chap 'at wur noan gradely reet went into th' heawse, one foine Sunday, an' geet owd ov his dinner an' ate it o. Well, hoo started a axin' her husband what owd Billy said, loike, abeawt goin' upstairs as he did, beawt axin' leov. " Why the man must be a fool," said th' lon'lord ; " I asked him if he knew he had been sleeping in our chamber, and his reply was, ' O, aw loiked sleepin' i' yond chamber very weel.' Really, Sarah, of all the customers we have ever had since we opened this place, this fellow beats them all. He is either mad or deaf."

Th' missis thowt hoo'd try her hand on him a bit, so hoo went up to him, an' sheawted, " Where do you come from ? "

" Now ; aw want no comb ; aw ne'er mak' a practice o' combin' my yead, only on a Sunday mornin'. Aw'm noan as preawd as some foalk. Aw let my yure grow as it's a moind, six days eawt o' th' seven."

" Really, my good man, you did not understand my question."

" Oh, aw see ; what will aw ha' to mi brekfast. Well, yo' can boil me a couple o' eggs, an' mak' me a sope o' coffee, iv yo' pleosen. Yo hanno' sich a thing as a bit o' cowd ham i' th' heawse, han' yo', missis ? "

" Have you ever been this road before ? " asked th' lon'lady.

" Eh dear, now, bless you ; aw couldn't eat four ; aw never eat no moor nor two eggs at a toime ; two ull be quite plenty. Aw ha' seen th' day, when aw'rn younger, when aw should ha' thowt nowt abeawt polishin' off hawve a dozen, but thoose days han' gone by long sin'."

Th' lon'lady stood hearkenin' him till hoo could howd no longer, for hoo turned to him, an' said, " I tell you what, you're a regular bore."

" Nay, aw shall want nowt no moor, as aw know on ; aw noather eat saut nor pepper to 'em. Neaw yo'll let 'em be new-laid uns, missis, iv yo' pleosen ; shop eggs are very oft rotten abeawt this time o' th' year."

" Sarah, get him some breakfast ready, and let us be without him. The sooner he goes and the better it will be for us, I can assure you. It's of no use wasting any more time with him."

So hoo started an' boil'd him a couple o' eggs, an' made him some coffee an' buttercakes, an' th' owd mon wur no' long afoor he had 'em put eawt o' th' seet.

" You seem to be rather deaf," said th' lon'lord, as he went an' ceawered him deawn near to owd Billy.

" Oh, yo' con eat what's left, con yo' ? Well, yo'll be welcome to o 'at aw leov, an' that'll noan be mich, aw con tell yo'. Aw've generally a good appetite in a mornin'. Heawever, yo' con sit here a bit, an' see heaw aw go on, an' then iv there is owt yo'll be ready for it."

When th' lan'lord yeard that, he begun a poikin' off as nicely as he could. Owd Billy cleant his plate as weel as iv it had been weshed. When he'd done, he buttoned his cooat, an' began a shapin' for goin' whom. Th' lan'lord thowt it wur abeawt toime to be lookin' after his brass, iv he wur to have ony, so he went and put his meawth close to owd Billy's earhole, and bawled eawt leawd enuff to be yeard welly a hawve-a-mile off,—" Let me see, I think you have not paid us yet ? "

" Nowt to pay, yo' sen, dun yo', mester ; o reet. Aw wur towd afoor aw coom 'at yo' charged nowt here. Well one con but thank yo'. Aw dar' say aw've bin a bit o' trouble to yo', bein' as aw'm so deof ; but yo'll happen think nowt abeawt that. Aw'm very much obliged to yo'."

" James," said th' lon'lady to her husband, you are not letting him go without paying, are you ? "

" I don't care whether he pays or not, if he will be off. If you think you can do anything with him he is there."

" Dear me, James, how annoying it is—a man coming as he has done, at twelve o'clock at night, wanting a supper getting ready, and then taking possession of the only bed we had unoccupied in the house ! "

" What a sayrious misfortin' it is to a body when they're deof,' said Billy, " aw should soa loike to yer what foalk are talkin' abeawt, but aw connot, yo' see. Aw've hard wark to mak' owt eawt 'at foalk sen to me. Aw dar say, iv one could yer 'em, th' brids are singin' as sweetly as con be eawt o' th' dur. Nowt used to pleos me better, when aw're younger, nor to have a ramble up into th' fields an' th' woods, to yer th' cuckoo sing. But aw con yer nowt o' that sooart neaw. Well, aw'll be makin' my way a bit shorter. Afoor aw leov yo', heawever, aw should just loike to say 'at aw've bin weel done to while here."

" Well, pay for it then," said th' lon'lady to owd Billy.

" Yo'll ha' no pay for it ; well, aw recon yo' winnot. Neaw, th' teetotallers may prate as hard as they loiken abeawt public heawses ; but aw've never yet cum across a smo'-drink establishment wheer they'd find a chap wi' supper, bed, an' breakfast for nowt. Aw dunno loike to go away beawt givin' yo' sum'at ; but, heawever, yo' mun co' at eawr heawse sometoime when yo' come eawr road, an' iv ever yo' want a bed, eawr Betty an' me ull let yo' have eawrs, wi' o th' pleasure i' th' world. So good mornin' to yo', an' thank yo', an iv ever aw happen to come this way agen aw shall be sure to gi' yo' a co.''

A WHOLESALE KESSUNIN' DOOMENT AT
TORRINGTON.

HATEVER is there to do neaw, aw wonder," said owd Matty Fletcher, as hoo stoode wi' her honds on her hips, starin' i' th' direction o' th' village church, wheer a lot o' foalk had collected together. "There's summat moor nor common, or there'd never be o yond sturrin."

It wur a foine frosty winter's day when these words wur uttered ; th' sun shone splendidly upo' th' hillsides, makin' 'em look as iv they'd bin weshed o'er wi' gowd. Th' greawnd looked soa warm that aw believe one met ha' baked fatcakes on it, hadn't it been 'at King Frost had bin th' neet afore, an' spread a lot o' cowd white stuff o'er it. Th' sparrows wur hoppin' abeawt fro' twig to twig, an' th' little robin redbreasts poppin' their yeads into th' cottages an' lookin' sensible enuff to ax th' occupants to send 'em a hon'full o' crums eawt. Th' cattle wur breawsin' i' th' meadows, an' pigs gruntin' i' their cotes. Th' poultry i' th' farmyards were amusin' theirsel's i' different ways ; some wur eightin', an' others wur feightin'. Aw believe there wur a cricket or two makin' their noise abeawt owd Gronny Gregory's foyar place, but aw dunnot feel quiet certain abeawt this, so connot speak positively. Here an' theer met be seen a toathry flees maunderin' abeawt, but they wurn't hawve as wick, nor nowt near so numerous, as they are i' owd Durty Molly's eatin' heawse i' th' middle o' July. There met ha' bin a few snails trailin' abeawt i' their cellars, or a lot o' grubs abeawt th' cabbages i' th' garden, for owt 'at aw know to th' contrary ; for aw didn't feel to care so mich abeawt it as to mak' ony inquiries. But one thing aw know, heawever, an' that is, 'at th' church bells o' Torrington wur ringin' reet merrily that mornin', as iv they wished to tell th' villagers there wur summat grand goin' to come off. Happenin' to be i' th'

village at this time, aw began to inquire what there were to do.
Some o' th' owder eend said they thowt at it wur th' foyar bell,
but a parcel o' lads 'at wur stondin' at a street corner said it
wur th' church bell, an' it wur ringin' becose it wur poncake
Tuesday. Heawever, it appears, 'at a week or two afore th'
toime 'at aw'm speakin' on, th' parson o' th' church had bin
reawnd th' nayburhood, an' foindin' at there wur a lot o' childer
'at had never bin kessund, he towd their parents 'at iv they'd
tak' 'em to th' church on a certain day he'd kessun 'em o for
nowt, an' it appears 'at this wur th' day 'at he'd fixed on.
Theer they wur,—men, women, an' childer gethered reawnd th'
church till it looked moor loike a rushbearin' nor a religious
ceremony.

> There wur Daff wi' his concertina,
>   An' Dorothy wi' hur choilt ;
> An' eh ! it wur some pratty,
>   Altho' a troifle spoilt.
> There wur Darron Bill among 'em,
>   An' th' woife in a bran new geawn ;
> An' th' choilt, wi' a spank new frock on,
>   Wi' tucks in th' haw've road deawn.
> Well, th' next coom Tom-o'-Mary's
>   An' th' woife—a charmin' pair !
> An' they'd wi' 'em two foine childer,
>   Real chucks, aw do declare !
> An' th' next wur a chap fro Canrow ;
>   Aw think they co' him Jim ;
> He's a noted breek for squintin',
>   An' th' woife's as good as him.
> These brought three woppin' childer,
>   An' had 'em kessund too ;
> Said Jim to th' woife at after,
>   " Wurn't this a rare chep do ? "
> " Ah, ah, it wur," said Betty,
>   " But, Jim, thee howd thi tongue ;
> Iv ever we mun save owt,
>   It mun be while we're young."
> " Well, well," said Jim to Betty,
>   " That's reet enuff, but come,
> Let's buy some sweets for th' childer,
>   An' then be trudgin' whoam."

" Stop a bit," said Betty, " th' parson hasn't done yet,
mon. There's Ned-o'-Jim's lad to do, an' Bill-o'Molly's, an'
Jim-o'-Robin's, an' another or two besides." Well, they wurn't
long afore they geet this business noicely o'er, but there were

some rare laffin' o'er it aw con tell yo. There wur one couple stood before th' parson 'at didn't seem so mich accustomed to that mack o' wark, for when his reverence held his honds for th' choilt, th' mother on't turned it o'er to him heels furst. Eh! but there wur a bonny titter i' that hole! But th' parson took it o i' good part. Aw thowt aw seed him laffin' a toime or two, an' no wonder, for some on 'em wur so very wooden. Aw could ha' done better misel, aw know. Yo would ha' laffed iv yo'd yeard th' childer, when the parson wur puttin' wayter on their faces. They sung eawt till yo couldn't yer a word at wur said. Heawever, they managed to get thro' this nomony someheaw, an' th' clerk finished up wi' sheawtin' "Amen." Everyone wur eawt o' that church i' quicksticks, an' when they'd getten noicely into th' street, they held a bit ov a ceawncil wheer they must put up at. They agreed to go to th' "Jolly Printers," an' have a saup o' their seawr rum, just to warm their throttles wi', an' they wurn't so very long afore some on em' began to be rayther jolly, while other some thowt it wur toime to be trudgin' tort whoam. Before doin' so, heawever, they collected some brass among 'em, an' bowt some ale, which they put in a bottle to drink on th' road. Havin' filled a bottle wi' black creom, they seet off eawt o' th' village to wheer they lived, wheer they soon londed, as it wur not so far off. When they geet theer, some on 'em wanted to go to th' "Frozen Mop," an' keep th' kessunin' up a bit longer, but others on 'em said 'at a mop wur no place for foalk to stick their yeads in 'at wanted to be comfortable. Ned o' Jim's said 'at they'd a besom at their heawse, 'at he'd back ogen ony mop they could foind 'i that quarter, so that settled th' matter at once, an' they o agreed to go to Mary o' Tommy's, fro' Tom Nook, an' spend th' neet eawt theer. When they geet to owd Mary's, they began to poo their brass an' their bottles eawt, an' shapin' for havin' a jolly good spree. One owd chap said iv they'd o be ov his moind, they'd ha' some gradely owd fashund drink, some 'at wouldn't tremble i' th' bag, but ston it greawnd. So it wur agreed on 'at they should send to th' "Mop" for a saup o' breawn steawt, unmixed wi' sooap. Well this coom, an' wur soon made warm an' gradely good, an' directly they wur sarvin' it reawnd, an' th' neet passed o'er very comfortably. At length, what wi' drinkin', singin', an' doancin', some on 'em began to get rayther sleepy, an' one or two on 'em wauted reet o'er i' th' owd woman's heawse, an' th' little childer wur lyin', some i' one corner an' some in another. Inneaw there wur one mon 'at seemed to ha' bin doin' a tidy business wi' John Barleycorn, tho' he didn't seem to ha' made sich a good bargin, bethowt him he'd go whoam, an' seein' 'at their Betty wur rayther flusht i' th' face, he thowt he'd better tak' th' choilt wi' him, which he did, an' they wur soon booth on 'em i' bed. Th' woife wurn't long afore hoo missed him, an' concludin' in her moind 'at he must be gone whoam, hoo nips up a choilt an' off hoo gooas; not knowin' 'at her husband had ta'en one an' o. Hoo geet into bed as quietly as hoo could, an' o went on reet enuff till mornin'. When they wackened, heawever, they were some surprised at seein' two childer i' bed! "Heaw's this," said Bill, "'at we'n getten two childer i' bed? Whoa's chilt has ta browt wi' thee, Betty?" "Whoy, aw've browt eawr own choilt, to be sure! Theaw must ha browt someb'dy's else. But, heawever, let's see which has browt th' reet un, an' which has browt th' wrong un." Soa after makin' th' examination, Betty said, "By th' mass, Bill, we've booath on us wrong this toime, for they noather on 'em belong to us, aw do declare!" "Well," said Bill, "we mun mak' th' best on't, an' say nowt abeawt it, for there'll be a bonny bother, there will for sure! Away wi' thee deawn th' lone, Betty, an' see iv theaw con yer owt o' onybody bein' beawt choilt, or onybody havin' a wrung un." Soa away Betty went deawn th' lone, but foindin' o very quiet, hoo turned her face tort whoam ogen; but hadn't gone fur afoor hoo met another on th' look eawt. "Well, Betty, lass, what's to do as theaw's sturrin' so soon this mornin'?" "Oh, nowt," said Betty, "only aw thowt aw'd have a bit ov a walk as it's a foine mornin', an' see if o wur reet after these kessunins." "Reet!" said th' woman, "theaw'll yer sich a row i' this lone as theaw never yeard afoor, aw con tell thee." "Well, whatever is there to do," said Betty. "Do! it'll be a country's talk, this will. Sithee, aw wouldn't ha' been mixed up wi' that lot iv aw'd known, now, not for summat. Theaw knows that chap 'at skens? Well, his woife lost her choilt, an' conno foind it nowheer; they'n bin up an' deawn o neet seechin' it, but wheer they are neaw aw conno tell. There's bin weary wark o'er it, aw con assure thee. Well, then, to mak' things wur, somebody's ta'en o th' best kessunin' things off Ponto's choilt, an' put it some other things on 'at arn't hawve as good as it own. It's bonny wark for sure, when one connot have a bit ov a kessunin' doo but they mun go an' rob one another o' their bits o' clooas, an' th' choilt lost in at th' bargain." "Well," said Betty, "let's hope 'at they'll foind their choilt ; as for th' bits o' clooas, they winno matter so very mich. But aw mun be goin', an' seein' abeawt gerrin' th' childer their brekfasts ready, and then gerrin' 'em off to th' schoo' !" Soa they bade one another " good mornin'," an' parted. After th' brekfasts wur o'er, an' th' husbands had getten to their wark, they began to meet together an' talk matters o'er. Soa th' woman 'at had lost her choilt wur sent for, an' very ill off hoo wur, yo may be sure. Heawever, owd Molly seemed to think o ud be made reet ogen, for hoo said 'at hoo could recollect bein' at a kessunin' when hoo wur young, an' it took 'em a three week afoor they o geet their own childer an' th' clooas reeted. But th' woman 'at had lost hur choilt wur very uneasy, an' wanted to know what plan could be adopted tort foindin' th' choilt, for her husband swore he'd very nee kill her iv it wur no' feawnd, when he coom whoam at neet. Soa we axed th' owd woman to put her wits to wark, an' hoo made a proposition 'at everyone 'at had had their childer kessund must meet that very day at one o'clock, an' bring their childer donned i' their kessunin' clooas, just as they wur th' neet afoor, an' thoose 'at wurn't theer at th' toime must be foined a shillin', to be spent among th' company. Soa they o agreed to this. When th' toime for meetin' coom, they wur o middlin' punctual except th' woman 'at wur beawt choilt an' Betty. Heawever, these two coom directly after, an' a bonny way Betty wur in. Hoo browt one o' th' childer, an' th' other hoo left awhoam. Well, they began to examine these childer, an' hadn't bin agate long afore Ponto bawled eawt, "Thoose are my choilt's clooas, chus heaw." "Well, then," said th' owd woman, " yo'd better examine th' choilt, an' see iv that's yo'rs an' o." Soa they looked at it, an' turned it o'er a toime or two, an' it proved to be hur choilt, an' that 'at hoo had belonged to Betty. Soa thoose two got reeted, an' Betty off whoam wi' hurs, an' said hoo'd be back i' toathry minutes, which hoo wur, an' browt th' other choilt wi' her. Th' woman 'at wur beawt choilt wur ceawered theer lamentin' aboon a bit, soa Betty, when hoo coom in, crommed th' choilt deawn into a creddle they had i' th'

heawse, as iv nowt wur. Th' women wur o gabberin' an'
talkin' ov a lump, an' took no notice o' noather Betty nor th'
choilt. Soa, after sendin' for a saup moor comfortin' cordial,
they supped reawnd, an' had this for th' tooast, "May th'
poor woman's choilt soon be feawnd ogen." Directly after this
tooast wur drunk (an' it looks queer to me 'at they should
drink tooast, as they used to ate it when aw wur a lad,
an' drank tay)—but, as aw wur sayin', they began to get
merry, an' this helped, to some extent, to droive th' woman's
sorrow away, an' hoo seemed for a toime to forget o abeawt
her choilt. Heawever, th' owd woman as wur th' cheermon
proposed havin' another look reawnd to see iv they could
meet wi' this lost choilt. Soa they o geet up to go a lookin',
but Betty managed to keep beheend a bit, and when they'd o
getten noicely eawtside, hoo bawled eawt, " Eh, aw say! some
of yo's leavin' yo're choilt ogen !" On yerin' this they o
stood stock still, an' began to stare at one another. Well,
they everyone declared they'd their own children wi' em, an'
Betty said hur's wur awhoam. Soa they agreed to go back
an' see what there wur. Th' woman 'at had lost her choilt
said hoo'd have a look an' see iv it wur hur's, so hoo went
back i' th' heawse, an' theer lay afoor her i' th creddle, "as
snug as a button," her own dearly beloved duck-a-darlin' !
Hoo had howd on it i' hawve a snifter, an' pressed it to her
bussom as if it had been missin' a week. " Th' choilt's mine,"
hoo said, "an' neaw aw'm as reet as a wooden clock." "Well,
come," said one on 'em, " as th' childer an' th' clooas are o
getten reeted, we conno do less nor send for a thimbleful o' th'
owd sooart." So they scraped up a bit o' brass among 'em, an'
sent for some moor drink, an' o went on as merrily as could
be, an' they'd as good a spree on th' second day as they had
o' th' furst. One o' th' women sung a song 'at hoo said hoo'd
made afoor hoo coom. Here it is :—

> One winter's day there coom this way
> A parson noan beawt thowt ;
> An' foindin' some childer unkessund i' th' place
> He promised to do 'em for nowt.
> Soa thinkin' this fair, there wur lots on us theer,
> An' some rare cracks o' laffin' we had ;
> For th' blunderin' wark 'at some on us made
> Wur really past tellin' for bad.

One fellow stood theer wi' his billycock on ;
  But this case wur noan one o' th' wurst,
For another, when hondin' to th' parson her choilt,
  Hoo gan it him th' wrong eend th' furst !
Eh, dear ! but there wur some rare titterin', too,
  But th' owd parson he let them a-be ;
He knew what a lot o' rum covies we wur,
  An' he cared nowt abeawt it, not he !

When we'd getten 'em kessund, we o left th' church,
  An' had a short meetin' i' th' street,
Wheer we clubbed up among us a foine lump o' brass—
  An' what do yo think we did we 't ?
We sent to owd Skeawter's, at th' four lone eends,
  For a saup o' their best seawer rum,
An' as true as aw'm here, afoor ten o'clock,
  We'rn o on us fuddled, by gum !

Well, this pleased 'em rarely, yo may be sure, an' th' owd
woman's heawse fairly rung ogen wi' th' noise they made. But
it wur gettin' toime to break up, which they did very soon after,
an' they o geet safe whoam. When th' husbands fun' it eawt
'at they'd getten o things reet an' square ogen, they agreed to
have another jollification, an' they kept at it till th' clock
fingers wur booath straight up. When they began o shapin'
for goin' whoam, th' husbands declared there should be noa
mishaps that neet, for they'd tak' care o' th' childer theirsels,
an' th' wives met follow after. This wur done, an' they o
managed to get whoam safe an' seawnd, wi' their own cloas
an' their own childer. Neaw this shows 'at there's bin great
an' important improvements i' kessunin' dooments sin' th'
owd woman wur young, when it took 'em three weeks to get
their childer an' their clooas o reet ogen. Neaw, yo seen, it's
done i' two days. Th' husbands sen at th' next kessunin' doo
they han they'll ha' th' childer properly marked wi' big letters
i' blue an' red, so that they con everyone know their own, an'
then there'll be noan o' this mak' o' bother no moor, some
tackin' th' wrong childer, an' others bein' left beawt. So neaw
o seems to be getten reet an' straight ogen, but iv aw should
happen to yer owt ony moor abeawt these kessunin's aw'll try
to let you know abeawt it at some other toime.

  "Adoo !" as poor Artemus Ward says—
    Kind readers an' hearers, adoo ;
  Aw dare say yo're getten weel toyart
    For one toime—well, soa am I, too.

LANCASHIRE KESMUS SINGIN' FIFTY YEAR' SIN'.

NE fine afternoon, last autumn, as I was walking leisurely along the turnpike road leading out of one of our large manufacturing towns in Lancashire, I was overtaken by an old man, apparently about 70 years of age. With the freedom usually manifested by country people, he accosted me thus: "It's a foine day, mestur." I said it was. "Aw think yo'r a stranger abeawt here, for aw connot recollect seein' yo afore, an' aw've lived i' this naybour-hood summat loike fifty or sixty year." I told him he was right, for I was a stranger in that part of the country; and asked him what trade the people followed in that locality. "Why some do one thing, an' some another, an' plenty do nowt at o, nobbut shankle abeawt wi' their honds i' their pockets. Th' biggest part on 'em are owd hondloom wayvers; aw'rn used to be one misel' when aw'rn younger, but aw've ne'er done noan neaw for this last four or five year'." "How do you manage to get your living, then?" I asked. I saw the tears trickling down the old man's cheeks, as he replied—"Well, to tell yo th' truth, mester, aw'm loike mony a one besoide me, at's getten owd, aw have to depend upo' other foalk." "Is your old woman living?" I inquired. "Nawe, hoo's been deod just two year' this September. We'rn livin' wi' a dowter o' mine, at that time, on i'th' cloof, yonder, but sin' hoo deed aw've bin livin' wi' mi owdest son, Jim, just across th' fielt theer. Will yo co' a bit an' have a poipe o' bacco wi' me? Eawr Jim's at his wark i'th' loom-heawse, an' th' childer are at th' schoo'; so if yo'n slip across wi' me we can have a comfortable chat

Y

together. Anxious to hear a little more of the old man's history, I thanked him for the invitation, and at once accompanied him to his dwelling. It was an old stone house, built, if I remember rightly, in the year 1760, and beautifully situated on a slight eminence, about two hundred yards from the turnpike road. As we approached the cottage, it appears we were observed by the old man's son, for he came to meet us at the garden gate, and holding out his hand to me, said, "Heaw are yo, sir? Aw dunno know yo, but aw reccon mi feyther does; come in, an' sit yo deawn. Aw'm expectin' eawr Betty in every minute, an' when hoo comes yo can have a sope o' tay wi' mi' feyther. Aw never ha' nowt o'th' soart misel', but aw loike to see other foalk have it, if they loiken it. Win yo have a poipe o' bacco with us? Yo happen dunno smook?" I told him I did not, but thanked him all the same.

"What rent may you pay for a house like this" I inquired. "We ne'er pay nowt, mestur; we wur used to pay thirty shillin' a year, but th' squire up at th' Ho' said he thowt we'd as mich as we could do, beawt payin' rent; he'd let us live a bit for nowt;—that's abeawt two year sin' an' we'n never paid a haupney fro' that day to this." "It is very kind of your landlord," I observed, "in allowing you to live rent free. Are any of your neighbours thus favoured?" "Nawe, not as aw know on. Aw reccon it's becose mi feyther's a bit ov a favourite wi' em. He used to play th' double bass up at th' chapel yonder, yo seen, an' they'n loike made a bit more ado on him on that akeawnt. Then there's another thing—mi mother wer'n th' cook up at th' Ho', afore mi feyther wed her, an' they'n allis taen to us a bit ever sin."

Just as Jim was concluding the last sentence, his wife came in, carrying a fine baby of some three months old. She seemed a little surprised at seeing a stranger in the house; it was something rather unusual, no doubt. She had not advanced many steps before her husband took the child from her arms, and, giving it a kiss, said to its mother, "There's a gentleman here, tha' sees, Betty; tha' mun make 'em a sope o' tay, lass, as soon us t'con; an' when they'n had sum'at t' eat they can sit an' chat together awhile. Mi feyther can tell yo some rare tales, mestur, iv he's a moind," he said, addressing himself to me. I told him I was exceedingly fond of tales, and should like to hear some good ones.

" Aw'll gie yo a bit of a skit or two, "said the old man, "when aw've getten some o'th' woind off mi stomach; for aw'm nowt at talkin' when aw'm hungry."

In a few minutes the good woman had the tea-things placed on the table, and, although I had partaken of dinner only about an hour before, I enjoyed their kind hospitality very much. Tea being over, I, along with my old friend, repaired to a wooden seat in the garden, the old man taking his pipe with him. We sat a few moments in silence, which was at length broken by my friend saying—" Well aw reccon aw shall ha' to try iv aw can tell yo a tale or two, neaw; an' as eawr Jim's towd yo at aw used to be a bit ov a music chap, aw'll tell yo one or two bits o' skits at aw remember very weel. Yo'll think they seawnden strange, no deawt, but aw can assure yo, they're quite true, an some o' th' characters mentioned are livin' yet.

" Well, one Kesmus neet—neaw abeawt fifty year' sin'— ther'n me an' a lot moor ov eawr singers at th' chapel, made it up among eawrsel's to go eawt a-singing th' Kesmus hymn, an' we agreed to meet at th' schoo' at eleven o'clock, an' have a bit ov a practice afore we started eawt. Aw conno' remember th' names ov o on 'em neaw, but aw con tell yo some on 'em. There were Simeon Carter, Ike-o'-Abram's, Sammy Hallsworth, Tommy Yetton, Tummy-o'-Sharp's, an' Jabez Barrowclough.

" Yo ne'er seed sich a seet i' o yo'r loife, as we looked, when we o stood in a reawnd ring i' th' middle o' th' floor !

" Owd Simeon Carter, a bass singer, had getten his woife's red cloak on, an' a great woollen shawl lapped reawnd his meawth, so that we could only just see his nose-end poppin' eawt. Ike-o'-Abram's had borrowed a top-coat off someb'dy 'at reached reet deawn to his feet; an he'd a pair o gloves on his honds 'at looked big enough for Daniel Lambert. Sammy Hallsworth had getten his feyther's breeches on th' top ov his own, an' his legs looked moor loike elephants legs nor owt else. Aw can assure yo we wur a bonny lot o together. Well, we tried th' Kesmus hymn, ' Hark, Hark,' an' toathry o' them things o'er, an' just as th' church clock struck twelve, we turned eawt. But aw'm forgettin' to tell yo abeawt Johnny-o'-Neddys, a chap 'at should ha' bin wi' us. Johnny aw understond, had a rare do wi' th' woife afore he seet off fro' whoam. Hoo didn't loike him to go a basoon playin', when he owt to be i' bed, an' wur freetund sum'ut ud happen him iv he went eawt; an' hoo

wur no' fur off reet, for on his way t' th' schoo', he had to cross
a wood, an' i' doin' so, as there wur nob'dy onywheer abeawt
he thowt he met as weel be tryin' a tune or two o'er. Well, he
geet owd ov his basoon, an started a puffin away. As it
happened, theer wur a bull noan fur off 'at yerd this noise 'at
Johnny wur makin', an' it began a tryin' to imitate him as weel
as it could.

"'What's that? What's that?' ax'd Johnny, lookin'
sharply abeawt him. 'Iv theawrt a musician let's yer thi
seawnd thi keighnote.' Well, he'd hardly getten th' words
eawt of his meawth afoor th' bull laid howd on him wi' it horns
an' threw him reet o'er it yead. His clooas wur ripped o to
rags, an' his basoon smashed o to pieces. Th' owd lad
scramblet off whoam as weel as he could, but he wur cured ov
his basoon playin' that neet—he ne'er played no moor.

"Well, neaw then, aw'll go back to mi tale agen. As aw
wur tellin' yo', we started eawt o' singin' at twelve o'clock.
There'n a parcel o' lads gethert reawn th' schoo' dur, an' as
soon as ever they seed us they seet up a great sheawt, an'
started a makin' remarks abeawt us. One on 'em said, 'Eh!
look theer at that mon wi' th' long top-cooat on; he looks
loike a clooas-prop dressed up.' An' then another young
rascal sheawted eawt, 'Wheer hast getten thi red cloak fro',
owd mon? What wilt' tak' for a whelp off it?' Sammy
Hallsworth, when he yeard that, began a poikin' off as noicely
as he could, for he knew iv they seed his breeches they'd hardly
ever ha' done makin' remarks abeawt 'em. Well, we geet o'er
this as weel as we could; owd Simeon grumbled at 'em a bit,
an' said iv he could only get owd on 'em he'd poo their ears till
they'rn as long as pig ears.

"Th' parson's heawse bein' close to th' schoo', we went
theer th' furst, an' started a singin' 'Christians, awake!'
When we geet to th' third loine, wheer it says 'Rise to adore,'
somb'dy sheawted eawt, 'Rise, an' let these chaps sup.' Well,
when we yeard that, one o' th' lads 'at wur singin' ceawnter
brasted eawt a-laffin', an' seet some o' th' others agate, an' we
broke deawn afore we geet to th' end o' th' furst verse. Aw
wur playin' th' double bass at th' toime, an' aw felt so vex'd at
aw up wi' th' fiddlestick, an' wur beawn to fot one on 'em a
crack o'er th' yead, but aw missed mi aim an' hit one o' th'
women singers a welt o'er her bonnet, an' made it as flat as a
poncake. Yo may guess what a row there'd be then.

"Tummy Yetton, a young fellow at purtended to cooart her a bit neaw an' then, ax'd me what aw'd done that for. He said he'd punse his foote thro' th' fiddle iv aw didn't keep that clumsy stick to mysel'. We wur o foin' eawt ov a lump for abeawt five minutes, an' aw wur freetened we should never be able to muster no moor; but owd Simeon coom an' stretched hisel' up among us, an' said it wur a shawm 'at we should be carryin' on i' that'n, an' a lot o' chapel singers as we wur; we should have o th' folk i' th' place talkin' abeawt us. Inneaw, who should come creepin' back but Sammy Hallsworth; he'd poo'd one o' th' pair o' breeches off, an' had 'em slung o'er his shooder. Well, we managed to get i' summat loike order agen, an' then we went forrard to owd Pogson's. (Owd Pogson wur th' clark o' th' chapel.) We started a singin' th' Kesmus hymn, an' geet thro' very weel to th' eend o' th' fust verse, an' then Skennin' Jonas, as we used to co him, began a thumpin' at th' dur, an' tryin' to wakken 'em up. When we'd getten to th' eend o' th' next verse, he gan it another bang wi' th' eend o' his knob-stick. Owd Pogson geet up and stuck his yead eawt o' th' window, an' towd us he wur very sorry, but he couldn't ger a leet—th' matches wur damp, or summat. Aw wur stondin' at th' side o' Skennin' Jonas at th' toime, an' yeard him mutter summat abeawt him loikin' his ale to weel hissel' to ger up an' give a poor body a sup. Well, after we'd bin to two or three moor places, we went to owd Daniel Whitley's, at th' Hey Barn. When we geet theer it wur abeawt two o'clock i' th' mornin', noice an' moonleet, but very cowd, for it wur freezin' keenly. We o stood reawnd th' dur, an' began a-singin'. Tummy-o-Sharps, 'at wur playin' th clarinett, cock'd up his yead tort chamber window, to see iv ony on 'em wur gerrin' up—for we'd rapped at th' dur to let 'em know 'at we'd go in iv they'd let us—an' to get a better seet, he walked back a foote or two. Neaw, reet facin' th' dur, but at th' other side o' th' fowt, wur a well, where they fot water fro' for th' ceaws, an' for weshin'-up wi'; but whether Tummy knew abeawt it or not, aw conno say, but at ony rate in he plopt, reet up to th' chin. By gum! didn't th' owd lad stare! an' his chin reet wackert agen wi' cowd, for it very nee froze him stiff. Nancy Greenhalgh—hoo wur his sweetheart, yo noan—when hoo yeard it wur Tummy 'at had backed into th' well, hoo seet up sich a skroike as aw ne er yeard afore sin aw'rn wick. 'For God's sake, ger him eawt,' hoo said ; 'do ger him eawt ! We should be wed o' th' twenty-second o' next month. Th' ring's bowt neaw, an' th' weddin' dress is very nee made. Jabez,' hoo said, to a great long chap as wur stondin' laffin', 'thee ger howd on him, theaw great starin' foo' ! What are t' laffin' at ? It's nowt to mak' fun abeawt, this isn't.'

"While Nancy wur makin' this bother, an' lettin' th' cat eawt o' th' bag, me an' two or three moor on us had managed to get Tummy eawt o' th' well. Didn't he look rare an' mad at Nancy, for he'd yeard every word hoo'd said. Th' owd lad shaked hissel' a bit, an' then poiked hissel' off whoam an' to bed as soon as he could. Well, when Tummy wur gone, owd Simeon coom an' fixed hissel' reet i' th' middle on us, an' said. 'Aw think we met as weel drop it neaw, folk. Th' clarinet player's gone, an' yo knoan we conno do mich beawt him. But afore we separate aw should loike to say a word or two respectin' th' way 'at we'n bin carryin' on. It seems very clear to my moind 'at it's nowt nobbut proide an' a hankerin' after other foalk's stuff 'at's bin th' cause o' th' misfortins we'n had to-neet. I' th' fust place, iv we'd turned eawt in us own clooas, as we owt to ha' done, i' th' stead o' makin' eawrsel's look loike a lot o' meawntebanks, th' lads would ne'er ha' sheawted us. I' th' next place, iv we'd gone eawt wi' a proper motive—that is, a-singin' th' Kesmus hymn in a gradely soart of a way, an' then goan abeawt us business—we should noan ha' brocken deawn as we did'n, when we'rn singin' at th' parson's heawse, nor that young woman wouldn't ha' had her bonnet spoiled wi' th' fiddlestick. Aw feel very ill hurt, for my own part, 'at Tummy-o'-Sharps has met wi' that misfortin. Its bin sich a lettin' deawn to him ; not only i' bein' letten deawn into th' wayter—that wur bad enuff, certainly—but yo see Nancy's letten it eawt abeawt th' weddin', an' there'n a ruck o' lads abeawt 'at yeard it as weel as us, an' no deawt they'll mak' it middlin' weel known. Let's go whoam, an' keep these things as quiet as we con, an' iv ever we go eawt a singin' ony moor let's do it in a gradely sperrit, as we owt, an' not be hankerin' so mich after mate an' drink. Heaw con we expect owt good to come eawt o' this mak' o' wark, think'n yo ? There's One up aboon yonder 'at knows heaw we'n bin carryin' on ; an' whoa knows but what Tummy-o'-Sharp's tumblet into th' wayter as a sooart ov a judgement on us for bein' so wicked. Sich things as these han happened afoor neaw, an' it's not at o unloikely at it is so i' this case.

" Well, when Simeon had finished his sarmonizin', Ike-o'-Abram's said he thowt we'd better go back to th' schoo' an separate in a respectable sooart ov a way. So we went, an' when we'd o getten sit deawn, aw geet up an' gan eawt a short-metre hymn ;—an' aw've forgetten neaw whoa it wur, but som'b'dy struck up wi' a long-metre tune ; so, to mak' it come in, we had to lengthen th' last words o' some o' th' lines ; an', as it happent, th' last word o' one o' th' loines we'rn ' Jacob,' so we sung it i' this road : Ja-fol-da-diddle-i-do-cob. Well, mestur," he said, " what dun yo think abeawt eawr Kesmus singin' ?" I said they had made a bad job of it. " A bad job on it ! Aw think we did."

" Aw reccon yo never knew owd Robin Dumplin-yead, as we used t' co him, did yo, mestur ?" I said I did not remember having heard the name before.

" Iv yo'n a moind aw'll tell yo heaw he once sarved a lot o' singers 'at went to their heawse. Yo known Robin wur a very eccentric sooart ov a chap. He wur no' mich of a chapel-goer hissel ; but, as he used to say, he could't abide to see religion bein' made a trade on ; an' these singers wur nowt nobbut a lot o' great awkart lads, an' toathry wenches 'at livt i' th' place, 'at wur goin' reawnd to get howd ov o they could, an' then have a spree with it. They went an fixed theirsel's under Robin's window, an' began a singin'. Robin yeard 'em, an' said to the woife, ' Yond's th' singers, Matty ; has't owt for 'em ?' ' Nawe, indeed I,' said Matty ; tha emptied th' last bottle we had i' th' heawse, afore we coom to bed. Has t' forgetten ?' ' Nawe, aw've noan forgetten, not I marry ; mi yead warches rather too ill for that. It's very kind on 'em comin' eawt a singin' ov a cowd frosty neet loike this, an' aw'll give 'em summat 'at ull satisfy 'em for th' next yer an' o, except they're ill to pleos.' ' Robin, tha knows very weel 'at we'n nowt to spare ; tha's had thi loom empty a week neaw, an' conno tell when tha'll get another warp. Tha's moor need to go reawnd wi' em an' try to mak' a bit o' summat nor give 'em owt ; that's what aw think, Robin.' ' Well, well, lass,

we're noan so weel off, aw know, but th' owd Book says 'at it's
better to give nor to receive; and iv tha conno believe me aw'll
gie thee a bit o' what they co'n hoccular demonstration, iv
tha'll ger eawt o' bed an' come wi' me to th' window.' So they
booath geet up an' went to th' chamber window, an' when
Robin oppened it they wur just finishin' th' last verse, an' very
nee o on 'em gaupin' an' starin' up at th' window.' ' Neaw
then,' said Robin, ' which on yo tak's it ?' So the leader
sheawted eawt ' Me.' ' Tak' that, then,' said Robin, emptyin'
a two-gallon potful o' water on 'em : ' tak' that, an' divide it
among yo; an' iv yo feel dry when it gets tort dayleet, iv yo'n
a moind to come this way ogen, aw'll see iv aw conno foind yo
a sope moor.' Well, mestur, aw think yo'll do for tales ; aw'll
have a poipe o' bacco, neaw."

When the old man had finished, I could not help saying,
" Thank you, thank you kindly, my old friend ; I am sorry to
have to leave you so soon, but I have an engagement about two
miles from here, which I am obliged to attend to." I wished
him good night, exclaiming to myself—

> Tha's noan so fur to tramp, owd friend ;
> Tha's welly reach'd thi journey's end ;
>   Trudge along.
> Thi fiddle's mony a toime bin strung,
> An' aw've no deawt bo what tha's sung
>   Mony a song.
> But neaw, owd mon, thi days are few,
> So, iv there's owt tha has to do,
>   Do it soon ;
> An' th' bit o' toime tha has to stop,
> Get ready for another shop
>   Up aboon.

LIST OF SUBSCRIBERS.

LIST OF SUBSCRIBERS

A

AGNEW, William, J.P.,
Pendleton and London   (2 copies)

AXON, W. E. A.,
47, Derby Street, Moss Side,
Manchester.   (2 copies)

AINSWORTH, John,
St. Annes-on-Sea.

ANDREW, John,
99, Hornby Road, Blackpool.

ALLEN, John,
Kilgrimol, South Drive,
St. Annes-on-Sea.

ASHWORTH, Albert,
87, Manchester Old Road,
Middleton.

ACKROYD, Thomas,
101, Hornby Road, Blackpool.

ANDREW, John,
138, Greengate Street, Oldham.

ANDREW, Herbert,
138, Greengate Street, Oldham.

AINSWORTH, William,
94, Eden Terrace, Stocks Lane,
Stalybridge.

AUTY, Charles,
Artist, Raikes View,
Blackpool (2 copies)

ASPEN, R. H.,
Woodland Cottage, New Moston,
Manchester.

ASHWORTH, James R.,
Castlelaw, York Road,
Chorlton-cum-Hardy.

AINSCOUGH, J. M.,
Crawford House, Wigan.

ALKER, Miss Elizabeth.
Commercial Inn, Aspull,
near Wigan.

ATKINSON, Barrett,
Scotland Road, Nelson.

ADDIE, R. Forrester,
Solicitor, Fleetwood.

ABBOTT, James H.,
Heaton Mersey.

ADSHEAD, G. H.,
Bolton Road, Pendleton.

ALLAN, George,
Blackett Street, Newcastle-on-Tyn .

ALLAN, Thomas,
Blackett Street, Newcastle-on-Tyne.

ALLEN, John,
24, Queensbury Road, Burnley.

ALLEN, Rev. G., M.A.,
Shaw.

ANDREWS, William, F.R.H.S.,
The Hull Press, Hull.

ARMITAGE, R. H.,
Lockwood, Huddersfield.

ASHTON, Squire,
45, Queen's Road, Oldham.

ASHTON, Herbert,
Lyndhurst, Windsor Road, Oldham.

ASHWORTH, Elijah,
Harefield Hall, Wilmslow.

ATKINSON, Rev. Canon,
Vicarage, Bolton.

ALDHOUSE, J. S.,
63, Temple Street, C-on-M,
Manchester.

ANDREW, Samuel,
12, Clegg Street, Oldham.

ASHTON, R.,
Librarian, Free Public Library,
Blackburn.

ASPDEN, Peter,
11, Higher Lawrence St., Darwen.

ARROWSMITH, James,
132, High Street West, Glossop.

ANDERTON, Mrs. Thos., sen.,
20, Moore Street, South Shore,
Blackpool.   2 copies.

ARNOTT, Wm. Hy., J.P., C.C.,
Limehouse, Lowton,
Newton-le-Willows.

B

BALFOUR, The Right Hon. A. J., (M.P.)
4, Carton Gardens, London, S.W.

BICKERSTAFFE, Robert,
Manager, Central Pier, Blackpool.
8 copies.

BARDSLEY, Isaac,
57, Lees Road, Oldham.

BARDSLEY, Joseph W.,
Clayton Hall View, Clayton,
Manchester.

* BOYLE, Robert,
Court Chambers,
15, Mawdsley Street, Bolton.

BAGULEY, Matthew,
922, Ashton Road, Fairfield.

BUCKLEY, W. H., J.P.,
Stamford Villa, Ashton-under-Lyne.

BARDSLEY, G. H.,
Dobu, British New Guinea.

BROWN, Henry,
Post Office, Revoe, Blackpool.

BARDSLEY, A. E.,
4453, Wakefield Street,
Germantown, Philadelphia, U.S.

BLAMIRES, Thomas,
Close Hill, Huddersfield.

BARDSLEY, Charles F.,
Corrparoo, Brisbane, Queensland.

BAYLIFFE, Roger,
17, Pitt Street, Oldham.

BARDSLEY, Isaac Ives,
57, Lees Road, Oldham.

BOTTOMLEY, Herbert,
County Bank, Stalybridge.

BOWES, Councillor James,
284, Oldham Road, Newton Heath.

BALMER, Rev. J. S.,
50, Park Road, Blackpool.

BUTTERWORTH, Councillor W., J.P.,
Oak Road, Crumpsall Park,
Manchester (2 copies)

BROOME, Robert,
140, Old Road, Heaton Norris.

BAILEY, W. H., Alderman, J.P.,
Summerfield, Eccles.

BAILEY, John,
New Brighton.

BARLOW, Charles,
9, Fern Street, Coppice, Oldham.

BARNES, Harold A., B.A.,
Summerfield, Great Lever, Bolton.

BARON, John, J.P.,
Manchester Road, Burnley.

BARON, Arthur,
Manchester Road, Burnley.

BELL, William,
19, January Street, Upper Brook
Street, Manchester.

BENSON, James,
94, Oxford Street, Oldham.

BENTLEY, James,
23, Park Street, Oldham.

BENTLEY, James W., J.P.,
Stakehill, Castleton, Manchester.

BLACKLEY CO-OPERATIVE
SOCIETY, Blackley, Manchester.

BLEARS, William,
108, Werneth Hall Road, Oldham.

BLEASDALE, T., Macauley House,
Royton.   2 copies.

BOLTON, T.,
3, Werneth Hall Road, Oldham.

BOOTH, C. H.,
113, Old Street, Ashton-under-Lyne.

BRADBURY, Joseph,
Solicitor, Saddleworth.

BREAR & CO. LD., Thomas,
Booksellers, &c., Kirkgate, Bradford.
2 copies.

BRIERLEY, Joseph,
21, Manchester Street, Oldham.

BROADBENT, E. J.,
Spring Gardens, Flowery Field,
Hyde.

BROCKBANK, William, F.G.S.,F.L.S.,
Brockhurst, Didsbury.

BROOKS, Peter,
36, Wellington Road, Oldham.

BROOKS, Richard Henry,
Meadow Bank, Urmston Lane,
Stretford.

BROOKS, S. H.,
Slade House, Levenshulme.

BROOKS, E.,
184, Rochdale Road, Shaw.

BROOME, W. B.,
137, Windsor Road, Oldham.

BROOME, Joseph,
Sunny Hill, Llandudno.

BROTHERTON, George,
16, Tennis Street, Burnley.

BROWN, James,
Hedge Lane, Salford.

BROUGHTON, Richard,
St. John's Terrace, Accrington
(Solicitor).

BUCKLEY, John,
Victoria Market, Oldham.

BUCKLEY, John,
92, Werneth Hall Road, Oldham.

BUCKLEY, Mark,
312, Ashton Old Road, Openshaw.

BURNLEY CO-OPERATIVE
SOCIETY.

BURNLEY MECHANICS'
INSTITUTION.

BUTTERFIELD, John,
Ormerod Road, Burnley.

BURGESS, Joseph (Workman's Times),
49, Wallace Street, Broughton,
Manchester.

BARRETT, George C., "The Washington," Central Parade, Blackpool. 2 copies.

BICKERSTAFFE, Alderman John, High Lawn, Hornby Rd., Blackpool.

BROADBENT, Alfred, 301, Waterloo Street, Oldham.

BLUNDELL, Councillor Gilbert, 47, Lytham Road, South Shore, Blackpool.

BOWMAN, John, 12, Red Earth Street, Darwen.

BROWN, Thomas, 30, Grasmere Terrace, Great Marton Road, Blackpool.

BANKS, Thomas, 286, New Hall Lane, Preston.

BUCK, James, St. Paul's Road, Preston.

BERRY, John, 15, London Terrace, Darwen.

BURY, Miss Fanny, 30, Quaker's Lane, Darwen.

BARLOW, Thomas, Dinting, near Glossop.

BUTLER, Edwin, Reciter, Barrowford.

BARDSLEY, R. S., Manchester Road, Burnley.

BROADBENT, Samuel, Stamford Road, Mossley.

BROOKE, Thomas, 28, Denbigh Street, Mossley.

BARROW, John, 34, Wellington Road, South Shore, Blackpool.

BICKERSTAFFE, Councillor Tom, 22, Foxhall Road, Blackpool.

BOLTON, James, 54, Eggrington Street, Rochdale Road, Manchester.

BUCKLEY, William, Gatehead House, Delph, Saddleworth.

BUCKLEY, C., 46, Broadway Street, Oldham.

BUCKLEY, Edwin, 80, Greengate Street, Oldham.

BROADHEAD, W. H., Prince of Wales Baths, Blackpool. 2 copies.

BRIGGS, Councillor Thomas, J.P., Park Field, Blackley, Manchester.

BLACKWELL, Walter, 77, Stocks Lane, Stalybridge.

BRADSHAW, Rev. Sandys Y. B., The Vicarage, South Shore, Blackpool.

BROOME, Frank, 45, Oxford Street, Heaton Norris.

BARLOW, John, 311, Market Street, Droylsden.

BENT, James, Superintendent, Police Station, Old Trafford, Manchester.

BRIGHT, Jacob, M.P., 31, St. James's Place, London, S.W.

BOOTH, Samuel Ogden, 449, Lees Road, Lees.

BROADBENT, Thos. Wm., 4, Athenaum Street, Sunderland.

BLACKBURN, James, 112, Lees Road, Nelson.

BRAMLEY, George, Rothwell Haigh, near Leeds.

BIRKBECK, Councillor Wm., Windsor Road, Clayton Bridge. 2 copies.

BAGSHAW, H.B., 77, Werneth Hall Road, Oldham.

BANKS, Mrs. G. Linnæus, 34, Fassett Square, Dalston, London.

BRINDLE, J., 23, East Street, Rochdale.

BATTLE, Farrel, Smithfield Market, Manchester.

BOLTON, H. Hargreaves, Newchurch-in-Rossendale.

BURTON, John 68, Yorkshire Street, Rochdale.

BRISCOE, J. Potter, F.R.H.S., Nottingham Free Public Library.

BRIERLEY, Wynford, Hollincross Lane, Glossop.

BARBER, Joshua, 86, Station Road, South Shore, Blackpool (2 copies)

BIBBY, Councillor J mes, 6, Exchange Street, Blackpool.

BLANE, Thomas, F.C.A., 9, Central Beach, Blackpool.

BRIERLEY, James, Fairfield House, Fairfield (12 copies)

BURGIN, John T., Dumall, Sheffield.

BEELEY, Samuel, Hollins Cottage, Stalybridge.

BRADLEY, Thomas, Local Board Office, St. Annes-on-Sea.

BENNETT, Robert J., 17, Cooper Street, Manchester.

BUTTERFIELD, George, 23, Banks Street, Blackpool.

BROWN, James, Crawford Villas, New Springs, nr. Wigan.

BARLOW, Samuel, J.P., (Mayor of Middleton), Stakehill House, Castleton, nr. Manchester.

BUTTERWORTH, Samuel, 43, Hornby Road, Blackpool.

BROADBENT, John, Auburn Bank, New Moston.

BASS, Joseph, 12, Hyde Road, Lytham Road, S. Shore, Blackpool.

BELLHOUSE, James,
38, Walnut Street, Cheetham,
Manchester.

BARLOW, R. G.
Cricketer, Raikes View, Blackpool.

BUCKLEY, W. H., Dentist,
15, Bottom-o'th'-Moor, Oldham.

BANCROFT, Samuel,
Adelaide Street, Blackpool (4 copies)

BURNETT, William,
Chemist, 72, Nugget Street,
Oldham.

BOOTH, Thomas,
8, Lorne Street, Burnley.

BOWMAN, John,
22, Barlow Street, Oldham.

BARLOW, Charles T.,
c/o S. Pope, Q.C., Parliament Street,
London.

BARBER, Henry,
Bank Manager, Spring Bank,
New Mills, nr. Stockport.

BAILEY, James,
Roodlands, Hornby Road,
Blackpool.

BULLOUGH, Thomas,
Heath Villas, Hindley.

BALDWIN, John,
Scotland Road, Nelson.

BERRY, James,
Union Bank of Manchester, Burnley

BUCKLEY, Charles,
Alt, near Ashton-under-Lyne.

BUTTERWORTH, Walter,
20, Burlington Road, Withington.

C

CARLETON, Will,
Author of "Farm Ballads," &c.,
420 Green Avenue, Brooklyn, U.S.

CARRITTE, W. L.,
20, Yorkshire Street, Oldham.

CAINE, W. S., M.P,
Clapham Common, London, S.W.

COLLINS, William,
12, Mumps, Oldham.

CROMPTON, James,
John Street, Liverpool   (12 copies)

CRANE, Cuthbert,
Central Station, Blackpool.

COCKER, Alderman W. H. (C. C.,)
Bloomfield Road, South Shore,
Blackpool (12 copies)

COCKER, Joseph,
66, Nottingham Street, Sheffield.

CORBITT, J.,
28, George Street, Chorley.

CHADWICK, John,
Vale House, Greaves Street,
Oldham.

CHEESEMAN, Rev. G. E.,
Priory Terrace, Stalybridge.

COULTHURST, Almeth,
Edward St., Moston, Manchester.

COLLISON, Richard D.,
Cleansing Department,
Town Hall, Manchester.

CHARLTON, D.,
105, Barlow Moor Road, Didsbury

CLOUGH, William,
c/o Manchester & Salford Bank,
Manchester.

CARTER, Thomas,
Auctioneer, Ashleigh, 253, Lytham
Road, S. Shore, Blackpool.

CROOK, Edward,
40, Pitt Street, Longridge,
Near Preston.

COCKER, James,
179, Park Road, Oldham.

CLEGG, John,
1, Windsor Place, Fleetwood.

CLAYTON, John,
22, Nelson Road, South Shore,
Blackpool.

CARSON, Dr.,
Union Street, Oldham.

CONNENLLY, Thomas.
Eastwood, Newton Heath.

CHEETHAM, J. M., M.P.,
Eyford Park, Burton-on-the-Water,
Gloucestershire.

CO-OPERATIVE SOCIETY,
Heywood, Lancashire.

CHARLSON, Thomas,
Beacon House, Wigan.

CRABTREE, JAMES,
68, Albert Road, Colne.

COULSTON, Wm.,
3, Victoria Buildings, Burnley.

CROASDALE, William,
Market Street Colne.

CLEGG, James,
4, Lune Street, Longridge,
near Preston.

CROWTHER, Joseph, J.P.,
Hay Green, Marsden.

CARRINGTON, Arthur W., J.P.,
18, Church Road, Lytham.

COLLETT, George,
Holly Bank, Failsworth.

CLEGG, W. S.,
Draper, Wilmslow.

COOK, Edmund,
Hornby Villa, Hoylake, Cheshire.

CO-OPERATIVE SOCIETY,
Educational Department, Mossley.

CO-OPERATIVE STORE LIBRARY
Bacup, per J. L. Wolfenden, Lib.

COUPE, Thomas,
13, Herbert Street, Burnley.

CROMPTON, Seville, Alderman,
Gloucester Street, Oldham.

CROMPTON, Ralph,
Market Hotel, Curzon Street,
Oldham.

CUNLIFFE, W. I.,
Beaufort Avenue, Brooklands,
near Manchester.

CLEGG, W. E.,
30, Market Place and Peter Street,
Oldham. 25 copies.

CLOUGH, Robert,
38, King-street South, Rochdale.

CHADWICK, William,
Chief Constable, Town Hall,
Stalybridge.

CLOUGH, Joseph,
Clock House, Manchester Street,
Oldham.

CHORLTON, Thomas
Solicitor, 32, Brazennose Street,
Manchester.

COLLIER, Joseph,
Norfolk Arms, Glossop.

COOPER, Councillor Robert,
Holly Bank, Royton.

CROOK, Thomas,
157, Church Street, Blackpool.
2 copies.

COLLIER, Edward,
South Terrace, Victoria Road,
Altrincham.

COOPER, William,
72, Brompton Street, Oldham.

CHEETHAM, James,
Strawberry Gardens, Glodwick,
Oldham.

COLLINS, William,
12, Mumps, Oldham.

CROSFIELD, Alderman J. H.,
Stone Wharf, Brewer Street,
Port Street, Manchester.

CROMPTON, F. E.,
Jolliffe Street, Princess Park,
Liverpool.

CANNON, George,
Curator, Alexandra Park, Oldham.

CHADWICK, Robert,
240, Greenacres Road, Oldham.

CHADWICK, Reuben,
Black Horse Inn, Lees Road,
Oldham.

CHADWICK, J. A.,
Burton Brewery, Wrexham.

CHAPMAN, Josiah Thomas, Thornlee,
Alexandra Road South, Manchester.

CLEGG, James,
Aldine Press, Rochdale. 11 copies.

CLOUGH, Miss,
Birchen Cottage, Hollinwood,
Oldham.

COCKCROFT, Wm.,
Solicitor, Rochdale.

CHADWICK, J. M. L.,
Chartered Accountant, The Orchard,
Rochdale.

D

DRONSFIELD, James,
54, Brunswick Street, Oldham.

DUNKERLEY,
Manchester Road,
Chorlton-cum-Hardy.

DUNDERDALE, Robert, J.P.,
Clifton House, Poulton-le-Fylde,
Near Blackpool.

DOLEMAN, Alexander H., M.A.,
26, Moore Street, South Shore,
Blackpool.

DUCKWORTH, Councillor James,
Mayor of Rochdale, Castlefield,
Rochdale.

DRONSFIELD, John,
39, Fern Street, Oldham.

DAWSON, James,
Gorton Brook, Gorton,
Manchester (2 copies)

DEARNALEY, Irvine,
Organist, Old Church,
Ashton-under-Lyne.

DYSON, George,
Argyle Street, Marsden, near
Huddersfield.

DIXON, James C.,
95, Windsor Road, Oldham.

DENT, W.,
Meadow Bank, Nelson.

DYSON, Councillor Haworth,
Arnold Street, Nelson.

DAVIES, Thomas W.,
81, Rooden Lane, Heaton Park,
Manchester.

DYSON, Councillor Wm.,
Bank House, Nelson.

DARBYSHIRE, Alfred, F.I.B.H.,
17, Brazennose Street, Manchester.

DEAN, Thomas, M.D.,
Burnley.

DODD, John, M.I.M.E., J.P.,
The Hollies, Werneth, Oldham.

DUCKWORTH, W. H.,
White Lion Hotel, Blackley.

DUNKERLEY, C. C.,
66, Port Street, Manchester.

DUNCKLEY, Henry, LL.D.,
9, Egerton Road, Fallowfield,
Manchester.

DUXBURY, James,
Bookseller, &c., 32, George Street,
St. Helens.

DYSON, A. K., J.P.,
Lee House, Sale, Cheshire.

DAWSON, James,
Accountant, 125, Union Street,
Oldham.

DEAN, James,
Stockport Road, Ashton-under-
Lyne. 2 copies.

DERHAM, John C.,
Chief Constable Blackpool.

DISHINGTON, Alex.,
Mottram Road, Stalybridge.

DIXON, Herbert,
82, Belvidere Road, Burnley.

DUCKWORTH, Miss R.,
128, Accrington Road, Burnley.

DICKSON, S.,
38, Bottom o' th' Moor, Oldham.

DIXON, Robert,
    101, Rochdale Road, Oldham.

DYSON, James, Spring Bank Place,
                  Nelson.

DUCKWORTH, Thos. Henry,
    Milton Brook Lodge,
        Stamford Bridge, Chester.

DAWSON, Maurice,
    55, Stamford Road, Mossley.

DIXON, David,
    194, Oldham-road, Ashton-under-
           Lyne.   2 copies.

DAVIES, John,
    157, King Street, Oldham.

DYSON, George.
    Argyle Street, Marsden,
           near Huddersfield.

DAWSON, Councillor Robert,
    Park Hill, Stalybridge.

E

EVANS, Geo., J.P.,
    Failsworth Lodge, Failsworth.

EDITOR, "Essex County Annual,"
    5, Horace Road, Forest Gate, Essex.

EMMOTT, Alderman A., J.P.,
    Woodfield, Oldham.

EDMUNDSON, Marmaduke,
    59, Rectory Road, Burnley.

EDMUNDSON, John,
    59, Rectory Road, Burnley.

EDMUNDSON, William,
    33, Belford Street, Burnley.

EDMUNDSON, Joseph,
    59, Rectory Road, Burnley.

ECKROYD, W.,
    Spring Cottage, Nelson, Burnley.

EASTWOOD, James,
    61, Greengate Street, Oldham.

EDGILL, John W.,
    Hulme Town Hall, Manchester.

ELLSEY, John,
    14, Cross Street, Radcliffe.   2 copies.

ENTWISTLE, Thomas,
    Apsley Villas, Adswood Lane East,
           Stockport.

EQUITABLE CO-OPERATIVE
    SOCIETY, Educational Department,
         Oldham.   2 copies.

EVANS, Thomas,
    54, Camden Square, London, N.W.

EVANS, Miss Fanny M.,
    South Shore, Blackpool.

EMMETT, Wm.,
    Berrycroft House, Stalybridge.

EMMETT, Mrs.,
    Berrycroft House, Stalybridge.

EMMETT, Thos.,
    Photographer, Stalybridge.

EMMETT, Wm. R.,
    Muskoka, Ontaria, Canada.

ECCLES, Joseph,
    Fairfield, Ashton-on-Ribble, Preston.

EDWARDS, Councillor John,
    458, New Chester Road, Rock Ferry.

EATOCK, William,
    380, Leigh Road, Westhoughton,
           Bolton.

EMBLETON, Thomas W., M.E.,
    The Cedars, Methley, Leeds.

EDWARDS, J. B.,
    62, Greengate, Salford.

F

FORREST, Alexander, J.P.,
    Heaton Chapel.   2 copies.

FERGUSON, H. S. Walmer,
    St. George's Road,
         St. Anne's-on-Sea.

FRANCE, Councillor James,
    327, Park Road, Oldham.

FISHER, Henry,
    Marsden, nr. Huddersfield.

FRIEND, A., Oldham.

FAZACKERLEY, Henry,
    Ancoats Vale Dye Works,
        Palmerston Street, Ancoats,
           Manchester.

FERNIHOUGH, C. B.,
    18, Park Avenue, Southport.

FITTON, Richard,
    44, Walnut Street, Cheetham,
           Manchester.

FITTON, James,
    56, Oldham Road, Royton.

FLETCHER, William H.,
    56, Smedley Road, Cheetham,
           Manchester.

FRANCE, James,
    Bank House, Uppermill, near
           Oldham.

FISHER, Henry, Mus. Doc.,
    117, Hornby Road, Blackpool.

FOXCROFT, Thomas W.,
    Castle House, Blackley, Manchester.

FOLKARD, Henry T.,
    Librarian, Public Library, Wigan.

FULLALOVE, Wm. T.,
    Town Clerk, Holly Mount, Burnley.

FORD, John France,
    Surrey Arms, Glossop.

FORD, William,
    1, Yorke Street, Burnley.

FAIR, Councillor Thomas,
    The Berks, Lytham.

FISH, Councillor Graham,
    Lynwood, Darwen.

FISH, John T.,
    Read's Villa's, Chapel Street,
         Blackpool.   2 copies.

FIRTH, James,
    Grasscroft, Greenfield, Saddleworth.

FRITH, W. E.,
Bryn Ciriog, Chirk, near Ruabon.

FLETCHER, John Robert, J.P.,
Kearsley Vale House, Stoneclough.

FAIRHURST, Thomas,
Parr's Bank, Altrincham.

FAIRBANK, Christopher,
Fern Bank, Newhey.

FIRTH, John,
285, Broad Street, Pendleton.
2 copies.

G

GREENWOOD, Thomas, F.R.G.S.,
20, Lordship Park, Stoke,
Newington, London, N.

GUEST, W. A.,
Arlington Place, 263, Oxford Road,
Manchester.

GRUNDY, Cuthbert, R.C.A.,
Lytham Road, South Shore,
Blackpool. 2 copies.

GRUNDY, J. R. G., R.C.A.
Lytham Road, South Shore,
Blackpool. 2 copies.

GIBSON, A.,
Grocer, Fleetwood.

GREEN, Geo.,
Dyer, Newton Heath.

GILLMORE, Robert,
Queen's Square, Blackpool.

GRAHAM, John,
1, Spring Lane, Lees,
Oldham. 2 copies.

GEE, Mrs. John,
24, Park View, Wigan.

GRIMSHAW, J.,
Albert Park, Wilmslow,

GILL, Frank,
8, Pollard Street, Nelson.

GODDARD, Richard,
Bankfield, Singleton,
Poulton-le-Fylde.

GANDY, James,
Windleshaw, St. Helens.

GARTSIDE, Benjamin,
Walk, Rochdale.

GASKELL, J. B. (Lieut.-Col.), J.P.,
Roseleigh, Woolton, Liverpool.

GEE, William,
42, Manchester Road, Oldham.

GELDART, William,
10, Fern Street, Oldham.

GILLESPIE, William,
253, Lees Road, Oldham.

GLEDHILL, Joseph,
1, Hunslet Street, Burnley.

GOODACRE, Rev. E. E., B.A.,
23, Manchester Road, Shaw.

GRADWELL, S.,
Holme Chapel, Cheshire.

GREEN, John,
21, Bath Street, Oldham. 2 copies.

GREENWOOD, Wm.,
Secretary Mechanics' Institute,
Bacup.

GREENWOOD, Stephen,
26, Westgate, Burnley.

GRINDROD, E.,
26, Barker Street, Oldham.

GRUNDY, J. H.,
Serpuckoff, near Moscow, Russia.

GIBBS, Henry,
29, St. Bride Street, London, E.C.

GOODMAN, Thomas,
255, Middleton Road, Oldham.
2 copies.

GRIER, Jeremiah,
105, Brompton Street, Oldham.

GARRITY, Edward,
Accrington House, 3, Kennington
Street, London, N.

GREENWOOD, Councillor John, J.P.,
Carr Road, Nelson.

GRIFFITHS, Edward,
Church Street, Burnley.

GRUNDY, Mrs. J. R. G.,
Lytham Road, South Shore,
Blackpool.

GREENHALGH, Councillor Andrew,
The Oaks, Radcliffe.

GILL, James, F.R.A.S.,
Nautical College, Liverpool.

GREENWOOD, Harry,
Bookseller, 38, Bull Green, Halifax.

GARTH, Joseph,
Harold Street, Oldham.

GLEAVE, Wm. Hanson,
5, Trafford Street, Rochdale.

GREEN, John Albert,
Hend Hill Street, Heywood.

GREGSON, Joseph,
45, Rawcliffe Street, South Shore,
Blackpool.

GOLDIE, John,
37, Victoria Road, Hyde Park, Leeds

H

HOLDEN, James,
Crystal Road, South Shore,
Blackpool.

HARRISON, S. J.,
1, Green Street, East Darwen.

HEATON, John,
43, Cambridge Street,
Stalybridge. 2 copies.

HEAP, B., J.P.,
Northwood, Prestwich.

HOTHERSALL, Rev. William,
York House, Oswaldtwistle.

HAMPSHIRE, Wm.,
27, Evening Street, Failsworth,
nr. Manchester.

HEYWOOD, Nathan,
3, Mount Street, Manchester.

HEYWOOD, Arthur,
  Spire Hollins, Combs,
                    Chapel-en-le-Frith.
HOLROYD, J. K.,
  3, Ash Street, Southport.
HELENS ST., FREE PUBLIC
  LIBRARY.   3 copies.
HALLAM, Wm.,
  333, Knutsford Road, Latchford,
                    Warrington.
HARREL, W. H.,
  153, Windsor Road, Oldham.
HALL, Robert,
  Vocalist, 40, Banks Street,
                    Blackpool.
HEGINBOTHAM Joseph,
  Woodbine Crescent, Stockport.
HOLT, Thomas,
  61, Rectory Road, Burnley.
HIBBERT, Right Hon. Sir J. T., M.P.,
  Hampsfield, Grange-over-Sands.
HANDLEY, Richard, J.P.,
  9, Carlton Terrace, Blackpool.
HARGREAVES, John Taylor,
  Ashton Road East, Failsworth.
HOWARTH, William Wallace,
  44, Dunfields, Sheffield.
HINMERS, Edward,
  St. Arnold's Road, Oak Park,
                    Worsley.
HARDMAN, David,
  212, Lytham Road, South Shore,
                    Blackpool.
HUNTINGTON, C. P., M.P.,
  Clock House, Chelsea Embankment,
                    London.
HARVEY, William,
  The Rookery, Nantwich, Cheshire.
HADWEN, William,
  Stamford House,
         Manchester Road, Fairfield.
HAMMOND, Thomas,
  16, Nelson Terrace, Blackpool.
HARGREAVES, Joseph,
  5, Church Street, Harpurhey,
                    Manchester.
HALLSWORTH, T. E.,
  37, Hyde Road, Ardwick,
                    Manchester.
HASTINGS, James,
  Higher Crowtrees, Entwistle,
             nr. Bolton. 2 copies.
HINDLE, J. M.,
  33, Dean Street, South Shore,
                    Blackpool.
HOLROYD, John,
  Lytham Road, South Shore,
                    Blackpool.
HARDMAN, William, M.D.,
  12, Albert Terrace, Blackpool.
HENTHORN, Elizabeth,
  Glodwick Road, Oldham.
HALL, Abel,
  37, London Road, Oldham.
HAYES, Samuel,
  Rose Lodge, Upton, Macclesfield.
HAIGHTON, Le Gender Starkie,
  Scotland Road, Nelson.

HARTLEY, Wm.,
  Thorn Hill, Manchester Road,
                    Burnley.   2 copies.
HARTLEY, James,
  Ormrod Road, Burnley.
HARTLEY, Job Whittam,
  Thorn Hill, Manchester Road,
                    Burnley.
HARTLEY, R. Burns,
  Bank Parade, Burnley.
HEATON, Mrs. Mary,
  99, Rectory Road, Burnley.
HEYWOOD, Frank,
  Spire Hollins, Chapel-en-le-Frith.
HUDSON J. C.,
  Chapel Hill, Littleborough.
HIBBERT, Emmanuel,
  Wicken Tree Lane, Failsworth,
HOOTON, W. A.,
  Vrandeg, Park Road, Blackpool.
                    2 copies.
HOLT, James,
  25, Hulton Street, Failsworth.
HALL, John,
  Solicitor, Chorley New Road,
                    Bolton
HARRIS, William,
  21, Cannon Street, Manchester.
HOLDEN, John, B.A.,
  Crystal Road, South Shore,
                    Blackpool.
HANSON, Geo.,
  178, Ramsay Street, Rochdale.
HADFIELD, George,
  Hollywood, Pendleton, Manchester.
                    2 copies.
HAINSWORTH, Lewis,
  120, Bowling Old Lane, Bradford.
HALL, Hiram George,
  24, Audenshaw Road, Audenshaw.
HALL, Oliver Ormerod,
  8, Half Edge Lane, Eccles.
HALLARD, Henry,
  132, Breckfield Road N, Everton,
                Liverpool.   2 copies.
HALSTEAD, David,
  Haslingden.
HALSTEAD, James,
  8, Rectory Road, Burnley.
HAMER, N.,
  Cropper's Hill, St. Helens.
HARDING, William,
  36, Manchester Road, Oldham.
HARDMAN, John,
  Stationer, Tyldesley.
HARGREAVES, G.,
  Bridge Mills, Rochdale Road,
                    Manchester.
HARPER, J.,
  Bookseller, &c., High Street,
                    Sandbach.
HARRISON, Inspector,
  Detective Office, Town Hall,
                    Manchester.
HARTLEY, J. T.,
  22, Nelson Square, Burnley.

HASLAM, J. W.,
25, Callender Street, Ramsbottom.

HAWORTH, William Henry,
Times Office, Rochdale.

HARGREAVES, H. L.,
Queen's Road, Oldham.

HAYES, Thomas Travers, J.P., C.C.,
Fairfield, Leigh.

HENSHALL, Henry,
8, Union Street, Oldham.

HEYS, Nathan,
4, Arcade, Colne.

HEPWORTH, James,
Hyde Lane, Hyde.   2 copies.

HEWITT, Thomas,
150, Leadenhall Street, London.

HEYWORTH, Richard,
Dearnley, near Rochdale.   2 copies.

HILTON, James,
16, Glodwick Road, Oldham.

HILTON, John,
19, Queen's Road, Oldham.

HINCHCLIFFE, James A.,
Fern Bank, Shaw.

HINDLE, Thomas,
District Chambers, Darwen.

HOLT, Jos. J. H.,
13, Manchester Street, Oldham.

HOLT, Squire,
5, Clegg Street, Oldham.

HOLT, William,
9, Clegg Street, Oldham.

HORROCKS, James,
Broad Oak Park, Worsley, near
Manchester.

HOSEGOOD, Samuel,
Surgeon, Swinton, Manchester.

HOUGH, Henry,
7, Blackfriars Bridge, Salford.

HOULDSWORTH WORKING MEN'S
CLUB, Reddish, near Stockport,
H. Lees, Secretary.

HOWARD, Jonathan,
Marland, near Rochdale.

HOWARTH, J.,
Florence House, Elm Grove,
Southsea.

HOWELL, Ed.,
Bookseller, Liverpool.

HUDSON, John C.,
Chapel Hill, Littleborough.

HULTON, John S.,
Sidebank, Greenfield, near Oldham.

HURST, James,
Chemist, 4, Greenacres Road,
Oldham.

HEYWOOD & SONS, Abel,
56 & 58, Oldham Street, Manchester.
5 copies.

HEYWOOD, John,
Deansgate and Ridgefield,
Manchester.   18 copies.

HEYWOOD, Frank,
Spire Hollins, Chapel-en-le-Frith.

HILL, Joseph,
Market Place, Marsden, near
Huddersfield.

HEAP, Councillor Joseph,
10, Raikes Parade, Blackpool.
4 copies.

HANSON, Wm.,
17, Marlborough Street, Oldham.

HOLT, John,
Liberty Ironworks, Stalybridge.

HALLAM, John,
11, Queen Street, Oldham.   2 copies.

HOLLINS, Frank, J.P.,
Preston.

HOWARTH, Daniel F.,
Grafton Place, Ashton-under-Lyne.

HEMMING, George J., Phrenologist,
61, Waterloo Road, South Shore,
Blackpool.

HEMMING, Mrs. G. J.,
61, Waterloo Road, South Shore,
Blackpool.

HOLLAND, William,
General Manager, Winter Gardens,
Blackpool.

HAWORTH, Thomas,
5, London Terrace, Darwen.

HARRISON, B.,
c/o Harrison & Clough,
Union Street, Oldham.

HUNTER, Councillor J.P.,
Talbot Road, Glossop.

HOWARD, James,
23, Spring Gardens, Middleton.

HORNER, Harry,
29, Manchester Road, Burnley.

HARTLEY, James,
18, Pitt Street, Glodwick, Oldham.

HALL, Alderman Edward,
98, Greengate Street, Oldham.

HAMPSON, Ralph,
22, Overens Street, Oldham.

HAMPSON, Jas. Richard,
Caxton House, Pendlebury.

HEYWOOD, Councillor Frederick,
Birchwood, Holland Road,
Crumsall.

HILL, Benjamin,
16, Victoria Street, Ashton-under-
Lyne.

HOYLE, William,
Bright Street, South Shore,
Blackpool.

HEAP, James,
Beach Hill, Blackley.   2 copies.

HEYWOOD, Tom,
Artist, Lyceum, Oldham.   2 copies.

HULLY, J. W.,
5, Orange Street, Ashton-under-
Lyne.

HOWARD, James,
(Carter & Howard, Auctioneers),
Blackpool.

HEAP, Robert T.,
2, Nelson Square, Burnley.

HAGUE, John Houghton,
  Artist, Wellington Road, Oldham.
  2 copes.
HIGSON, John T.,
  Red Lion, Market Place, Oldham.
HEAP, James,
  37, Rochdale Road, Heywood.
HILTON, James,
  10, Firth Street, Oldham.
HOLT, Miss,
  c/o Mrs. Chas. Lees, Werneth Park,
  Oldham.

I

IRVING, Henry,
  Lyceum Theatre, London.
INNES, Robert,
  Princess Street, Stalybridge.
INGHAM, Samuel,
  325, Park Road, Oldham.
INNES, David,
  47, Melbourne Street, Stalybridge.
IRVIN, David,
  Woodvill, Longridge, near Preston.
IRLAM, William Henry,
  55, High Street West, Glossop.
  2 copies.
IRLAM, John W.,
  Worthington, Princess Street,
  Glossop.
ISHERWOOD, F. G.,
  West View, Windsor Road, Oldham.
IRVIN, David,
  Woodville, Longridge, near Preston.

J

JACKSON, James,
  Soho Ironworks, Oldham.
JACKSON, John,
  1, Bonny Street, Blackpool.
JACKSON, Joseph,
  Druggist, Talbot Road, Blackpool.
  2 copies.
JACKSON, John,
  Alexandra Villas, Stalybridge.
JOHNSON, E. A.,
  15, Vineyard, Lees Road, Oldham.
JOB, Francis Geo.,
  62, Belmont Avenue, Gt. Marton Road,
  Blackpool.
JOPSON, Daniel,
  30, Sadler Street, Middleton.
JOHNS, Henry Maxwell,
  2, Temple Street, Blackpool.
JONES, John,
  36, Princess Street, Bury.
JACKSON, Edward,
  16, Fox Platt Terrace, Mossley.
JACKSON, Vernon L.,
  231, Park Road, Oldham.

JACKSON, Joseph,
  Greaves Street, Oldham.
JAGGER, Eli,
  142, Lee Street, Oldham.
JOHNSON, John,
  Woodstock, Higher Crumpsall,
  Manchester.
JOHNSON, Rev Samuel,
  The Manse, Buckley via Chester.
JOHNSON, Alfred,
  Oak Lee, Dukinfield.
JONES, F. L.,
  Hart Street Works, Blackburn.
JONES, Robert,
  307, Waterloo Street, Oldham.
JOHNSON, James Henry,
  Hall Garth, Overkellet, Carnforth.
  2 copies.
JACKSON, Edward, J.P.,
  Wheelton, Chorley.
JACKSON, Thomas,
  43, Great Ducie Street, Manchester.
JACKSON, Mrs. Joseph,
  82, Greenwood Street, Oldham.

K

KINGSBURY, Geo. C., M.D.,
  3, Brighton Parade, Blackpool.
  2 copies.
KAY, John,
  58, Cannon Street, Manchester.
KERSHAW, William,
  Sunny Beach, St. Annes-on-Sea.
KNOTT, John Fred.,
  Stoneleigh, Stalybridge.   2 copies.
KNOWLES, Robert,
  South Drive, St. Annes-on-Sea.
KERSHAW, Cooper,
  Mill Manager, Oldham Road,
  Failsworth.
KELLETT, Robert,
  22, Manchester Road, Burnley.
KITSON, Sir James, Bart., M.P.,
  Gledhow Hall, Leeds.
KNOTT, A. W.,
  Uppermill, Saddleworth.
KAY, Abraham,
  Dingle Bank, Prestwich Park,
  Prestwich.   2 copies.
KAY, Thomas, J.P.,
  Moorfield, Stockport.
KELSALL, Joseph Edward,
  8, Belmont Street, Oldham.
KERSHAW, Henry,
  Park Hill, Rochdale.
KIRKHAM, William,
  Lorne House, Regent Street,
  Chorley Old Road, Bolton.
KITCHINGMAN, Joseph,
  Seabank Nook Promenade, Liscard.

KNIGHT, Rev. George,
826, Oldham Road, Newton Heath.

KERSHAW, Joseph,
Moston House, Failsworth.

KIRTLAND, S. R., Mus. Bac.,
382, Lytham Road, Blackpool.

KENYON, Robert, F.R His. S.,
The High School, South Shore,
Blackpool.

KERFOOT, Edwin,
Market Street, Leith, Lancashire.

KNIGHT, J., The Waverley Hotel,
Talbot Road, Blackpool.

KINNEAR, Henry,
Manager Commercial Inn,
Stalybridge.

KAY, Tom W.,
Solicitor, Pelham Mount, Blackpool.

KENWORTHY, O.,
106, Werneth Hall Road, Oldham.

KEGAN PAUL, TRENCH, TRÜBNER
& Co. Ltd., Paternoster House,
Charing Cross Road, London, W.C.

L

LEE, Helen,
Poulton-le-Fylde.

LAYCOCK, John,
6, Grosvenor Street, Stalybridge.

LAYCOCK, E. B.,
Post Office, Westwood, Oldham.

LATHAM, James,
168, Bolton Old Road, Atherton.

LAWTON, Peter.
Beechwood, Middleton.

LORD, James,
St. Annes Road, St. Annes-on-Sea.

LORD, J. M.,
Albert Terrace, Blackpool.

LAW, William,
Littleborough.

LAWLESS, Richard,
Union Club, Oldham.

LEACH, R. A.,
Wellington Terrace, Rochdale.

LEAVER, R.,
Hilton Arcade, Oldham.

LEE, Thomas,
1, Rushton Lane, Bolton.

LEES, Edward B.,
Thurland Castle, Kirkby Lonsdale.

LEES, Henry,
86, Brompton Street, Oldham.

LEES, John, J.P.,
Cartref Melies, Conway, North
Wales.   2 copies.

LEES, Joseph,
40, Chelmsford Street, Oldham.

LEVY, James, J.P.,
9, Verulam Buildings, Grays Inn,
London.

LIBRARY, Free Public,
Oldham.   2 copies.

LINSLEY, Henry,
20, Peru Street, Salford.

LOCKWOOD, Arthur,
Barnsley.

LOFTHOUSE, George M.,
77, Strand Street, Douglas, I.O.M.

LOMAX, William,
16, Meanley Street, Tyldesley.

LORD, Lawrence,
60, Devonshire Road, Burnley.

LUPTON, Albert,
58, Colne Road, Burnley.

LUPTON, Arthur,
12, St. Matthew Street, Burnley.

LUPTON, Benjamin,
136, Manchester Road, Burnley.

LUPTON, J. T.,
7, Carlton Road, Burnley.

LIBRARY, Feilden Free,
Fleetwood.

LYTHGOE, Gilbert,
Foxhall Road, Blackpool.   2 copies.

LANCASTER, John,
Hornby Road, Blackpool.

LENNARD, James,
1, Rutland Gate, Claremont Park,
Blackpool.

LUCAS, Rev. J. E.,
Claremont College, Blackpool.

LONSDALE, Wm.,
135, Hartley Terrace, Bacup.

LONSDALE, Thomas,
49 and 51, Market Street, Colne.

LAYCOCK, Joseph,
37, Barker Street, Queen's Park,
Manchester.

LIGHTBOWN, Ainsworth,
19, Harwood Street, Darwen.

LAYCOCK, Peter,
71, Lord Street, Liverpool.   4 copies.

LEES, William,
312, Manchester Road, Hollinwood.

LAYCOCK, Samuel, J.P., C.B.C.,
Airedale House, Park View, Wigan.

LONGBOTTOM, A.,
64, Nugget Street, Oldham.

LAYCOCK, James,
515, Rochdale Road, Manchester.

LAHEE, M. R.,
Rochdale.

LEES, Elliott, J.P.,
14, Queen Anne's Gate, London,
S.W.

LORD, Abraham,
417, Park Road, Oldham.

LIBRARY, Free Public and Museum,
Bootle.

LEE, Henry C.,
11, King Street, Oldham.

LIBRARY, BIRKENHEAD PUBLIC
FREE, (per Wm. May, Librarian).

LIBRARY, ROCHDALE PUBLIC
FREE, (per Geo. Hanson, Librarian.)

LEIGH, Arthur G., F.R.S.L.,
Chorcliff House, Chorley.

LOWE, Bennett,
19, Bright Street, South Shore,
Blackpool.   2 copies.

LEE, Moses,
Cotton Street, Ashton-under-Lyne.

LINDLEY, William,
35, Green Lane, Sheffield.

LUMB, Henry, Broughton Road,
Marsden, near Huddersfield.

LORD, Silvanus,
Manufacturer, Woodtop Mills,
Burnley.

LONGRIDGE INDUSTRIAL
CO-OPERATIVE SOCIETY,
Longridge.

LEEMING, John,
Green Lane, Longridge.

LEXTON, Alfred,
Beehive, Marsden, nr. Huddersfield.

LETHAM, James,
153, Yorkshire Street, Oldham.

LETHAM, William,
99, Belgrave Road, Oldham.

LANCASTER, Rev. A.,
61A, Manchester Old Road,
Middleton.

LUPTON BROTHERS,
Booksellers, Manchester Road,
Burnley. 12 copies.

LAWTON, David,
Spring Grove, Greenfield,
near Oldham.

LAWTON, Josef,
Musical Director, The Park,
Rochdale.

LIBRARY, OLDHAM FREE,
(per S. Barlow, J.P.)

LIBRARY, ROCHDALE FREE,
(per S. Barlow, J.P.)

LIBRARY, MIDDLETON FREE,
(per S. Barlow, J.P.)

LIBRARY, CO-OPERATIVE
SOCIETY, FAILSWORTH.

LIBERAL CLUB, BLACKPOOL.
(per M. G. Wilde)

LIBRARY, MANCHESTER PUBLIC
FREE, King Street, Manchester,
(per C. H. Sutton). 10 copies.

LAWSON, Samuel,
29, Scotland Road, Nelson.

LORD, Edward,
5, Albion Street, Burnley.

LOWE, E.,
c/o W. H. Rushton, Mineral Water
Co., King Street, Stalybridge.

LIBRARY, FREE PUBLIC, St. Helens
3 copies.

LORD, William,
1, York Street, Burnley.

LANG, E. S.,
2, Preston Street, Oldham.

LYCEUM, Oldham,
(per Arthur Tait, Secretary).

M

MATLEY, Andrew.
Warrington Street, Stalybridge.

McMURDO, James,
Hardman Lane, Failsworth.

MATTHEWS, Henry,
41, Union Street, Oldham.

MELLOR, John,
68, Talbot Road, Blackpool

MONKS, Thomas,
Cliftonville, 58, Duke Street,
Southport.

MARSDEN, John,
Auctioneer, Queen's Square,
Blackpool.

MIDDLETON, James,
Manchester Road, Hollinwood.

MOORE, Robinson,
Auctioneer, 30, Abingdon Street,
Blackpool.

MARSDEN, George,
Marsden, near Huddersfield.

MILLS, Jesse,
3, Wellington Road, Coppice,
Oldham.

MAYCOCK, William C.,
Wencobank, Sheffield.

MAYCOCK, Emma,
Wencobank, Sheffield.

MOORHOUSE, Thomas,
115, London Road, Oldham.

MURGATROYD, Robert,
70, Gee Street, Moss Side,
Manchester.

MALLALIEU, John,
32, Hartley Street, Oldham.

MEADOWCROFT, William,
Eagle and Child Hotel, Bury.

MELLING, Samuel, J.P.,
Sycamores, Wigan.

MANLEY, James,
80, Stockton Street, Moss Side,
Manchester.

MATHER, Wm., Albert,
13, Claremont Terrace, Nelson.

MARLAND, Thomas,
88, Manchester Road, Burnley.

McCOURT, Walter,
8, Baron Terrace, Healey Wood,
Burnley.

MERCER, Councillor R.,
Ighten Holme, Burnley.

MURGATROYD, W. C.,
Spring Bank Place, Nelson.

MITCHELL, Joseph,
St. Andrew's Road South,
St. Annes-on-Sea.

MITCHELL, Councillor John, J.P.,
Woodend House, Mossley.

MACKIE, W.,
Priory Chambers, 77, Union Street,
Oldham.

MANDLEN, William,
7, Salter's Road South, Gosforth.

MAUDSLEY, Pearson J.,
The Elms, Cherry Tree,
near Blackburn.

MATLEY, Levi,
Rochdale.

MELLALIEU, William,
55, Chadderton Road, Oldham.

MELLOR, J. H.,
24, Stanley Road, Hollinwood.

MELLOR, Miss P.,
52, Bridge Street, Worksop.

MIDDLETON, Mrs.,
23, Lord Street, Oldham.

MILLS, John,
West Hill, Oldham.

MILNER, Edward,
Hartford Manor, Northwich.

MILNER, George,
President Manchester Literary Club.

MITCHELL, Jeremiah,
19, Green Terrace, Padiham.

MUCKELT, John,
102, Portland Street Manchester.

MUNRO, John,
Fair View, Rudyard, Staffordshire.

Mc'FARLANE, James,
98, Smedley Road, Cheetham.

MARSHALL, James Henry,
83, Dunkerley Street, Oldham.

MATHER, William, M.P.,
Salford Ironworks, Salford.
2 copies.

MILLS, Felix,
Elocutionist, Lee Street, Oldham.

MALLALUE, Rev. Wm. Revoe,
Blackpool.

MONKS, J.P.,
Solicitor, 9, Fold Street, Bolton.

MARSDEN, T. R.,
3, Barlow Street, Oldham.

MIDDLETON, George,
Poppythorn, Prestwich.

MARSLAND, Wain,
54, Lees Road, Oldham.

MELLOR, R. H.,
59 and 61, Henshaw Street, Oldham.

MELLOR, Samuel Dixon,
8, Market Place, Oldham.

MORT, James,
Old Corn Exchange, Manchester.

MELLING, Alderman John,
34, Victoria Street, Manchester.

MONK, Councillor F.,
Walton Old Hall, near Warrington.

MONK, Councillor Josiah,
Brookfoot Farm, near Padiham.

MASON, Thos. & Son,
Oxford Mills, Ashton-under-Lyne.

MILNES, Charles,
Bamford, near Rochdale.

MARTIN, John,
5, King Street, Westhoughton.

MILLS, George, J.P.,
Brookbottom, Mossley.

MARCROFT, William, jun.,
7, Union Street, Oldham.

MANN, Tom,
London Reform Union, Granville
House, 3, Arundel Street, Strand,
London, W.C.

MEADOWCROFT, Wm.,
" Eagle and Child " Hotel,
Stanley Street, Bury.

MACKEY, Matthew,
8, Milton Street, Newcastle-on-Tyne.

METCALFE, James,
2 Mosley Street, Barnoldswick.

MILLER, M. H., M.J.I., F.R. Hist. S.,
" Times " Office, Leek.

MIDDLETON, John,
Cab Proprietor, Leigh,
near Manchester.

N

NEVILLE, Ralph, M.P.,
42, Cadogan Terrace, London, S.W.

NEWALL, Richard,
Pawnbroker, Oldham Road,
Manchester.

NEEDHAM, Isaac,
The Green, Poynton, via Stockport.

NEWSHOLME, Rev. John,
23, Bright, Street, South Shore,
Blackpool.

NEWSOME, E. L.,
Coal Merchant, Nelson Road,
South Shore, Blackpool. 2 copies.

NAYLOR, Thomas,
Church Street, Blackpool.

NICKSON, Charles,
" Guardian Office," Altrincham.

NUTTER, Henry,
Darwen House, Burnley.

NEILD, William,
56, Fern Street, Oldham.

NEWBIGGING, Thomas,
Eccles, Manchester.

NEWBIGGING, W.,
Bruxfield, St. Annes Road,
St. Annes-on-Sea.

NUTTER, William Henry,
Park Road, St. Annes-on-Sea.

NUTTALL, James,
St. Chad's Terrace, South Shore,
Blackpool.

NEWTON, Isaac,
135, Bolton Street, Oldham.

NASH, William,
23, Queen's Road, Oldham.

NEIL, Alexander,
Ironfounder, Hope House, 82,
Eccles Old Road, Eccles.

NUTTER, Henry,
Queen's Gate, Burnley.

NAYLOR, John H.,
Nelson Terrace, Blackpool.

NORTON, S. Walter,
221, Fern Park Road, Hornsey, N.

NEEDHAM, Councillor George, J.P.,
    483, Rochdale Road, Manchester.
NORRIS, Councillor John, J.P.,
    15, Seymour Grove, Old Trafford.
NEWSOME, Ernest Lodge,
    13, Kent Road, Blackpool.
NEEDHAM, James,
    Beach Street, West Beach, Lytham.

O

OWEN, Edward,
    1, Kay's Terrace, Blackpool.
OGDEN, John,
    Stonemason, St. Annes-on-Sea.
ORRELL, Thomas,
    216, Stony Lane, Hindley,
                    nr. Wigan.
OGDEN, A.,
    43, Frederick Street, Oldham.
OLDFIELD, George,
    6, Lansdowne Place, Bradford,
                    Yorks.
ORRELL, J. Andrew,
    Solicitor, 18, St. Ann Street,
                    Manchester.
ORMEROD, Thomas,
    80, Norroy Road, Putney, London,
                    S.W.
OGDEN, George A.,
    21, Henshaw Street, Oldham.
OGDEN, J. N.,
    54 and 56, Oldham Road,
                    Manchester.
OLIVER, Thomas,
    Lithographic Artist, 8, King Street,
        Manchester.   2 copies.

P

POPE, Samuel, Q.C.,
    38, Parliament Street,
                Westminster, London.
POLLARD, George,
    Hazel Villa, Hayfield, via Stockport.
PLATT, Samuel,
    Strawberry Gardens, Oldham.
PLATT, Thomas G., J.P.,
    Thornbank, Mossley Road,
                    Ashton-under-Lyne.
PLATT, James,
    Greenacres Road, Oldham
PRINCE, Daniel,
    23, Elliston Street, Poulton-le-Fylde,
                    Blackpool.
PAYNE, Charles,
    Laburnum Villas, George Street,
                    Cheetham Hill.
PAYNE, John,
    Jeweller, Market Street, Blackpool.
PASHLEY, Frank,
    Balaclava, Sheffield.

PORRITT, William John, J.P.,
    Stoneleigh, North Parade,
                    St. Annes-on-Sea.
PORRITT, Harold,
    North Beach, North Parade,
                    St. Annes-on-Sea.
PEERS, Joseph,
    87, St. Andrew's Road,
                    St. Annes-on-Sea.
PARKER, Mrs.,
    Belmont Villas, South Shore,
                Blackpool.   3 copies.
PARSONS, William,
    Market Street, New Mills,
                    Derbyshire.
PLATT, Samuel,
    194, Greenacres Road, Oldham.
PLATT, Thomas,
    Brunswick Hotel, Ashton-u-Lyne.
PILLING, Rev. Samuel, F.G.S.,
    Regent Road, Blackpool.
PHILLIPS, Alderman Jonathan,
    Mayor of Wigan.
PENDLEBURY, J., J.P.,
    Crawford House, Wigan.
PLATT, Hugh Hague,
    16, Sand Street, Stalybridge.
PARKIN, John W.,
    4, Bradley Road, Nelson.
PARKINSON, Albert W.,
    45, Ormrod Road, Burnley.
PRINCE, J. E.,
    Abingdon Street, Blackpool. 2 copies.
PAINE, Ernest John,
    Wheelock Street, Manchester.
PARKER, Henry,
    73, Rumford Street, Manchester.
PEARSON, Rev. Thomas, M.A.,
    24, Latham Street, Preston.
PEEL, Martin,
    606, Stockport Road, Manchester.
PHILLIPS, John, J.P.,
    Brown Hill, Burnley.
PICKAVANCE, Edward,
    67, Bridge Street, Warrington.
PICKLES, Joseph,
    38, Allen Street, Burnley.
PICKUP, George,
    Moorside, Oldham.
PILKINGTON, W.,
    Dinting Vale, Glossop.   2 copies.
PLATT, James E., J.P.,
    Bruntwood, Cheadle, Cheshire.
PLATT, James,
    Penwortham Lodge, Cambridge
                Road, Southport.
POTTER, William Henry,
    34, Market Place, Oldham.
POWER, Robert,
    28, Moorhead Villas, Shipley, Yorks.
                    7 copies.
PRESCOTT, Thos.,
    122, Turf Lane, Hollinwood.

PRESTON INDUSTRIAL CO-OP.
SOCIETY LD., Educational
Department, 80, North Road,
Preston.
PRIESTLEY, L. J.,
St. James's Street, Bacup. 2 copies.
PROCTOR, John,
45, Rectory Road, Burnley.
POLLARD, William,
Hazel Villas, Hayfield *via* Stockport.
PONTEFRACT. Matthew,
Hepworth, near Huddersfield.
PROCTOR, Richard,
Oak Mount, Burnley.
PLATT, Thomas Shaw,
Wellfield, Uppermill, Saddleworth.
PEMBERTON, James,
79 and 83, Harwood Street,
Blackburn.
POLLARD, Thomas,
Daisy Hill, Westhoughton.
PRATT, Thomas,
Drysalter, &c., Brierfield.
PRESCOTT, R. M.,
Town Clerk, Nelson.
POLLARD, James,
Leigh Road, Westhoughton.
PERKINS, George,
Artist, Harpurhey, Manchester.
2 copies.
POLLARD, William, jun.,
Hazel Villas, Hayfield, near
Stockport.
PIMBLOTT, William,
Swiss Cottage, Upton, Macclesfield.
PETRIE, George, J.P.,
Rochdale.
PADWICK, F. G., M.A.,
Downham House, Rochdale.
PLATT, John, J.P.,
Clifton Lodge, Llandudno.
PORRITT, Wm. John.,
Helmshore, near Manchester.
PILLING, Samuel,
Rosemount, Helmshore.
PEARSON, James,
21, Fitzwarren Street, Pendleton.

R

RICHARDSON, W. H.,
Teacher of Music, Stamford Street,
Stalybridge.
RIDGWAY, Frank,
White House Hotel, Stalybridge.
RUSHTON, Ralph,
Beach Hotel, Blackpool.
RILEY, Richard,
89, Albert Road, Colne.

ROTHWELL, Councillor W. T., J.P.,
Heath House, Newton Heath
(2 copies)
RHODES, Abel,
177, Moorhey Street, Oldham.
RUSHWORTH, Luke,
Edge Lane, Droylsden.
ROBINSON, Thos. F.,
Fern Bank, Williams Road, Moston.
ROBINSON, Jonathan,
288, Dickenson Road, Rusholme,
Manchester.
RILEY, G. E.,
Rose Cottage. New Moston.
RYECROFT, John,
Every Street, Nelson.
RAWLINSON, Jonedab,
Pendle Street, Nelson.
ROBINSON, County Ald'rm'n J.B., J.P.
The Inner Hey, Marsden.
REAY, Thomas,
16, Withington Street, Pendleton.
RILEY, Thomas,
Fleetwood.
RAMSDEN, W. H. F.,
Sunnyside, Dobcross, near Oldham.
RAWLINSON, Jos.,
Top o' th' Wallsuches, Horwich.
2 copies.
RICHARDS, Mrs. Mary, Old England
Hotel, Bowness, Windermere.
RIDDICK, James,
9, Fountain Street, Manchester.
RILEY, Thomas,
Rosthwaite, Stafford Road, Eccles.
RENNIE, W.,
59, Windsor Road, Werneth,
Oldham. 4 copies.
ROBERTS, S.,
211, Lees Road, Oldham.
ROBERTS, T. H.,
Solicitor, Burnley.
ROBINSON, John Augustine, J.P.,
Southport.
ROBINSON, Alderman Stephen,
Stamp Office, Stockport.
ROGERS, M. C.,
Flowery Field, Hyde.
ROGERSON, Thomas,
Fair Field, Heaton Chapel.
2 copies.
ROWBOTTOM, John,
48, Manchester Road, Werneth,
Oldham.
RUSSELL, William,
Ironfounder, 80, Fitzwarren Street,
Pendleton, Manchester.
RYLANCE, William,
Solicitor, 76, Mosley Street,
Manchester.
ROBINSON, William
Artist, King Street Manchester.
2 copies.
RYDINGS, Harold,
Southcote Road, Bournemouth.

RICHARDSON, Walter,
71, Guide Lane, Hooley Hill.

RHODES, Thomas,
High School, Hornby Road,
Blackpool.

REED, Councillor William,
Pendle Street, Nelson.

RYDINGS, Amos,
583, Oldham Road, Failsworth.

RUSHTON, Rev. Adam,
Swiss Cottage, Upton, Macclesfield.

RIDINGS, Gilbert,
Castle Inn, Market Street,
Blackpool.

ROYDS, Clement, M., J.P.,
Greenhill, Rochdale.

RATCLIFFE, Chas. G.,
Park House, Colne.

RUSHWORTH, Joseph,
397, Oldham Road, Failsworth.

ROYTON CO-OPERATIVE SOCIETY
Limited, Educational Department,
per Thos. Bleasdale.

S

STANLEY, Alderman, G. T.,
Moxley Road, Crumpsall,
Manchester. 10 copies.

SCHOFIELD, Sim,
Auburn Bank, New Moston,
3 copies.

SHAW, Samuel,
Manufacturer, Stalybridge.

SHAW, W. H.,
17, Marsh Street, Oldham.

SMITH, William,
Brookfield Villa, Morley, nr. Leeds.

SMITH, E. W. B.,
Bookseller, Bury.

SOUTHERN, Councillor, J.W., J.P.,
Burnage Lodge, Burnage,
Manchester.

SMITH, Joseph, Raikes Road,
Blackpool.

SIDDALL, Thomas,
Dale House Fold, Poynton,
via Stockport.

SCHOFIELD, Mrs. Sim,
Auburn Bank, New Moston
(3 copies)

SUTTON, Chas. W.,
Free Reference Library, Manchester.

SINCLAIR, J., M.D.,
250, Oxford Road, Manchester.

SAYNOR, John,
25, Rawcliffe Street, South Shore,
Blackpool.

SCHOLES, Thos. H.,
18, Chester Street, Oldham.

SEED, G. H.,
87, Lansdowne Road, Didsbury.

SHAW, Giles,
72, Manchester Street, Oldham.

SHAW, Tom,
Mumps, Oldham.

SHORROCK, Peter,
56, Mosley Street, Manchester.

SMITH, Francis,
Registrar County Court, Salford.

SMITH, Wm. H.,
Prince Albert Hotel, Oldham.

SOWDEN, Job,
28, Clegg Street, Oldham.

SOWERBUTTS, Eli, F.R.G.S.F.J.
Inst., &c., 44, Brown Street,
Manchester.

STOTT, James,
Coldhurst Hall, Oldham.

STOTT, Sidney,
Retiro Buildings, Yorkshire Street,
Oldham.

STUTTARD, Ernest,
57, Burns Street, Burnley.

STUTTARD, Luther,
57, Burns Street, Burnley.

SUBSCRIPTION LIBRARY,
Bolton, per J. R. Waite.

SWAILES, George,
Birks House, Waterhead, Oldham.

SWINDLEHURST, Robert Henry,
M.I.C.E., Wynesdale House,
Chorley Old Road, Bolton.

SWINGLEHURST, Henry, J.P., D.L.,
Hincaster House, near Milnthorpe.
2 copies.

SUTCLIFFE, Thomas,
Librarian Co-operative Society,
8, Dale Street, Todmorden.

SIMPKIN, MARSHALL, HAMILTON,
KENT, & CO. LD., 4, Stationers'
Hall Court, London, E.C.
8 copies.

SMETHURST, Jas.,
North Moor Church School, Oldham.

SPENCER, Councillor James,
Engineer, Hollinwood.

SHARPLES, George,
Dean Villa, South Shore, Blackpool.

SPARLING, H. Halliday,
8, Hammersmith Terrace,
London, W.

SYMONDS, Arthur G. M.A.,
50, Haworth's Buildings,
Cross Street, Manchester.

SCHOFIELD. Geo. Ernest,
207, Ripponden Road,
Watersheddings, Oldham.

SCHOFIELD, John Wm.,
Hon. Sec. Literary Society,
Waterhead.

STANDRING, Joseph,
558, Oldham Road, Failsworth.

SWIRE, Hezekiah,
27, Red Lion Street, Burnley.

STUTTER, Isaiah,
65, Busk Street, Oldham.

SMITH, Benjamin,
  6, William Street, Colne,
                    Lancashire.
SUTCLIFFE, John,
  43, Chesterfield Street, Oldham.
SHAW, Joseph,
  Accountant, 19, Retiro Street,
                    Oldham.
SIDDALL, Councillor A. W.,
  Grafton Place, Ashton-under-Lyne.
SUTHERS, William,
  197, Glodwick Road, Oldham.
SMITH, Councillor T. H.,
  Houldsworth Lodge, Blackpool.
SPENCER, Councillor John,
  Scotland Road, Nelson.
SUTCLIFFE, John,
  19, Market Street, Colne,
                    Lancashire.
STOTT, John,
  24, Wilkinson Street, Leigh,
                    Lancashire.
SMITH, Robinson,
  Jeweller, 48, Plumbe Street,
                    Burnley.
SMITH, John,
  Plumber, Curzon Street, Burnley.
STAFFORD, Samuel,
  Ash Cottage, Whittle, New Mills,
                    Derbyshire.
SHACKLETON, J.,
  Artist, Rose Bank, Moston Lane,
                    Moston.   2 copies.
SIDDALL, Wm. T.,
  Literary Institute, Altrincham.
STOTT, Charles,
  276, Oldham Road, Rochdale.
SMITH, E. W. B.,
  5, Haymarket Street, Bury.
SCHOFIELD, Miss Mary Ann,
  24, Schofield Street, Failsworth.
SHARP, Robert,
  Endowed School, Bisphan,
                    Poulton-le-Fylde.
SCHOFIELD, Mrs. Jenny,
  24, Schofield Street, Failsworth.
SANDERS, John,
                    Ancoats, Manchester.
SEED, Captain Thomas,
  Ash Road, Tranmere Park,
                    Birkenhead.
SCOTT, C. H.,
  West Bank, Heaton Mersey,
                    Stockport.
SEDDON, Edward,
  Groby House, 56, Duke Street,
                    Southport.
SHORE, Luke,
  Central Parade, Blackpool.
SWINDELLS, Geo. H.,
  Heaton Moor, nr. Stockport.
STEAD, William,
  Bookseller, 100, Yorkshire Street,
                    Oldham.   2 copies.
STANHOPE, Philip, M.P.,
  2, Great Cumberland Place,
                    Hyde Park, London, W.

SNAPE, Thomas, M.P.,
  (Heywood Division) The Gables,
                    Croxteth Road, Liverpool.
SPENCER, C. C.,
  Barleycroft, Oldham.
STANSFIELD, A.,
  Rectory Road, Burnley.
STOREY, Sir Thomas,
  Lancaster.   2 copies.
STREET, Samuel,
  23, Colwyn Street, Oldham.
SIMPSON, John,
  1, Shrewsbury Street, Oldham.
SWIRE, J. L.,
  67, King's Road, Rochdale.

T

TINKER, Henry,
  Schoolmaster, 8, Stamford Street,
                    Stalybridge.
TWEEDALE, Isaac,
  Glenside, Moston, nr. Harpurhey.
TURNER, J.T.,
  Queen Street, Oldham.
TREVOR, Councillor, Wm., J.P.,
  Heathfield, Newton Heath. 2 copies.
TREVOR. Rev. John,
  Rulow, Macclesfield.
TAYLOR, John, K.,
  116, Roundthorn Road, Oldham.
TAYLOR, Tom,
                    Bungalow, St. Annes-on-Sea.
TAYLOR, William,
  13, Mumps, Oldham.
THOMPSON, Fred,
  107, Camp Street, Broughton,
                    Manchester.
TAYLOR, Radcliffe,
  2943, North Fourth Street,
                    Philadelphia, U.S.
TAYLOR, John Wm.,
  c/o Mr. Colthard, Crescent, Salford.
TAYLOR, Mrs. James,
  23, Park View, Wigan.
TEARLE, James,
  Market Street, Colne.
THORNTON, Robert James,
  14, Carr Road, Nelson.
THORNTON, Charles,
  15, Carr Road, Nelson.
TAYLOR, Frank, J.P.,
  Ash Lawn, Heaton, Bolton.
TAYLOR, Thos. B.,
  171, Windsor Road, Oldham.
TAYLOR, Rev. W. H.,
  Warmington Rectory, Banbury.
THOMASON, William,
  167, North Road, St. Helens.
THOMPSON, Thomas,
  Melbourne Villa, New Moston, near
                    Failsworth.

TAYLOR, James,
  Butcher, 14, Bottom o' th' Moor,
                              Oldham.
TAYLOR, Joseph,
  100, Oldham Road, Failsworth.
TAYLOR, Alfred,
  Bookseller, 94, Northgate,
                              Wakefield.
THOMPSON, John W.,
  Langley Cottage, Prestwich.
THORP, Wm.,
  St. Mary's Road, Glossop.
TAYLOR, John,
  Auctioneer, 28, Chapel Street,
                              Blackpool.
TONG, Samuel,
  15, Pole Lane, Failsworth, near
                              Manchester.
TAYLOR, John,
  Lord Rodney Brewery, Ancoats,
                              Manchester.
TATTERSALL, Councillor L.,
  Book Stationer, &c., 67, Scotland
                          Road, Nelson.
TURNER, John,
  Mayor of Stockport, Ingersley,
    Shaw Heath, Stockport. 4 copies
TURNER, J. Horsfall, F.R.H.S.,
                          Idel, Bradford.
TAYLOR, S. E.,
  19, Hill Street, Oldham.

U

UTTLEY, Joseph,
  Alliance Hotel, Manchester.
UNWIN, Councillor John,
  7, Park Crescent, Southport.

W

WARD, Councillor John,
  Hazel Bank, Moston.
WRIGLEY, John,
  Albert House, Seascale, Cumberland
                              2 copies.
WOOD, Alderman, J.P.
  Middleton   (2 copies)
WOOD, Wright, J.P.,
  16, Chester Square, Ashton-u-Lyne.
WOOD, Geo. Thos.,
  16, South-hill Street, Oldham.
WALKDEN, John,
  Lagos House, Prestwich.
WILDE, Isaac,
  52, Raikes Road, Blackpool.
WILDE, Edward,
  Langsett Road, Sheffield.
WILDE, Samuel Exley,
  Rochdale.

WARD, James,
  36, Bonny Street, Blackpool.
WAINWRIGHT, Joel,
  Finchwood, Compstall, via Southport
WHITEHEAD, Sam,
  Clough Lee, Marsden, Huddersfield.
WARDLEWORTH, Richard,
  Old Road, Blackley, Manchester.
WARDLEWORTH, J. S.,
  1, Gordon Street, Rawtenstall.
                              2 copies.
WHILEY, Henry,
  Town Hall, Manchester.
WHITEHEAD, Wm.,
  15, Turley Street, Cheetham Hill,
                              Manchester.
WILLIAMS, John,
  47, St. Andrew's Road,
                          St. Annes-on-Sea.
WARD, Alfred,
  Swan Street, Manchester.
WITHAM, William,
  93, St. Andrew's Road,
                          St. Annes-on-Sea.
WHITWORTH, John,
  Solicitor, Booth Street Chambers,
                          Ashton-under-Lyne.
WARBURTON, Samuel,
  10, Witton Polygon, Cheetham Hill,
                              Manchester.
WIGGINS, William,
  Photo Artist, South Shore,
                              Blackpool.
WHITEHEAD, George,
  Ollerton Farm, Lord Lane,
                              Failsworth.
WHITESIDE, John,
  Dickson Street, Blackpool. 2 copies.
WILDMAN, Councillor, Wm.,
  Stamp Office, Blackpool.

WALMSLEY, Edward,
  St. Andrew's Road,
                          St. Annes-on-Sea.
WHITTAKER, Aaron,
  1, Wicken Tree Lane, Failsworth.
WHITTAKER, Sam,
  Bank Terrace, Bacup.
WALKER, Thos. A.,
  66, Leyland Road, Southport.
WALLWORK, Joseph H.,
  57, Chief Street, Oldham.
WARBURTON, John,
  32, Oak Road, Withington, near
                              Manchester.
WARD, Orlando,
  83, Napier Street East, Oldham.
WARDLE, Joseph,
  45, Werneth Hall Road, Oldham.
WEST, John,
  Belgrave Road, Oldham.
WHATMOUGH, Elizabeth,
  Yorkshire Street, Rochdale.
                              2 copies.
WHITEHEAD, Edwin,
  4, Thursley Road, Burnley.

WHITTAKER, Edwin,
   Sun Ironworks, Oldham.

WHITTAKER, George,
   Pole Lane, Failsworth.

WARD, James, B.A.,
   Literary Society Library, Leigh.

WILSON, Titus, J.P.
   Aynam Lodge, Kendal.

WRIGHT, Richard D'Aubney,
   18, John Dalton Street, Manchester.

WORTH, John T.,
   Solicitor, 182, Drake Street,
               Rochdale.

WILD, Robert,
   38, Standish Street, Burnley.

WHITEHEAD, Joseph,
   Assistant Overseer, Oldham.

WILD, James,
   7, Regent Street, Mumps, Oldham.

WILD, Jonathan,
   Wren Nest Mills, Shaw.

WILD, Mrs.,
   24, Thornham Road, High Crompton.

WILDE, Asa,
   Jessamine Place, Hollinwood.

WILSON, Edgar,
   Mare and Foal Hotel, Oldham.

WINTERBURN, George,
   65, Deansgate, Bolton.   3 copies.

WOOD, Alexander,
   Thornly, Saltcoats, Glasgow.

WOOD, Thomas,
   497, Middleton Road, Oldham.

WOOD, Thomas,
   3, Hamilton Street, Oldham.

WOOD, William,
   184, Market Street, Droylsden.
                   2 copies.

WOOLEY, George S.,
   Victoria Bridge, Manchester.

WORRALL, Francis,
   Newtown Rampside, Barrow-in-
               Furness.

WORTHINGTON E.,
   5, Rodney Street, Wigan.

WRIGLEY, Geo.,
   Spotted Cow, 122, Henshaw Street,
               Oldham.

WRIGLEY, Roscoe,
   114, Werneth Hall Road, Oldham.

WARDLEWORTH, T. R.,
   18, Brown Street, Manchester.
                   6 copies.

WILSON, Frank,
   22, Sefton Street, Southport.

WRIGLEY, Joseph,
   Byram's Buildings, Shaw Hall,
           Greenfield, near Oldham.

WOLSTENHOLME, Richard,
   62, King Street, Blackburn.

WHITEHEAD, Abraham,
   3, Exchange Street, Oldham.

WHITTAKER, W. T.,
   Greenbank, Middleton.

WILKINSON, J. S.,
   Binchem Street, Wakefield.

WILKINSON, C.,
   35, Alexandra Road, Wimbledon,
               London.

WILSON, John, J.P.,
   Gloucester Place, Ashton-under-
           Lyne.   2 copies.

WORTHINGTON, Councillor George,
   44, Bonny Street, Blackpool.

WILDE, David,
   Church Street, Blackpool.

WILDE, Milton Gough,
   Photo Artist, Talbot Road,
          Blackpool.   2 copies.

WADDISON, James,
   3, Abbotsford Terrace, Darwen.

WHITTAKER, Handel,
   Failsworth, near Manchester.

WHITTAKER, Alderman John, J.P.,
   Woodlands, Nelson.

WOOD, Edward, Red Lion Hotel,
      Bottom o' th' Moor, Oldham.

WARD, Wm.,
   23, Lees Road, Oldham.   2 copies.

WOODARD,
   110, Pitt Street, Oldham.

WILSON, Councillor William,
   Old Works, Worsley.

WILKINSON, Jas. F.,
   Printer, Bury Street, Pendleton,
              Manchester.

WELLS, Councillor J. W., J.P.,
   Sunny Bank, Cliff Grove,
         Newton Moor, Stockport.

WILKINSON, F.,
   Bell Street, Oldham.

WHITEHEAD, Thomas,
   Wesley Street, Failsworth.

WIGMORES, James,
   46, Churchill Street, Oldham.

WHITHAM, Thomas,
   Police Station, Preston.

WALSH, T.,
   10, Cragg Street, Colne.

WILLIAMS, Rev. J. G.,
   70, George Street, Blackpool.

WORTHY, R.,
   49, King's Road, Rochdale.

WOOD, James B.,
   Hudson Street, Hollinwood.

WRIGLEY, Colonel, D.L.O.Y.C.,
   13, Riding Street, Southport.

WILDE, Thomas,
   99, Vaudrey Street, Stalybridge.

WILLIAMSON, Aaron,
   93, Oldham Road, Ashton-under-
               Lyne.

WHITHAM, C.,
   144, Pitt Street, Oldham.

WORSLEY, Thomas,
Postmaster, St Andrew's Road,
St. Annes-on-Sea.

WAINWRIGHT, Albert,
3, Canal Street, Stalybridge. 2 copies.

WOLSTENHOLME, W. H.,
95, Manchester Old Road, Middleton

WOLSTENHOLME, John,
Imperial Cottage, North Shore,
Blackpool. 2 copies.

WOLSTENHOLME, Samuel,
Photo. Artist, Wellington Terrace,
Blackpool.

WHITTAKER, Horatio,
41, Warren Road, Stockport.

WOOLLEY, Edward,
64, Mottram Road Stalybridge.

WOOLLEY, Harry,
64, Mottram Road, Stalybridge.

WOOLLEY, James,
5, St. Helen's Road, Bolton.

WARTON, Colonel,
Capernwray, Carnforth.

WHITTAKER, Masha,
Slater Street, Failsworth.

WILKINSON, Aaron,
8, Westbourne Grove, Harpurhey,
Manchester.. 2 copies.

WHITTINGTON, John,
4. Central Beach, Blackpool.

WALKER, T. H.,
Wellington Terrace, Blackpool.

WATSON, Joseph,
Gladstone Grove, Heaton Moor,
Stockport.

WILD, James,
548, Oldham Road, Failsworth.

WHARTON, Dr. Joseph,
Lees Road, Oldham.

WALL, Stephen,
86, Edward Street, Oldham.

WHITEHEAD, A. P.,
4, Edna Street, Hyde.

WILD, Herbert,
41, Spring Street, Oldham.

WIGLEY, J.,
11, Spring Gardens, Manchester.

WATSON, John,
3, Manchester Road, Nelson.

WALTON, Robert,
66, Rectory Road, Burnley. 2 copies.

WHITHAM, R. M.,
Craven Lodge, Burnley.

WINTERBOTTOM, John,
24, Derby Street, Colne.

WILKINSON, Thomas,
Barleyfield House, Nelson.

WILMORE, Thomas,
Cross Street, Nelson.

WILKINSON, Fergus,
Lancashire Reciter, Westwood,
Nelson.

WILKINSON, William,
Lancashire Reciter,
79, Scotland Road, Nelson.

WILKINSON, John,
Every Street, Nelson.

WATSON, Charles,
69, Windsor Road, Oldham.

WESTBURY, Claude Frederic,
2, Northolme Road, Highbury Park,
London, N.

WOOD, Joseph,
The Grange, Hollinwood.

Y

YOUNG, Arthur,
47, Dale Street, Manchester.

YATES, John,
Primrose Cottage, Wigan.

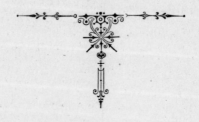

OPINIONS OF THE PRESS.

———o———

Mr. Laycock's genial philosophy in his " Welcome, Bonny Brid," will find a sympathetic response in thousand of homes, and from thousands of hearts. . . . The writer finds a "spirit of good in things evil;" he sees " the silver lining to every cloud ;" his humour is genial, his pathos is genuine, his sympathies with right, with goodness, and true manliness, are strong, and healthy, and pure. In the gloomiest hour he is neither puling nor cowardly, nor fierce ; he is a man in all things, and manly under all trials.

Huddersfield Examiner, June 18th, 1864.

———

Mr. Laycock is a far-off follower of the lyrist who showed the world that the human nature of the poor man was not always sterile and stunted, but had a laugh left in it, and a keen keeking eye for the absurdities around it. Nor would he stand much chance of doing any justice to the Lancashire poor unless he had some of the Scottish bard's sound-hearted good sense and inexpressible humour. . . . The author excels most, however, in his humours of local characters. He cannot do better than follow out this predelection, and he will find much that is quaintly natural in the obscure nooks of human life—especially in his native county.

Atheneum, April 13th, 1864.

———

In our humble opinion these rhymes are calculated to do much good. They are not the dawdling, purposeless twaddle with which the public has been surfeited by the thousand and one poetasters that have latterly sprung up, but they are pregnant with incentives to virtue, and contain many sparks of fire fresh and warm from the anvil of conviction.

Ashton-Under-Lyne Reporter.

———

The author of these rhymes has rightly regarded the demand for the single sheets, in which form most of them have previously appeared, as indicative of the hearty welcome they meet with generally. . . . They contain some good lessons, spiced with the pleasantry which makes them go down pretty good humouredly with the class not always the most patient under reproof. Neatly bound, got up in pretty good type, with glossarial notes, notwithstanding its homely literary pretentions, it will be a cherished volume in many a home We wish it a good circulation.

London Review.

The best proof that verses marked with the sterling homely strength of Mr. Laycock's rhymes do find their way to the heart of the Lancashire weaver is to be found in the fact that forty thousand copies of these particular poems had been sold in single sheets before the author collected them into a volume. . . . Throughout there is nothing unwholesome or of questionable tendency. None of Mr. Laycock's rhymes could imitate class prejudices, or turn the thoughts of his readers to narrowness or bitterness. If their local popularity is genuine, it says a good deal for the kindly and manly character of the Lancashire weaver.

Saturday Review.

Few temperance orators have pleaded with such force against drunkenness as has our author in two sets of verses which he entitles " A Little Bit o' Boath Sides," and those who read " Th' Coartin' Neet " will find that there is much good, though homely, philosophy to be found in it. But to our mind the best thing in the book is the piece entitled " Thee an' Me." The extracts which we have given from this book are of themselves sufficient to show that the author has considerable talent, and that his talent is wisely employed. . . . We like to see men of his class engaged in any kind of intellectual labour, and would do what we could to make such labour advantageous to themselves, and stimulating to their fellows.

A LANCASHIRE LAD.

Preston Herald, February 20th, 1864.

Here is another Lancashire poet—another songster who comes from the cottage. We give him welcome. He sings the songs of the poor, with a knowledge of the poor. He has the humour of the humble-fated. He is not all tears ; were he, he would not be a true representative of Lancashire. His main purpose—one that does him honour—is to thank the givers to the great Lancashire fund. The song is homely ; but it has that " best majesty " earnestness. Where the poet sings a lively song, that has a most powerful under-current to it, he is happiest. His greeting to a little stranger that comes to a scantily-furnished house is, to us, deeply touching. Mr. Laycock is not unknown among the cheerful and courageous people of Lancashire. His poems have been eagerly bought up in broadsheets, and they deserved collection in the present form.

Lloyd's Newspaper.

The " Welcome, Bonny Brid," by Samuel Laycock, to which we have already referred, will probably be known to many of our readers, but it deserves to be known widely beyond the county Palatine, and though the dialect may afford a little difficulty, none can mistake the genuine tenderness and sweetness of the ballad, which are worthy of the best efforts of Burns. " Bowton's Yard," by Samuel Laycock, in which Hood's humour and descriptive powers are blended with Lancashire quaintness and shrewdness, will probably be new to the majority of our readers. These are but a few samples out of scores, of the high literary merit of the modern Lancashire ballad.

Manchester Examiner.

OPINIONS OF THE PRESS.

Any work which tends, in however slight a degree, to the moral and intellectual improvement of the labouring and artizan classes is deserving of every consideration, and this little collection of rhymes, by Samuel Laycock, we think is particularly adapted to such a purpose, not only because the poetry is homely, simple, and interesting in itself, but also on account of its being written in the dialect of our language, which is commonly used and understood in the large manufacturing district in and around the county of Lancaster.

Weekly Review, February 27th, 1864.

The author of these "Homely pictures of the people," Mr. Laycock, belongs to the humble toiling class, whose quaint habits, manners, and strange speech, he has so truthfully and musically depicted. The rough truths, and occasional witty hits of these simple rhymes, must strike home even to the polished and supercilious : while the feeling tone that pervades some of them, having reference to the trials of the operatives of the cotton districts during the present distress, cannot fail to touch the generous chords of the heart. A strictly moral vein runs through the whole of the rhymes, and we have no hesitation in expressing a belief that the lessons inculcated in them are calculated to effect much good amongst the class for whom they are intended.

Stockport and Cheshire County News, February, 1864.

Perhaps, after Waugh, no Lancashire song-writer has attained such popularity as Mr Samuel Laycock, whose separate poems originally published on fly-sheets), sold to the extent of forty thousand copies before they were collected into permanent form. as a book ; and, although his writings are somewhat unequal, there can be no doubt that he amply merits the applause he has received. The native humour and subdued pathos of "Welcome, Bonny Brid," have made it a universal favourite ; but the finest poem he has yet produced is "Bowton's Yard," which describes in homely rhymes the fortunes and characters of each denizen of the now famous yard.

Folk-Song and Folk-Speech of Lancashire
on the Ballads and Songs of the County Palatine,

W. E. A. AXON, F.R.S.L.

These rhymes are healthy in tone and sentiment. They are principally descriptive of the manners and customs of the Lancashire operatives, and are in the Lancashire dialect. Mr. Laycock is a real poet, and he has sung of the joys and sorrows of the people in a way that cannot but prove acceptable to readers in general. We have no lack of poetasters of the Mortimer Collins and "poet close" school, but too few real poets who make the noble struggles, the joys, and aspirations of the toiling masses their principal themes. There is a vein of sly humour in many of Mr. Laycock's rhymes, while a genuine kindliness pervades them all. Mr. Laycock sings not of "perfumed ringlets," "brows of snow," and "rosy lips," the usual stock-in-trade of bardlings, but sketches with striking fidelity the various phases of operative life in the homeliest style. Such lays are refreshing, and deserve a large circulation. Many persons, we hope, will purchase the volume for its poetic excellence, and the admirable way in which it deals with "the short and simple annals of the poor."

Public Opinion.

Samuel Laycock, although a writer of Lancashire dialect poems, is a Yorkshireman by birth, having first seen the light at Marsden, not far from the borders of Lancashire, which accounts for many words appearing in his works which are common to both the dialects of Yorkshire and Lancashire, such words being common to the people on both sides the border. . . . One of Laycock's best known songs is "Bowton's Yard," which is as well known in the North of England as Edwin Waugh's "Come Whoam to thi Childer an' Me." Like most Yorkshiremen, Samuel Laycock is proud of his native county, if we may judge by his many references to it in his songs and poems. As instances we may mention his song, "Mi Gronfeyther," where he says :—

He wur allis straightforrad i' o' 'at he did,
An owd-fashioned Yorkshire John Bull.

Hull and East Riding Good Templar, July, 1881.

Bro. Samuel Laycock has placed the Temperance cause, the Band of Hope organisation, and our Good Templar brotherhood under heavy obligations by his numerous productions, which when either read or recited at our festive meetings, never fail to merit encore or to secure exciting applause. There is an ease, naturalness, and humour in his pieces, which stamps him as one of the most wonderful men, as well as pleasing, ingenious, and popular poets and public readers of our time. He is of the ranks, and delights to be in the ranks, and his fertile pen has done no little towards giving a healthy and vigorous tone to the electoral and educational agencies in his native counties of Lancashire and Yorkshire—for both counties claim him as their honoured son. He is only yet in middle life [this article was written 17 years ago], and gives sunshine to his loving family at Blackpool. . . . His fugitive pieces are very numerous in both prose and poetry, and he has likewise published a neat volume of his best compositions. Brother Laycock is in sympathy with every aspect of the Temperance cause, and disinterestedly devotes himself, as a man in humble circumstances, by both pen, purse, and person, to the extension of its beneficient principles. · B. H.

The Good Templars' Watchword, February 2nd, 1876.

Every one knows Waugh's tender, humorous verses, "Come Whoam to th' Childer an' Me," and we are not surprised to hear that he is the most popular of Lancashire song-writers. But to our thinking, Samuel Laycock, to whom we are glad of an opportunity of introducing our readers, equals him in humour, and surpasses him in the depth of his tenderness and the refinement of his thought. Nor is Mr. Laycock behind in humour, as witness his account of the mischievous old Bellman's description of a lost baby. . . . To him, too, we are indebted for a cordial song of thanks for all that the rich did in the time of the Lancashire Distress, but much as we should like it, we cannot afford Mr. Laycock any more of our space.

The Spectator, March 20th, 1875.